MULTIVARIATE PROCEDURES FOR THE BEHAVIORAL SCIENCES

WILLIAM W. COOLEY
Assistant Professor of Education
Harvard University

PAUL R. LOHNES
Associate Professor of Education,
University of New Hampshire

John Wiley & Sons, Inc., New York · London

MULTIVARIATE PROCEDURES FOR THE BEHAVIORAL SCIENCES

to our wives, Cynthia and Kathleen

Preface

This book describes some of the more useful multivariate techniques and how to compute and report them. It is intended to implement rather than to constitute a course in multivariate analysis. The first chapter presents a general description of multivariate analysis and the specific techniques outlined in this book. Each subsequent chapter briefly describes the mathematics of a particular procedure, presents computed examples to illustrate that type of analysis, provides flow charts for programming any digital computer for the procedure, and concludes with listings of FORTRAN-coded, tested, and proven computer programs. The final chapter gives utility subroutines for matrix inversion and methods for extracting latent roots and vectors as used in the various computing programs.

Although a knowledge of basic statistics is assumed, we give numerous references for the reader who wishes to familiarize himself more thoroughly with the mathematical bases of the multivariate procedures considered. References are also provided for research workers who are not yet familiar with electronic computers or FORTRAN coding. Therefore we also view this book as a possible basic guide for the behavioral scientist who wishes to familiarize himself with recent developments in multivariate analysis and to apply these procedures in his work.

We cannot hope to provide individual acknowledgments for the many teachers and authors whose works have influenced our conceptions of multivariate analysis. We do wish to state explicitly our great sense of indebtedness to Professor Phillip J. Rulon, who introduced us to most of the matters treated in this book, and to Professor John B. Carroll, who introduced us to factor analysis. We are also indebted to the Massachusetts Institute of Technology and the International Business Machines Corporation, which have provided New England scholars with the M.I.T. Computation Center. At this computer installation we accumulated the experience on which much of this book is based. Moreover, the half-time appointment as I.B.M. Research Associate at the M.I.T. Computation Center from the University of New Hampshire, which P. R. Lohnes has held for two years, has made it possible for him to devote his time to this project.

Many of the computed examples reported here are drawn from the data of the "Career Development of Scientists" project which W. W. Cooley has in progress as Cooperative Research Project Number 436, supported by the United States Office of Education.

Three important computer programs we report are developments of other workers who have generously allowed the reproduction of their programs here. The FORTRAN program for the Kaiser Varimax criterion was written by Lynn C. Hayward, Biostatistics Unit, University of California Medical Center at Los Angeles. General advisory information was given by Professor W. J. Dixon, Department of Preventive Medicine, and Professor A. L. Comrey, Department of Psychology, University of California at Los Angeles. Professor Henry F. Kaiser provided the information on the location of this successful Varimax program. The FORTRAN program MATINV for the computation of matrix inverses, determinants, and solution of simultaneous equations was written by Burton S. Garbow, Applied Mathematics Division, Argonne National Laboratory. The FORTRAN program HDIAG for the computation of eigenvalues and eigenvectors of a real symmetric matrix was developed by F. J. Corbato, Associate Director, M.I.T. Computation Center, and his staff. Professor Eugene C. Lee, School of Education, University of Texas, participated in developing the analysis-of-variance program for factorial designs.

We would also like to thank Professors G. Watson of the University of Toronto and R. Sitgreaves of Columbia University, who reviewed the original manuscript and who offered many helpful suggestions.

To the persons and agencies mentioned, to colleagues and students who have read and criticized the text, to the authors whose books and papers appear in chapter references, to persons whose data and/or analyses of data are included as examples in various chapters (and are identified there), to Frederick Seiler and his colleagues at John Wiley and Sons, to Naomi Alperen and Cynthia Cooley who labored on the manuscript, the writers utter a heartfelt "thank you." Our mistakes we made ourselves despite your ministrations.

WILLIAM W. COOLEY

PAUL R. LOHNES

Cambridge, Massachusetts
Durham, New Hampshire
September, 1962

Contents

CHAPTER ONE

An introduction to multivariate analysis and computer programming

1.1 Definition of Multivariate Analysis and Introduction to Matrix Algebra

Multivariate analysis is generally considered to include those statistical procedures concerned with analyzing multiple measurements that have been made on a number N of individuals. The important distinction is that the multiple variates are considered in combination, as systems. The specific multivariate procedure selected for analyzing a given set of variables based on N observations depends, of course, on the question the investigator wishes to ask of his data.[1]

A basic concept useful in considering several variates together is the test space concept. If m measurements have been made on N individuals, each individual can be represented as a point in the m-dimensional space. Each point (individual) has a unique location depending on the combination of the m scores resulting from the m measurements.

Consider the case when two test scores are obtained for ten students; $m = 2$ and $N = 10$. This case results in ten points in a two-dimensional space, which is represented by the generally familiar bivariate score roster (Table 1.1) and the two-dimensional plot (Figure 1.1). Students having similar test score combinations will occupy similar regions of the test space. In the bivariate example each student can be represented by a vector, and student 2 is so represented in Figure 1.2.

Symbolically, the vector for the same student may also be represented as [1 2]. Thus a score vector is a row or column of numbers, the numbers being the m scores or m coordinates for the m axes of the test space. The ten rows of the roster of Table 1.1 represent ten vectors. Together the ten rows form a matrix, an ($N \times m$) or (10×2) matrix in this case. (The size of a matrix is notated $r \times c$, or r by c, with r rows and c columns.)

In multivariate analysis, the bivariate techniques are extended so that more than

---

[1] A good introduction to the nature and scope of multivariate analysis is found in Kendall (1957), Chapter 1.

Note: In this text, references are found at the end of each chapter.

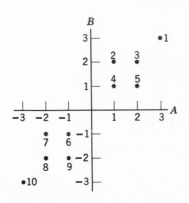

TABLE 1.1

Student	Test A	Test B
1	3	3
2	1	2
3	2	2
4	1	1
5	1	2
6	−1	−1
7	−2	−1
8	−2	−2
9	−1	−2
10	−3	−3

Figure 1.1. Two-dimensional test space.

two variables can be considered, the m variables becoming the m axes of the test space. Of course, it is difficult to diagram spaces of more than two or three dimensions, but matrix algebra makes it possible to consider m-dimensional systems. Most mathematics of multivariate analysis involve the manipulation of matrices. The raw score roster, for instance, an $N \times m$ matrix, can be converted to a correlation matrix by a few simple steps, which are outlined in Section 2.1.

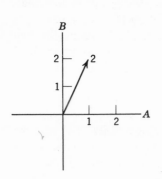

Figure 1.2

Procedures of multivariate analysis are often concerned with the problem of reducing the original test space to the minimum number of dimensions needed to describe the relevant information contained in the original observations. Multivariate procedures differ in the types of original information they preserve. For example, the procedure called multiple-group discriminant analysis finds the minimum number of dimensions or discriminant functions required for the description of group differences.

Because some understanding of matrix algebra is essential to using and understanding multivariate analysis, a review of basic matrix operations should be undertaken by the "uncertain" reader before proceeding. The following section is a very brief introduction to matrix algebra and is presented for those readers who have not previously been exposed to this field. The reader may also wish to consult Harman's (1960) chapter on "Matrix Concepts Essential to Factor Analysis."

Introduction to Matrix Algebra. As has been stated, a vector is a one-dimensional array of numbers arranged either as a column or as a row. Thus, $\mathbf{v} = \begin{bmatrix} v_1 \\ v_2 \end{bmatrix}$ and $\mathbf{y}' = [y_1 \quad y_2 \quad y_3]$ are vectors. A matrix is a two-dimensional array of numbers.

Thus $\mathbf{A} = \begin{bmatrix} a_{11} & a_{12} \\ a_{21} & a_{22} \end{bmatrix}$ is a matrix. In general, a_{ij} identifies the element of the $\mathbf{A}$ matrix which is found in the ith row and the jth column. Matrices are added or subtracted by adding or subtracting corresponding elements of the matrices. Thus,

given $$\mathbf{A} = \begin{bmatrix} a_{11} & a_{12} \\ a_{21} & a_{22} \end{bmatrix} \quad \text{and} \quad \mathbf{B} = \begin{bmatrix} b_{11} & b_{12} \\ b_{21} & b_{22} \end{bmatrix},$$

$$\mathbf{A} + \mathbf{B} = \begin{bmatrix} a_{11} + b_{11} & a_{12} + b_{12} \\ a_{21} + b_{21} & a_{22} + b_{22} \end{bmatrix} \quad \text{and} \quad \mathbf{A} - \mathbf{B} = \begin{bmatrix} a_{11} - b_{11} & a_{12} - b_{12} \\ a_{21} - b_{21} & a_{22} - b_{22} \end{bmatrix}.$$

Matrix multiplication involves the computation of the sum of the products of elements from a row of the first matrix (the premultiplier) and a column of the second matrix (the postmultiplier). This sum must be computed for every combination of rows and columns. Given the $\mathbf{A}$ and $\mathbf{B}$ we just defined,

$$\mathbf{A} \cdot \mathbf{B} = \begin{bmatrix} a_{11} \cdot b_{11} + a_{12} \cdot b_{21} & a_{11} \cdot b_{12} + a_{12} \cdot b_{22} \\ a_{21} \cdot b_{11} + a_{22} \cdot b_{21} & a_{21} \cdot b_{12} + a_{22} \cdot b_{22} \end{bmatrix}.$$

Note that if $\mathbf{A}$ is a $k \times m$ and $\mathbf{B}$ an $m \times n$ matrix (meaning that $\mathbf{A}$ has k rows and m columns and $\mathbf{B}$ has m rows and n columns), the product of $\mathbf{A} \cdot \mathbf{B}$ is a $k \times n$ matrix, and that if $k \neq n$, it is not possible to form the product $\mathbf{B} \cdot \mathbf{A}$.

Numerical examples may help to clarify these operations. If

$$\mathbf{A} = \begin{bmatrix} 5 & 6 \\ 3 & 7 \end{bmatrix} \quad \text{and} \quad \mathbf{B} = \begin{bmatrix} 3 & 2 \\ 1 & 5 \end{bmatrix},$$

then

$$\mathbf{A} + \mathbf{B} = \begin{bmatrix} 8 & 8 \\ 4 & 12 \end{bmatrix}, \quad \mathbf{A} - \mathbf{B} = \begin{bmatrix} 2 & 4 \\ 2 & 2 \end{bmatrix}, \quad \text{and} \quad \mathbf{A} \cdot \mathbf{B} = \begin{bmatrix} 21 & 40 \\ 16 & 41 \end{bmatrix}.$$

To multiply a matrix by some scalar, we multiply each element of the matrix by that scalar.[2]

An m-element row vector times an m-element column vector produces a scalar product. An m-element column vector times an m-element row vector produces an $m \times m$ square matrix as a product. Premultiplying a matrix that has m rows by an m-element row vector produces a row vector having as many elements as the matrix has columns. Postmultiplying a matrix having m columns by an m-element column vector produces a column vector that has as many elements as the matrix has rows. It is not possible to premultiply a matrix by a column vector or to postmultiply a matrix by a row vector. The matrix product $\mathbf{x}' \cdot \mathbf{A} \cdot \mathbf{x}$, where $\mathbf{x}$ is a column vector and $\mathbf{x}'$ is a row vector containing the same elements as $\mathbf{x}$, produces a scalar; this scalar product is called a quadratic form.

[2] Ordinary algebraic quantities (real and complex numbers) are called scalars in order to distinguish them from matrices.

Matrix division involves an operation called inverting a matrix. That is, the quotient $\mathbf{A}/\mathbf{B}$ is expressed as $\mathbf{B}^{-1} \cdot \mathbf{A}$, where the matrix $\mathbf{B}^{-1}$ (pronounced $\mathbf{B}$ inverse) has the property that $\mathbf{B}^{-1} \cdot \mathbf{B} = \mathbf{I}$, where $\mathbf{I}$ is a matrix of the form

$$\mathbf{I} = \begin{bmatrix} 1 & 0 & 0 & \cdots & 0 \\ 0 & 1 & 0 & \cdots & 0 \\ 0 & 0 & 1 & \cdots & 0 \\ \cdot & \cdot & \cdot & & \cdot \\ \cdot & \cdot & \cdot & & \cdot \\ \cdot & \cdot & \cdot & & \cdot \\ 0 & 0 & 0 & \cdots & 1 \end{bmatrix}.$$

$\mathbf{I}$ is called an identity matrix.

There are various methods of computing $\mathbf{B}^{-1}$ from $\mathbf{B}$, one of which is discussed briefly in Chapter 9. In addition, an excellent inversion program is reported in that chapter.

The determinant of a square matrix is a single number that represents a unique function of the numbers in the matrix. Therefore the determinant is a useful index to a square matrix. Two programs for computing determinants are given in Chapter 9. The determinant of $\mathbf{A}$ is notated $|\mathbf{A}|$. Of particular interest in statistics is the determinant of a square symmetrical matrix $\mathbf{D}$ whose diagonal elements are variances and off-diagonal elements are covariances, i.e.,

$$\mathbf{D} = \begin{bmatrix} s_1^2 & s_1 s_2 r_{12} & \cdots & s_1 s_m r_{1m} \\ s_2 s_1 r_{21} & s_2^2 & \cdots & s_2 s_m r_{2m} \\ \cdot & \cdot & & \cdot \\ \cdot & \cdot & & \cdot \\ \cdot & \cdot & & \cdot \\ s_m s_1 r_{m1} & s_m s_2 r_{m2} & \cdots & s_m^2 \end{bmatrix},$$

because $|\mathbf{D}|$ represents as a single number the generalized variance in a set of m tests.

The characteristic equation of a square matrix is formed by subtracting some one value λ from each of the diagonal elements of the matrix, where λ is selected so that the determinant of the resulting matrix is equal to zero. Thus the characteristic equation of a second-order matrix $\mathbf{A}$ may be written

$$\begin{vmatrix} a_{11} - \lambda & a_{12} \\ a_{21} & a_{22} - \lambda \end{vmatrix} = 0.$$

This may also be written $|\mathbf{A} - \lambda \mathbf{I}| = 0$. The number of different nonzero λ's, or roots, that satisfy the characteristic equation of a square matrix will be equal to or less than the order of the matrix (order referring to the number of rows or columns) and will determine the rank of the matrix. Solving for the λ's (usually called the eigenvalues or latent roots of the matrix) may be approached in a variety of ways, three of which are described in Chapter 9.

Associated with each eigenvalue will be a vector $\mathbf{x}$, called the eigenvector or latent vector, which satisfies the matrix equation $\mathbf{A} \cdot \mathbf{x} = \lambda \cdot \mathbf{x}$. If the complete set of eigenvectors of $\mathbf{A}$ are placed as columns in a matrix $\mathbf{X}$, and the complete set of corresponding eigenvalues are placed in the diagonal elements of a matrix Λ, where the off-diagonal elements are zeros, the following relationship holds: $\mathbf{A} \cdot \mathbf{X} = \mathbf{X} \cdot \Lambda$. The eigenvectors of certain matrices play important roles in multivariate statistics as the weights in linear functions of variables that maximize or minimize various criteria. Chapter 9 contains information on methods of calculating eigenvectors.

Before going to the mathematical details and computing procedures, a survey of types of multivariate procedures may be useful. Each class of procedures we shall briefly describe is treated in a separate chapter of this book. Our brief survey is followed by an introduction to the FORTRAN (FORmula TRANslation) language used in programming the multivariate techniques described herein.

1.2 Types of Multivariate Procedures

The best-known method of multivariate analysis is multiple-regression analysis, which is used to examine the relation between a criterion or dependent variable and two or more predictors or independent variables. Thus grade point average might be predicted from several aptitude scores. One example in Chapter 3 involves an attempt to predict the quality of independent laboratory work by talented high-school students from a linear combination of a set of ten temperament measures. Another example in Chapter 3 involves a reasonably successful prediction of the final class rank of some high-school students from a set of six mental-ability measures.

For the simplest case of two predictor scores, the problem can be visualized by using the test space concept described in Section 1.1. The criterion score and two predictors form a three-dimensional test space. A plane is located in that space, such that the sum of the squared distances of all the score points from the plane, when those distances are measured parallel to the criterion axis, is smaller than for any other plane that could be located in the test space. The sum of the squared distances divided by the appropriate number of degrees of freedom is an estimate of the variance of the criterion scores about the regression plane. The estimate of an individual's criterion score is computed as a linear function of the two predictor scores. When $m - 1$ predictors are used, the test space is m-dimensional, and the plane becomes a hyperplane. A hyperplane lying in the m space is analogous to the plane lying in the three-dimensional space. It is a subspace of $m - 1$ dimensions.

The weights for the different predictor variables can be scaled to indicate the relative contributions of the variables to the prediction of the criterion, and a coefficient of multiple correlation is available as an indication of the prediction's accuracy. The square of this coefficient represents, as a decimal fraction, the proportion of variance on the criterion that is predictable from, or explained by, the linear combination of the $m - 1$ predictors. There is an analysis-of-variance test of the statistical significance of the multiple-correlation coefficient, and the significance of each predictor variable's contribution can also be tested. When the investigator is interested in determining one characteristic of a set of objects which is measured as a continuous variable by a set of other characteristics similarly measured, multiple correlation often provides an excellent analytic tool. Presumably, before the scientist applies the model to his data, he will review its several assumptions. In fact, our reservation regarding the suitability of a model's assumptions applies to all the techniques discussed in this book, although it will not be repeatedly mentioned.

Another popular multivariate procedure is multiple-discriminant analysis, used when the scientist is interested in examining or predicting the group membership of individuals on the basis of a set of attributes of those individuals, the attributes measured as continuous variables. The example reported in Chapter 6 involves the computation of discriminant functions based on scores of ninety-six male college students on six study-of-values scales to predict the postcollege membership of the men in three career criterion groups, namely (1) research, (2) applied science, and (3) nonscience. The distinction of this problem is that the criterion is categorical rather than continuous. The approach is to locate a line in the m space for which the separation of the groups is optimized when the individual points of the different sample groups are projected on to it. Actually, the ratio of the among-groups to the within-groups sums of squared deviations is maximized. Since in general this first discriminant function may not exhaust the power of the test battery to separate the groups, additional functions, mutually orthogonal,[3] may be fitted. The limit to the number of discriminant functions that may be required in an analysis is the smaller of m and $g - 1$, where g is the number of groups sampled.

A test of the statistical significance of the separation of the g groups in the m space is standard; an approximate test of the significance of separation of the groups by individual discriminants is also available. It is also possible to scale the weights for the variables in each discriminant function to show the relative contributions of the variables to the discriminant. Computing and plotting the "centroids" (the vector of group means or "mean vector") in the discriminant space often provides a helpful map of the location of the groups in the reduced space, particularly if only two or three discriminant functions are required to describe the observed group differences.

The test of the discriminating power of the battery, which we have mentioned, is so important that it is given separate treatment in the chapter on generalizations of the analysis of variance. The research question behind these generalized tests is whether two or more sample groups should be thought of as arising from a single population or from two or more different populations. One example in Chapter 4 involves testing the separation of four academic-interest groupings of talented

[3] Independent, or uncorrelated.

boys by quantitative and linguistic-aptitude scores. The major example in Chapter 4 involves testing the separation of science-career-oriented males from science-teaching-oriented males by a set of twelve scales in the personality modalities of interests and temperament. The null hypothesis for each test asserts that the sample statistics arose from two or more samplings of a single population, or single swarm of subjects in the multivariate space.

The most useful test of the discriminating power, called Wilks' lambda (Λ) test, determines a probability level for the null hypothesis of equality of population centroids (mean vectors), on the assumption of equality of dispersions (variance-covariance matrices). The assumption is analogous to that of homogeneity of variance in the univariate F ratio test of equality of means. A test of this assumption of equality of population dispersions will be presented later.

Attention is directed to a procedure for multivariate analysis of variance with covariance controls which has not been encountered by the authors in published reports of educational or psychological research, but which seems to have great promise for these fields. For example, in curriculum research it would be possible to test the separation of a number of treatment groups on a set of m achievement variables with covariance adjustment for differences on a set of c aptitude variables. In Chapter 4 one example asks whether a set of group aptitude test scores can separate academic-interest groups after covariance removal of those components of variation which are predictable from individual intelligence test scores. Another example in Chapter 4 asks whether students taught by two different approaches will differ significantly on five criterion measures after adjustment has been made for differences in aptitude and initial knowledge. Descriptions and programs are also presented for two- and three-way factorial designs, with covariance control possible for as many as five adjuster variables. The example in Chapter 5 is a three-way design, the factors being (1) instructional method, (2) teacher type, and (3) course content. Two covariance control variables are utilized, the pretest score on the criterion scale and a scholastic-aptitude score.

It is sometimes desirable to compute actual predictions for new samples of subjects in order to test previous findings as in replication studies, or to provide a basis for practical decisions in applying the findings. Programming the computation of linear functions that yield estimated scores is described in this text. We have also developed programs for determining the probability of an individual being a member of each of a number of groups on the basis of his test scores, discriminant scores, or factor scores. Probabilities of this type have been found especially useful in the study of occupational choice. These procedures make it possible to determine, at any point in the test space, the probable density of the different groups located in that test space. An example used in Chapter 7 involves probabilities of college students' membership in several career fields computed on the basis of their scores on certain discriminant functions.

Psychometricians have been very active in recent years in the study of the logical implications of systematic intercorrelations within sets of tests. They have published many approaches to the reduction of dimensionality in correlated systems of measurements and the rotation of a reduced number of axes to more meaningful positions. This is the general task of factor analysis. Correlations among tests are conceptualized within a sample space model, where the cosine of the angle of separation of two normalized test vectors is equal to the coefficient of correlation between the two variables. This sample space (or person space) model differs from the test space model in that in the sample space the initial N reference axes represent individuals, and the points or vectors represent tests. The problem is to select a smaller set of orthogonal reference axes (factors) to span the swarm of points. One solution of the factor analysis problem, called principal-components analysis, has the advantage of being easily integrated into multivariate statistics, but it does not usually lead to reference axes acceptable to the psychologists or other theoreticians. Therefore some scheme for rotating the derived components to interpretable locations is generally demanded. The method reported here is Kaiser's Varimax solution. In Chapter 8 a description of a principal-components factor analysis and a Varimax rotation of forty-eight Rorschach test scores for 213 college males will be found.

1.3   Introduction to FORTRAN and Flow Diagrams

The programs reported and listed here are written in an IBM coding language called FORTRAN. This language is acceptable to the IBM 704, 709, and 7090 computers, which are the largest and fastest scientific computers IBM has placed in general service. FORTRAN can also be used with the IBM 650 and 1620 computers, which are the old and the new smaller "intermediate"-class IBM computers. It is noteworthy that coding languages for a number of non-IBM machines resemble, or are identical to, FORTRAN. Examples of other machines with FORTRAN compilers are Autonetics' RECOMP, Control Data Corporation's 1604, the Philco 2000, the Honeywell 800, and the Univac 1107.

There are some modifications of the language for each machine, and indeed for each installation. Thus it is necessary to check the listings of the programs locally and correct some details, particularly in the input and output procedures used. The smaller IBM machines accept only a subset of the FORTRAN language statements employed in our programs, which were written for and tested on the IBM 709. Therefore modifications are sometimes required to adapt the programs to the 650 or 1620. Memory restrictions in these smaller machines make it necessary to segment some of the longer analyses and run them in parts, and/or to assemble the programs with smaller dimension statements controlling the maximum sizes of matrices and vectors, and thus of the test space analyzed. The 709 used by the authors has 32,768 word memory locations, whereas many of the small machines have only 2000.[4]

The great advantage of FORTRAN is that it closely approximates the everyday

[4] Recently a 1620 with augmented memory of 4000 ten-digit locations has become available at the University of New Hampshire (hereafter referred to as U.N.H.) Computation Center, and Mr. Lohnes has begun to adapt the 709 multivariate analysis programs reported in this book to it. Readers interested in 1620 applications are invited to communicate with him.

usage of English-speaking mathematicians, scientists, engineers, and, in our case, statisticians. Anyone who has explored the ways in which modern digital computers "think" realizes that their internal machine language usually consists exclusively of binary-coded numbers, which are very difficult for human beings to use. In addition, instead of a single instruction which the human perceives as a simple command (such as, "Read the following list of things: A, B, C, D"), a computer must be presented with an extremely long sequence of binary-coded instructions. In short, if we had to communicate with these machines in their own language, most of us would probably turn to problems capable of solution on desk calculators. Fortunately, programs called compilers have been devised which enable the machines to translate English-like language terms into machine language instructions, and to assemble programs the machine can obey from statements the human user can easily write and appreciate. FORTRAN is such a compiler.

The following list pairs FORTRAN statements on the right with English explanations on the left to show the similarities. This sample of FORTRAN statements illustrates the major features of the language.

English Statement	FORTRAN Statement
Reserve memory cells for a matrix **A** of maximum 50 × 50 size and for a vector x of maximum 50 elements size.	DIMENSION A(50, 50), X(50)
Read according to format 1 the problem number.	READ 1, PROBNO
Print by format 2 the problem number.	PRINT 2, PROBNO
Specification as format 1 an input or output card, line, or tape record which contains a five-digit integer.	1 FORMAT (I5)
Place B in storage location A (Set $A = B$).	A = B
Set $A = B + C - D \cdot B/C$.	A = B + C − D * B/C
Set $A = B^n$.	A = B**N
Set $A = \sqrt{B}$.	A = SQRTF (B)
Set $A = |A|$.	A = ABSF (A)
Set $X_i = A \cdot \sqrt{Y_i}$ for $i = 1, 2, \ldots, N$.	DO 1 I = 1, N
	1 X(I) = A * SQRTF (Y(I))
Transfer to statement 7.	GO TO 7
Test N; if it is negative go to 2, if it is zero go to 3, if it is positive go to 4.	IF (N) 2, 3, 4
Call subroutine HDIAG, which will operate on the symmetric matrix **X**, of order M, to extract its eigenvalues and eigenvectors, placing the former in the diagonal of **X** and the latter in matrix **U**.	CALL HDIAG (X, M, O, U, R)

The most important feature of FORTRAN language in mutivariate statistical work is the easy handling of subscripted variables, which facilitates matrix manipulations. The "DO loop" and nests of DO loops are the key to this facility. A

DO-loop instruction causes a subscript to take on each of its possible values successively. A DO nest causes two or more subscripts to vary systematically. For example, the following nest causes the writing in the cells reserved for matrix $\mathbf{B}(N \times M)$, the transpose of matrix $\mathbf{A}(M \times N)$.

$$\text{DO 10 I} = 1, \text{M}$$
$$\text{DO 10 J} = 1, \text{N}$$
$$10 \ \text{B(J, I)} = \text{A(I, J)}.$$

The outside (or first) DO sets I = 1. This is held constant while the inside DO causes statement 10 to be executed for values of J from 1 to N. Then the outside DO changes I to 2 and the inside DO is repeated, running J from 1 to N again. This sequence continues through I = M. As a further example, note how the following DO nest creates the lower triangle of a symmetric matrix A from the established upper triangle.

$$\text{DO 10 I} = 1, \text{M}$$
$$\text{DO 10 J} = \text{I}, \text{M}$$
$$10 \ \text{A(J, I)} = \text{A(I, J)}.$$

In the next example a matrix product $\mathbf{C}(M, N) = \mathbf{A}(M, L) \cdot \mathbf{B}(L, N)$ is created.

$$\text{DO 10 I} = 1, \text{M}$$
$$\text{DO 10 J} = 1, \text{N}$$
$$\text{C(I, J)} = 0.0$$
$$\text{DO 10 K} = 1, \text{L}$$
$$10 \ \text{C(I, J)} = \text{C(I, J)} + \text{A(I, L)} * \text{B(L, J)}.$$

As this example illustrates, "DO 10" actually means "execute each of the following instructions through the one numbered 10."

Among the other significant advantages of FORTRAN are its great flexibility of input and output procedures, achieved through the FORMAT statement, and the subroutine, which allows the writing and testing of building blocks out of which a main program can be assembled. In the set of programs presented in the following chapters, three service subroutines have been employed extensively. (1) Subroutine CORREL takes in raw score vectors on subjects and computes sums, sums of squares and cross products, mean and standard deviation vectors, and dispersion and correlation matrices. It is explained in Chapter 2. (2) Subroutine HDIAG computes the eigenvalues and eigenvectors of a real symmetric matrix. (3) Subroutine MATINV computes the inverse of a matrix, the determinant of the matrix, and solutions of linear equations. These latter two subroutines are discussed in the final chapter.

A complete FORTRAN program, for computing the average score for each subject, is illustrated in the statements that follow. The computer is directed to read one score card which contains a five-digit identification number (ID) for a subject in the first five columns and a number (M) of two-digit scores (maximum M = 25 in this case) in three column fields beginning with Column 6. Then the machine is to compute the average score for the subject and print a line containing the subject's ID number and his average score. Finally, it is directed to repeat the process as long as there are cards to be read. As a help in reading the program, it should be mentioned that cards with a "C" in Column 1 are comment cards, which do not become part of the machine-language program. The statement "EM = M" is required to convert M, an integer, into EM, which is a floating-point number, so that the floating-point division that creates AV may be done. "END" is not an instruction in the program but simply a means of informing the compiler that it has all the statements of the program.

```
C     FORTRAN PROGRAM TO COMPUTE AVERAGE SCORE FOR EACH SUBJECT.
C     FIRST CARD CONTAINS M = THE NUMBER OF SCORES PER SUBJECT IN
C     COLUMNS 1–2. SUBSEQUENT CARDS CONTAIN SUBJECT ID IN
C     COLUMNS 1–5 AND SCORES IN 3 COLUMN FIELDS BEGINNING IN
C     COLUMN 6.

      DIMENSION X(25)
      READ 2, M
    2 FORMAT (I2)
      EM = M
    1 READ 3, ID, (X(I), I = 1, M)
    3 FORMAT (I5, 25F3.0)
      SUM = 0.0
      DO 4 I = 1, M
    4 SUM = SUM + X(I)
      AV = SUM/EM
      PRINT 5, ID, AV
    5 FORMAT (I5, F10.4)
      GO TO 1
      END
```

The preceding discussion should give the reader some idea of what FORTRAN is. There are excellent IBM manuals from which a detailed knowledge of FORTRAN may be rapidly obtained, and which will enable the reader to understand all the steps in the listed programs of this book and to adapt these programs as desired. The reader should request a current *FORTRAN Primer* and *FORTRAN Reference Manual* from the IBM computer installation he intends to work with or directly from IBM.[5]

A very useful step between the specification of the mathematical and logical methods of a proposed analysis and the actual coding of a program is flow diagramming. A flow diagram exhibits the flow of events through the computer, and is thus a sort of map of the computational process. We present flow diagrams for two reasons. First, they may make the computational processes more transparent and understandable. Secondly, they provide an important aid to persons wishing to code the processes in languages other than FORTRAN.

[5] International Business Machines Corportation, 590 Madison Avenue, New York 22, New York. Another "how to" FORTRAN manual is McCracken (1961).

In the flow diagrams certain block shapes are used in systematic ways. Ordinarily, a rectangle encloses a description of an arithmetic operation. When it encloses a description of an input or output procedure or of an operation to be performed by a subroutine the labels *INPUT, OUTPUT, SUBROUTINE* are used. Conditional transfers based on a test of a variable are indicated as in the accompanying diagram.

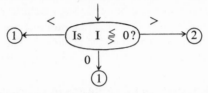

This diagram means that the current value of I is to be compared with zero. If I is less than or equal to zero, control is to be transferred to transfer point 1. If I is greater than zero, control is to go to point 2.

In order to make the important characteristics of our programs stand out in the flow diagrams, only the significant decision points in the programs have been diagrammed as conditional transfers. The enormous number of routine conditional transfers, or loops, required to perform the standard matrix manipulations such as transposing, adding, subtracting, and multiplying have not been diagrammed. Instead, these operations have simply been described within the rectangles. For this reason the flow diagrams presented should be viewed as descriptions of the FORTRAN-coded programs rather than as specifications of them. In Diagram 1.1, notice the simplicity of the flow diagram as compared with the FORTRAN listing given earlier in this section. Details of programming such as DIMENSION statements, FORMAT statements, and appropriate conversion of integers to floating-point variables are ignored in the flow diagram, which makes it possible to "see" the process in its bare essentials.

1.4 Introduction to Computer Usage

One problem that continually seems to harass the research worker who has not previously used a computer facility is that of having a problem computed. Old hands at computer usage seldom seem to appreciate the difficulty the uninitiated have in seeing just how to go about using the machine. Once the data are in punched cards, the type of analysis is decided on, and the computer program is selected, what do we do next? This is a simple question, but it is almost never considered in general discussions of computers and programming.

Probably one reason for the question's neglect is the wide variety of possible answers, since the right one depends on the particular computing facility. At some computer centers, individuals must actually operate the computer themselves. Such an entirely "open shop" is usually only possible for small and intermediate machines and is not particularly desirable for the worker who does not want to be bothered with the details of actually operating the machine himself.

At the other extreme is the completely "closed shop," actually a kind of service bureau, in which all programming and computer operation is performed for the research worker. One problem that often arises here is that through misunder-standing or insufficient definition of the problem the computations are not con-ducted exactly as the investigator wants it run. It is also a very expensive type of operation.

We tend to favor a facility where the research worker is responsible for his own programming and submits ready-to-run decks to the computer center, but experienced operators run the computer. This gives the research worker complete control over the actual analysis with a minimum of detailed involvement with computer mechanics. This may not be the most desirable organization for individuals developing new programs, but for behavioral scientists who will be using existing programs primarily (with minor modifications to suit their particular problems), this seems like the best type of center. In the following discussion we assume that this is the installation available to the reader.

What is a ready-to-run deck? Although the answer varies from center·to center, certain generalizations are possible. The first task is to obtain the program needed for the type of problem to be run. If it is one of the FORTRAN programs provided here, the next task is to make it conform to the center's conventions for input and output. This can be done either by having a consultant at the center check the program over or consulting the center's procedures handbook, which most computer centers provide. The READ and WRITE statements in our programs may not call for the tape numbers used for reading and writing at other centers. In addition, the PRINT statements in our programs are interpreted as WRITE OUTPUT TAPE 2 by the center at which these programs were developed. If PRINT means on-line printing at your center, you will want to change the PRINT statements to WRITE OUTPUT TAPE statements.

At this point it would be desirable to inspect the output statements in the program being prepared for compilation, to be sure that all the desired results will be available, and in their most useful form. The type of output research workers need varies, and so it is impossible to write a program that will satisfy all the possible users. Small changes in the FORTRAN listing will make intermediate results available, however, or will change printed output to punched output, etc. The output available from each of the programs listed here is indicated by its title.

Once the FORTRAN program listing conforms to local conventions, the statements are punched into cards and converted to an object program (a binary-coded machine language program). The conversion is done by requesting FORTRAN compilation. The computer converts the FORTRAN statements into the sequence of detailed machine steps that actually controls the operation of the computer during the data processing. The time it takes to compile a program on the IBM 709 is approximately:

$$\text{Minutes} = \frac{\text{Statements}}{20} + 1.$$

Thus forty FORTRAN statements can be compiled in about three minutes.

The next step is to set up the data deck according to the directions provided by the comment cards of the source program. (See p. 25 for an example of these directions.) This involves preparing the control cards describing the particular run and sequencing the cards and data in the proper order.

Once the data deck is set up, the total job deck is prepared. Computer centers may vary in the way this is to be done. The sequence of cards in the total job deck might be as follows, where cards marked with an asterisk are specified by the center at which the problem is computed.

(1) *ID. This card describes the problem number, the estimated time runs will take, estimated output, etc.

(2) *XEQ. A card indicating that the problem is to be executed. (As distinguished from runs in which only program compilation is involved.)

(3) The program deck.

(4) *DATA. A card indicating that computer control is now to be turned over to the program, which has just been completely read in.

(5) The data deck, including the control cards specified by that particular program.

Readers should consult their center's procedures handbook for a precise description of the control cards needed for computer runs.

Most general programs call for format cards. These tell the program where the data are in the cards. For example, subroutine CORREL might be used (see p. 25) for a job involving ten variables. They are in the data deck as follows:

Variable	Columns
X_1	11–12
X_2	13–15
X_3	16–17
X_4 to X_{10}	18–24

The format statement would be (starting in column 1 with the parenthesis):

$$(10 \text{ X, F 2.0, F 3.1, F 2.0, 7F 1.0}).$$

This tells the computer to skip the first ten columns, then to read a two-digit variable, followed by a three-digit variable with the decimal point after the first digit on the right,[6] another two-digit variable, and seven one-digit variables. It is possible to skip fields between variables if necessary.

This brief description of computer usage is necessarily incomplete due to center variations, but the point should be clear. Computers are *easy* to use once the "rules of the game" at the local center are understood. A visit to the center will clarify most of them for the reader.

---

[6] This assumes that the decimal point was not punched. See the FORTRAN manual for more detailed directions regarding format statements.

Flow Diagram for Computation of Average Test Score for Each Subject

INPUT
Read M, N, where M is the number of test scores for each subject and N is the
number of subjects.

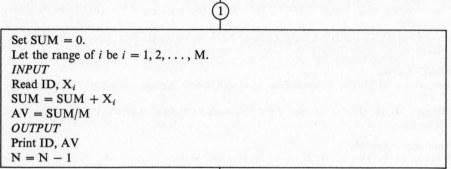

Set SUM = 0.
Let the range of i be $i = 1, 2, \ldots, M$.
INPUT
Read ID, X_i
SUM = SUM + X_i
AV = SUM/M
OUTPUT
Print ID, AV
N = N − 1

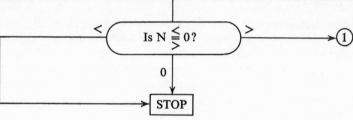

1.5   References

Computers
McCracken, D. D. (1957). *Digital Computer Programming.* New York: John Wiley and Sons, Chapter 1.

FORTRAN
General Information Manual: FORTRAN (1961). White Plains, N.Y.: IBM Data Processing Division.
McCracken, D. D. (1961). *A Guide to FORTRAN Programming.* New York: John Wiley and Sons.

Matrix Algebra
Faddeeva, V. N. (1959). *Computational Methods of Linear Algebra.* New York: Dover Publications.
Harman, H. H. (1960). *Modern Factor Analysis.* Chicago: University of Chicago Press, Chapter 3.

Multivariate Analysis
Kendall, M. G. (1957). *A Course in Multivariate Analysis.* New York: Hafner Publishing Company, Chapter 1.

Other Computer Applications
Borko, H., editor (1962). *Computer Applications in the Behavioral Sciences.* Englewood Cliffs, N.J.: Prentice-Hall.

CHAPTER TWO

Computing the basic matrices and vectors

2.1 Mathematics of Basic Matrices and Vectors

The first task in multivariate analysis is to accumulate the sums and sums of squares and cross products of scores for the sample group. This preliminary reduction of the data is always necessary, regardless of the type of multivariate analysis to follow. From these summations, the deviation sums-of-squares-and-cross-products matrix, the variance-covariance matrix, and the correlation matrix can be computed. One of these three matrices is then used in subsequent computations, depending on the kind of multivariate analysis to be performed. Because these first steps are similar in any multivariate analysis, a general subroutine, called Subroutine CORREL, has been written to form the initial matrices and vectors for most of the main programs in this book.

Because the program CORREL is of basic importance, and because the mathematical aspects of these operations are familiar to most readers, CORREL is explained in detail so that the relations among familiar algebraic formulas, matrix notation, and FORTRAN statements can be more easily seen. In other chapters the reader is referred to the flow charts and accompanying FORTRAN programs for a detailed understanding of the computational procedures. Hence the flow chart for CORREL should be consulted as the reader progresses through the following discussion.

Before proceeding, a word about notation is necessary. In this text, upper-case **boldface** type is used for matrices and lower-case **boldface** type for vectors. The symbols used in FORTRAN are all upper case, including subscripts written in parentheses. When a matrix is defined, the elements of the matrix are usually written in standard algebraic statistical notation, with the matrix symbol on the left and the FORTRAN symbol on the right. Multiple letters are generally used for variable names in FORTRAN, and so those symbols are frequently different from their algebraic or matrix equivalents.

The initial accumulations CORREL forms are defined algebraically as follows:

$$\sum_{i=1}^{N} X_{ij} = \text{sum of scores on test } j \text{ for all } N \text{ individuals.}$$

$$\sum_{i=1}^{N} X_{ij}^{2} = \text{sum of squares of scores on test } j \text{ for all } N \text{ individuals.}$$

$$\sum_{i=1}^{N} X_{ij}X_{ik} = \text{sum of cross products of scores on tests } j \text{ and } k \text{ for the } N \text{ individuals.}$$

The sums are formed for each test or pair of tests; i.e., $j, k = 1, 2, \ldots, m$, where m is the total number of tests. Now in terms of vectors and matrices, the desired sums can be defined as **a** and **B**:

Matrix Notation   FORTRAN Notation

$$\mathbf{a} = \quad [\Sigma X_1 \;\; \Sigma X_2 \; \ldots \; \Sigma X_m] \qquad = \text{SX(I)}$$

$$\mathbf{B} = \begin{bmatrix} \Sigma X_1^{2} & \Sigma X_1 X_2 & \ldots & \Sigma X_1 X_m \\ \Sigma X_2 X_1 & \Sigma X_2^{2} & \ldots & \Sigma X_2 X_m \\ \cdot & \cdot & & \cdot \\ \cdot & \cdot & & \cdot \\ \cdot & \cdot & & \cdot \\ \Sigma X_m X_1 & \Sigma X_m X_2 & \ldots & \Sigma X_m^{2} \end{bmatrix} \qquad = \text{SS(I, J)}$$

If **X** is a score roster matrix, with N rows and m columns, **B** could be formed as follows:

$$\mathbf{X'X} = \mathbf{B}$$

This involves multiplying the $m \times N$ matrix $\mathbf{X'}$, which is the transpose of **X**, times the $N \times m$ matrix **X**. The product is the $m \times m$ matrix **B**. This method of computing **B** would, however, require a very large memory for even an average-size sample, for the entire score roster would have to be stored as the matrix **X**.

CORREL forms **a** and **B** [denoted SX(I) and SS(I, J) in FORTRAN] by reading one score vector at a time, i.e., one row of **X** at a time, and then adding these scores, their squares, and cross products to the appropriate locations in SX(I) and SS(I, J). After SX(I) and SS(I, J) are set equal to zero, the first set of m scores [X(I)] is read in and the following steps take place:

DO 260 I = 1, M

SX(I) = SX(I) + X(I)

DO 260 J = I, M

260 SS(I, J) = SS(I, J) + X(I) * X(J).

Then the second score vector is read in, and these four statements are repeated. This process is repeated for each of the N score vectors. Notice that only the upper triangle in SS(I, J) is being formed because matrix **B** is symmetric; hence the number of multiplications is halved. Then, after all the score vectors have been read in and accumulated in $SX(I)$ and $SS(I, J)$, the elements of the lower triangle are set equal to the upper triangle by the following DO loop

$$DO\ 265\ I = 1,\ M$$

$$DO\ 265\ J = I,\ M$$

$$265\ SS(J, I) = SS(I, J).$$

The deviation sums of squares and cross products matrix **C** is then formed from **B** and **a**. The following algebraic relationships are used in this particular case (lower-case is used for deviation scores):

$$\sum x_1^2 = \sum X_1^2 - \frac{(\sum X_1)^2}{N},$$

$$\sum x_1 x_2 = \sum X_1 X_2 - \frac{\sum X_1 \sum X_2}{N}.$$

In matrix algebra this can be written $\mathbf{C} = \mathbf{B} - \left(\dfrac{1}{N}\right) \mathbf{a}'\mathbf{a}$

where $\left(\dfrac{1}{N}\right)\mathbf{a}'\mathbf{a}$ is

$$\begin{bmatrix} \dfrac{(\sum X_1)^2}{N} & \dfrac{\sum X_1 \sum X_2}{N} & \cdots & \dfrac{\sum X_1 \sum X_m}{N} \\ \dfrac{\sum X_2 \sum X_1}{N} & \dfrac{(\sum X_2)^2}{N} & \cdots & \dfrac{\sum X_2 \sum X_m}{N} \\ \cdot & \cdot & & \cdot \\ \cdot & \cdot & & \cdot \\ \cdot & \cdot & & \cdot \\ \dfrac{\sum X_m \sum X_1}{N} & \dfrac{\sum X_m \sum X_2}{N} & \cdots & \dfrac{(\sum X_m)^2}{N} \end{bmatrix}.$$

The FORTRAN statement for this step is:

$$SSD(I, J) = SS(I, J) - SX(I) * SX(J)/ENG.$$

This step is performed for all combinations of values for I and J, from 1 to m. The resulting matrix is:

$$\mathbf{C} = \begin{bmatrix} \sum x_1^2 & \sum x_1 x_2 & \cdots & \sum x_1 x_m \\ \sum x_2 x_1 & \sum x_2^2 & \cdots & \sum x_2 x_m \\ \cdot & \cdot & & \cdot \\ \cdot & \cdot & & \cdot \\ \cdot & \cdot & & \cdot \\ \sum x_m x_1 & \sum x_m x_2 & \cdots & \sum x_m^2 \end{bmatrix} = SSD(I, J).$$

The dispersion or variance-covariance matrix $\mathbf{D}$ is formed from $\mathbf{C}$ by dividing each element of $\mathbf{C}$ by $N - 1$.

$$\text{Variance:} \quad s_1^2 = \frac{\sum x_1^2}{N - 1} = s_{11}.$$

$$\text{Covariance:} \quad s_1 s_2 r_{12} = \frac{\sum x_1 x_2}{N - 1} = s_{12}.$$

To simplify notation, the symbols s_{11} and s_{12} are used for designating elements of the variance-covariance matrix.

$$\mathbf{D} = \begin{bmatrix} s_{11} & s_{12} & \cdots & s_{1m} \\ s_{21} & s_{22} & \cdots & s_{2m} \\ \cdot & \cdot & & \cdot \\ \cdot & \cdot & & \cdot \\ \cdot & \cdot & & \cdot \\ s_{m1} & s_{m2} & \cdots & s_{mm} \end{bmatrix} = D(I, J).$$

The FORTRAN statements for forming $\mathbf{D}$ from $\mathbf{C}$ are:

DO 441 I = 1, M

DO 441 J = I, M

D(I, J) = SSD(I, J)/(ENG − 1.0)

441 D(J, I) = D(I, J).

Finally, the correlation matrix $\mathbf{R}$ is formed from $\mathbf{D}$ by using the relationship

$$r_{12} = \frac{s_1 s_2 r_{12}}{s_1 s_2}$$

where the values for s_i in the denominator are obtained by taking the square root of the diagonal elements of $\mathbf{D}$, and the covariances in the numerator are the off-diagonal elements of $\mathbf{D}$. In the matrix notation, $\mathbf{R} = \mathbf{EDE}$ where $\mathbf{E}$ is an $m \times m$ diagonal matrix, the diagonal elements of which are $1/\sqrt{s_{ii}}$, and s_{ii} are the corresponding diagonal elements of $\mathbf{D}$.

$$\mathbf{R} = \begin{bmatrix} 1.00 & r_{12} & \cdots & r_{1m} \\ r_{21} & 1.00 & \cdots & r_{2m} \\ \cdot & \cdot & & \cdot \\ \cdot & \cdot & & \cdot \\ \cdot & \cdot & & \cdot \\ r_{m1} & r_{m2} & \cdots & 1.00 \end{bmatrix} = R(I, J).$$

In FORTRAN, R(I, J) is formed as follows:

DO 486 I = 1, M

DO 486 J = I, M

R(I, J) = D(I, J)/SD(I) * SD(J)

486 R(J, I) = R(I, J).

where SD(I) are the square roots of the diagonal elements of D(I, J), that is, the standard deviations.

It is suggested that the reader go over the flow chart and FORTRAN statements for Subroutine CORREL, using this description of the mathematical operations involved. Then he will have the background needed to understand the more unfamiliar aspects of this text—matrix notation, flow diagrams, and FORTRAN.

2.2   Example of Reporting Basic Matrices and Vectors

Readers of research reports are not generally interested in seeing all the basic matrices and vectors computed for sample groups. Usually it suffices to report the

TABLE 2.1

Aptitude Variables, Jervis-Congdon Data

Variable		Mean	S.D.
A.C.E.[1]	Q	33.6	5.61
A.C.E.	L	84.0	13.37
A.C.E.	T	118.1	14.22
CoopRdg.[2]	V	57.8	8.33
CoopRdg.	S	66.2	8.82
CoopRdg.	C	61.7	7.10
CoopRdg.	T	63.0	7.57
Watson-Glaser[3]		69.9	8.12
Raven Prog. Matrices[4]		24.8	4.17
WAIS[5]	VI	14.5	1.63
WAIS	V2	16.5	2.29
WAIS	V3	13.8	2.08
WAIS	V4	14.1	2.10
WAIS	V5	12.4	2.92
WAIS	V6	15.2	2.00
WAIS	Verbal	131.1	7.10
WAIS	P1	11.9	2.21
WAIS	P2	12.7	2.14
WAIS	P3	13.2	2.60
WAIS	P4	12.7	2.66
WAIS	P5	11.7	3.10
WAIS	Performance	117.5	10.53
WAIS	Total	126.8	6.96
WAIS	V − P	34.6	11.77

[1] American Council on Education Psychological Examination.
[2] Cooperative Reading Tests.
[3] Watson-Glaser Critical Thinking Appraisal.
[4] Raven Progressive Matrices.
[5] Wechsler Adult Intelligence Scale.

TABLE 2.2

Correlations among Aptitude Variables for 105 Boys in Jervis-Congdon Data

	A.C.E.	CoopRdg.				W P									WAIS							
	L	T	V	S	C	T	G	M	1	2	3	4	5	6	V	1	2	3	4	5	P	T	V–P
Q	.49	*	.26	*	*	*	*	.29	*	*	.52	*	.20	*	.28	.24	.21	.28	.21	*	.35	.41	*
L		.86	.65	.56	.35	.39	.61	*	.42	.25	*	.25	*	.54	.47	*	*	*	*	*	*	.30	.27
T			.58	.63	.49	.59	.22	*	.40	.30	.23	.21	*	.49	.51	*	.21	*	*	*	*	.42	*
V				.79	.59	.87	.37	*	.35	*	*	*	*	.68	.44	−.21	*	*	*	*	*	.24	.30
S					.49	.80	.27	*	.44	.26	*	.23	*	.43	.46	*	*	*	*	*	*	.25	.33
C						.62	*	*	.26	*	*	.29	*	.33	.38	*	*	*	*	*	*	.33	*
T							.50	.50	.41	.24	*	.29	*	.55	.49	*	*	*	*	*	*	.30	.30
WG								.50	*	*	*	.30	*	.24	.24	*	*	*	*	.24	.28	.23	*
PM									*	*	.33	*	*	*	*	*	*	*	*	*	.28	.28	*
V1										.28	*	.29	*	.48	.62	*	*	*	*	*	*	.34	.43
V2											*	.26	*	.32	.53	*	*	*	*	*	*	.39	.25
V3												*	*	*	.47	*	*	.22	.23	*	.24	.45	*
V4													*	.31	.56	*	*	*	*	*	*	.40	.27
V5														*	.49	*	*	.21	*	.20	*	.42	*
V6															.64	*	*	*	*	*	*	.36	.42
V																*	*	*	*	*	.47	.71	.46
P1																	*	.22	*	*	.47	.39	−.36
P2																		.37	.21	.31	.61	.48	−.50
P3																			*	.47	.71	.57	−.57
P4																				.24	.59	.46	−.48
P5																					.70	.55	−.57
P																						.79	−.79
T																							.27

* Indicates r < .195, p > .05.

vectors of group means and standard deviations and the correlation matrix, or some similar selected part of the results. The example reported here is drawn from test data on 105 academically superior male high-school students who attended the St. Paul's School (N.H.) summer program in 1959.[1]

Table 2.1 gives the mean and standard deviations for twenty-four aptitudinal measures, and Table 2.2 gives the intercorrelations of these tests for the group of subjects. These data will be discussed and analyzed further in subsequent chapters.

In reporting a large correlation matrix, the reader is usually aided by the deletion of insignificant correlations. This enables us to focus more easily on those relations in which we have confidence. Since the matrix is symmetrical, only the upper triangle need be reported. The r's for one variable with all others can be found simply by reading down the column of that variable until the last element in that column is reached, then reading from there across the row just below that last element.

---

[1] These data were collected by Dr. Fred Jervis and Dr. Robert Congdon of the U.N.H. Counseling Center. The investigation is unpublished; the data will be referred to hereafter as the Jervis-Congdon data.

Flow Diagram for Basic Matrices and Vectors (Subroutine CORREL)

(Enter CORREL from main or calling program.)
INPUT
Read T, NG where T is the number of variables and NG is the number of subjects in this group.

Throughout this program let the range of i be $i = 1, 2, 3, \ldots, T$ and let the range of j be $j = 1, 2, 3, \ldots, T$.
Set $SX_i = 0$ and $SS_{ij} = 0$ for initialization.
CASES = NG

①

INPUT
Read X_i where X_i is the score vector of the ith subject.

$SX_i = SX_i + X_i$ accumulating raw sums.
$SS_{ij} = SS_{ij} + X_i^2$ accumulating raw sums of squares and
                           cross products.
CASES = CASES − 1

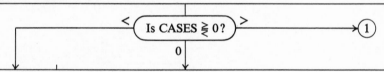

Is CASES $\gtreqless$ 0?   →①

0

$SSD_{ij} = SS_{ij} - SX_i \cdot SX_j/NG$ forming deviation s.s.c.p.*
$XM_i = SX_i/NG$ forming means.
$D_{ij} = SSD_{ij}/(NG - 1)$ forming dispersion matrix.
$SD_i = \sqrt{D_{ii}}$ forming standard deviations.
$R_{ij} = \quad D_{ij}/(SD_i \cdot SD_j)$ forming correlation matrix.

OUTPUT
Print and punch T, NG, SX_i, SS_{ij}, SSD_{ij}, XM_i, SD_i, D_{ij}, R_{ij} as desired, with labels.
(All these products of CORREL are also reported to the main or calling program.)

RETURN

* Here and subsequently in the flow diagrams, the abbreviation s.s.c.p. is used for "sums of squares and cross products."

FORTRAN SOURCE PROGRAM FOR SUBROUTINE CORREL

```
C       SUBROUTINE CORREL.

C            THIS SUBROUTINE PERFORMS A COMPLETE CORRELATION ANALYSIS FOR
C       UP TO 50 VARIABLES. SEVERAL OUTPUT OPTIONS ARE AVAILABLE.  WITH
C       THE MAIN CALLING PROGRAM FOR CORREL (SEE CALL CORREL).
C       CORRELATION ANALYSIS FOR ANY NUMBER OF GROUPS CAN BE PERFORMED IN
C       ONE RUN.
C       SUBROUTINES MPRINT AND MPUNCH ARE REQUIRED.

C       INPUT.

C            THE FIRST CONTROL CARD FOR EACH GROUP IS DEFINED AS FOLLOWS.
C       COL.1-2  M = T = NUMBER OF VARIABLES (MAX. OF 50)
C       COL.3-7  NG = ENG = NUMBER OF SUBJECTS IN GROUP
C       COL.8    L1 = 1 TO COMPUTE DISPERSION AND CORRELATION MATRIX,
C                        OTHERWISE 0.
C       USE THE FOLLOWING CODE FOR VALUES OF L2 THROUGH L5.
C            1 = DO NOT PUNCH MATRIX
C            2 = PUNCH MATRIX IN F, NOT E(10X 10F7.2).
C            3 = PUNCH MATRIX IN E, NOT F(10X 5E14.7).
C            4 = PUNCH MATRIX IN BOTH F AND E.
C            (F IS USED FOR MAKING ADDITIONAL PRINTOUTS FOR RESEARCH
C            REPORTS, ETC. E IS USED IF MATRIX IS NEEDED FOR SUBSEQUENT
C            COMPUTATIONS)
C       COL. 9   L2 = RAW SUMS OF SQUARES AND CROSS PRODUCTS (SS OR B)
C       COL.10   L3 = DEVIATION SUMS OF SQUARES AND CROSS PRODUCTS (SSD OR C)
C       COL.11   L4 = DISPERSION MATRIX (D)
C       COL.12   L5 = CORRELATION MATRIX (R)
C       COL.13   L6 = 1 TO PUNCH MEANS AND STANDARD DEVIATIONS IN E,
C                        OTHERWISE 0.
C       COL.14   L8 = 0 PRINT ONLY THE MEANS, STANDARD DEVIATIONS, AND
C                        CORRELATION MATRIX.
C                L8 = 1 PRINT ALL MATRICES.
C       COL.15-17  IPROB = PROBLEM NUMBER FOR IDENTIFYING PUNCHED OUTPUT.

C            THE SECOND CARD CONTAINS GROUP TITLE IN COLS. 1-72.
C       CARDS 3-5 CONTAIN THE VARIABLE FORMAT FOR DATA CARDS.  FIRST
C       SCORE CARD IS CARD NUMBER SIX.


C       OUTPUT.

C            OUTPUT IS PRINTED AND PUNCHED AS DEFINED BY THE FIRST CONTROL
C       CARD OUTLINED ABOVE.  PUNCHED MATRICES ARE IDENTIFIED IN COLUMN 5
C       AS FOLLOWS.
C            B = RAW SUMS OF SQUARES AND CROSS PRODUCTS MATRIX
C            C = DEVIATION SUMS OF SQUARES AND CROSS PRODUCTS MATRIX
C            D = DISPERSION OR VARIANCE-COVARIANCE MATRIX
C            R = CORRELATION MATRIX
C       PROBLEM NUMBER IS PUNCHED IN COLUMNS 1-3.
C       ROW NUMBER IS PUNCHED IN COLUMNS 7-8.
C       SECTION OF ROW IS PUNCHED IN COLUMNS 9-10.
        SUBROUTINE CORREL (T,NG,SX,SS,SSD,D,R,XM,SD)
        DIMENSION FMT(36),FMR(36),X(50),SX(50),SS(50,50),SSD(50,50),
       1D(50,50),R(50,50), XM(50), SD(50), TITLE (12)
        READ 21, T,NG,L1,L2,L3,L4,L5,L6,L8,IPROB
     21 FORMAT(F2.0,I5,7I1,I3)
        READ 22, (TITLE(I), I=1,12)
     22 FORMAT (12A6)
```

```
      L12=L3+L4+L5+L6
      IF (L12-4) 210, 210, 207
  207 PUNCH 22, (TITLE(I), I=1,12)
  210 M=T
      ENG=NG
      READ 22, (FMT(I), I=1,36)
      DO 230  I=1,M
  220 SX(I)=0.0
      DO 230  J=1,M
  230 SS(I,J)=0.0
      CASES=ENG
  240 READ FMT, (X(I), I=1,M)
      DO 260 I = 1,M
      SX(I)=SX(I)+X(I)
      DO 260 J = 1,M
  260 SS (I,J) = SS(I,J) + X (I)* X(J)
C     RAW SUMS OF SQUARES AND CROSS PRODUCTS
      CASES=CASES-1.0
      IF (CASES)  280,280,240
  280 DO 286  I=1,M
      DO 286  J=1,M
      SSD(I,J)=SS(I,J)-SX(I)*SX(J)/ENG
      SS(J,I) = SS(I,J)
  286 SSD(J,I)= SSD(I,J)
C     DEVIATION SUMS OF SQUARES AND CROSS PRODUCTS
      DO 295  I=1,M
      XM(I)=SX(I)/ENG
  295 SD(I)=SQRTF(SSD(I,I)/(ENG-1.0))
C     MEANS AND STANDARD DEVIATIONS
      PRINT 31, (TITLE(I), I=1,12)
   31 FORMAT (26H1CORRELATION ANALYSIS FOR , 12A6)
      PRINT 32, T
   32 FORMAT (23H0NUMBER OF VARIABLES = , F3.0)
      PRINT 33, NG
   33 FORMAT (36H0NUMBER OF SUBJECTS IN THIS GROUP = , I5)
      PRINT 34
   34 FORMAT (20H0MEANS OF THIS GROUP)
      PRINT 35, (XM(I), I=1,M)
   35 FORMAT (5F14.7)
      PRINT 36
   36 FORMAT (34H0STANDARD DEVIATIONS OF THIS GROUP)
      PRINT 35, (SD(I), I=1,M)
  355 CONTINUE
  360 IF (L6)  370,370,365
  365 PUNCH 34
      PUNCH 39, (XM(I), I=1,M)
   39 FORMAT (5E14.7)
      PUNCH 36
      PUNCH 39, (SD(I), I=1,M)
  370 IF (L8)  385,385,375
  375 PRINT 376
  376 FORMAT (39H1RAW SUMS OF SQUARES AND CROSS PRODUCTS)
      CALL MPRINT (SS, M, 2, 6HRAW SS)
  385 GO TO (400, 386, 387, 386),L2
  386 CALL M PUNCH (SS, I PROB, 1HB, M, 1)
      IF (L2-4) 400,387,400
```

```
387 CALL M PUNCH (SS,I PROB, 1HB, M, 2)
400 IF (L8)  415,415,405
405 PRINT 406
406 FORMAT (45H1DEVIATION SUMS OF SQUARES AND CROSS PRODUCTS)
    CALL MPRINT ( SSD, M,2,6HDEV SS)
415 GO TO (430, 420, 425, 420),L3
420 CALL M PUNCH (SSD, I PROB, 1HC, M, 1)
    IF (L3-4) 430, 425, 430
425 CALL M PUNCH (SSD, I PROB, 1HC, M, 2)
430 IF (L1) 700, 700, 435
435 DO 441   I=1,M
    DO 441   J=1,M
    D(I,J)=SSD(I,J)/(ENG-1.0)
441 D(J,I)=D(I,J)
C       DISPERSION MATRIX
    IF (L8)  460,460,450
450 PRINT 451
451 FORMAT(27H1VARIANCE-COVARIANCE MATRIX)
    CALL M PRINT (D, M, 2, 6HD MAT )
460 GO TO (475,465,470,465),L4
465 CALL M PUNCH (D, I PROB,1HD, M, 1)
    IF (L4-4) 475, 470, 475
470 CALL M PUNCH (D, I PROB, 1HD, M, 2)
475 DO 486 I = 1,M
    DO 486   J=I,M
    R(I,J) = D (I,J)/(SD(I)* SD(J))
486 R(J,I)=R(I,J)
C       CORRELATION MATRIX
    GO TO (625, 497, 498, 497),L5
497 CALL M PUNCH (R, I PROB, 1HR, M, 1)
    IF (L5-4) 610,498,610
498 CALL M PUNCH (R, I PROB, 1HR, M, 2)
610 CONTINUE
625 IPNO=1
628 PRINT 50, (TITLE (I), I = 1,12), NG, I PNO
 50 FORMAT (21H1CORRELATION MATRIX, , 12A6,1X2HN= , I4, 6X9HPAGE NO. ,
   1I2)
    CALL MPRINT(R, M, 2, 5HR MAT)
    PRINT 62 ,(XM(J), J= 1,M)
 62 FORMAT(6H0MEANS4X10F11.2/(10X10F11.2))
    PRINT 63, (SD(J), J= 1,M)
 63 FORMAT(8H0STD DEV2X10F11.2/(10X10F11.2))
700 RETURN
    END


C     SUBROUTINE MPRINT

C         THIS SUBROUTINE WILL PRINTOUT SQUARE MATRICES UP TO 50 X 50.
C     ALL ROWS AND COLUMNS ARE APPROPRIATELY LABELED.
C     DEFINITIONS OF SUBROUTINE ARGUMENTS
C     R(I,J) = MATRIX TO BE PRINTED
C     M = ORDER (MAX. OF 50)
C     L = 1 FOR 20F5.2 OUTPUT OR 2 FOR 10F12.2
C     TI IS A SIX-CHARACTER DESIGNATE OF THE MATRIX
```

```
      SUBROUTINE  MPRINT  (R, M, L, TI)
      DIMENSION  R(50,50),  J(50)
      IF  (L-1)  2,2,4
    2 L1=19
      GO TO 5
    4 L1=9
    5 J1=0
      J2=0
      JSEC = 0
      DO 8   I= 1,M
    8 J(I) = I
    9 J1 = J2 +1
      J2 = J1 +L1
      IF  (J2 - M)  13,13,12
   12 J2=M
   13 JSEC = JSEC + 1
      IF  (JSEC -1)   18, 18 , 19
   18 PRINT 17,  TI, JSEC
   17 FORMAT (1H0, A6, 9H  SECTION I3/)
      GO TO   201
   19 PRINT 20,  TI, JSEC
   20 FORMAT (1H1, A6, 9H  SECTION I3/)
  201 IF(L-1) 21, 21, 26
   21 PRINT 22, (J(I), I=J1,J2)
   22 FORMAT(6H0  ROW 3X2OI5)
      DO 23 I=1,M
   23 PRINT 24, I, (R(I,J), J=J1,J2)
   24 FORMAT(I6, 4X2OF5.2)
      GO TO 31
   26 PRINT 27,(J(I), I=J1,J2)
   27 FORMAT(6H0  ROW 3X10I11)
      DO 29 I=1,M
   29 PRINT 30, I, (R(I,J), J= J1,J2)
   30 FORMAT (I6, 4X 10F11.2)
   31 IF (J2-M) 9,32,32
   32 RETURN
      END


C      SUBROUTINE MPUNCH

C          THIS SUBROUTINE WILL PUNCHOUT SQUARE MATRICES UP TO 50 X 50.
C      ALL ROWS AND SECTIONS OF ROWS ARE IDENTIFIED IN FIRST TEN COLUMNS.
C          DEFINITIONS OF SUBROUTINE ARGUMENTS
C      R = THE SQUARE MATRIX TO BE PUNCHED
C      IPROB = THE PROBLEM NUMBER , PUNCHED IN FIRST 3 COLUMNS
C      ATYP = A ONE-CHARACTER DESIGNATE OF THE MATRIX TYPE, PUNCHED IN
C      COLUMN 5
C      M = THE ORDER OF THE MATRIX
C      L = 1 MATRIX PUNCHED IN 10F7.2
C      L = 2 MATRIX PUNCHED IN 5E14.7
C      THE SECTION OF THE ROW WHICH IS IN EACH CARD IS INDICATED IN
C      COLUMN 10.

      SUBROUTINE MPUNCH (R, IPROB, ATYP, M, L)
      DIMENSION R(50,50)
```

CORREL PROGRAM (CONTINUED)

```
      IF(L-1) 8, 8, 22
   8  J1 = 0
      J2 = 0
      JSEC = 0
   9  J1 = J2 + 1
      J2 = J1 + 9
      IF (J2 - M) 13, 13, 12
  12  J2 = M
  13  JSEC = JSEC + 1
      DO 15 I = 1,M
  15  PUNCH 16, IPROB, ATYP, I, JSEC, (R(I,J), J = J1, J2)
  16  FORMAT (I3, 1XA1, I3, I2, 10F7.2)
      IF (J2 - M) 9, 19, 19
  19  CONTINUE
      GO TO 32
  22  DO 30 I = 1,M
      J1 = 0
      J2 = 0
      JSEC = 0
  24  J1 = J2 + 1
      J2 = J1 + 4
      IF (J2 - M) 26,26,25
  25  J2 = M
  26  JSEC = JSEC +1
      PUNCH 28, IPROB, ATYP, I, JSEC, (R(I,J),J = J1, J2)
  28  FORMAT (I3, 1XA1, I3, I2, 5E14.7)
      IF (J2- M) 24,30,30
  30  CONTINUE
  32  RETURN
      END
```

MAIN PROGRAM TO CALL CORREL FOR ANY NUMBER OF GROUPS

```
C      CALL CORREL.

C          SET UP EACH GROUP AS REQUIRED BY SUBROUTINE CORREL.  A CARD
C      IS PLACED AT THE BEGINNING OF THE FIRST GROUP WHICH HAS,
C      IN COL. 1-2, THE NUMBER OF GROUPS TO BE RUN.  ALL OUTPUT IS  FROM
C      SUBROUTINE CORREL.

       DIMENSION SX(50), SS(50,50),  SSD(50,50), D(50,50), R(50,50),
      1  XM(50), SD(50)
       READ 11, JOBS
   11 FORMAT (I2)
  101 CALL CORREL    (T,NG,SX,SS,SSD,D,R,XM,SD)
       JOBS = JOBS - 1
       IF (JOBS) 103, 103, 101
  103 CALL EXIT
       END
```

CHAPTER THREE

Multiple and canonical correlation

3.1 Mathematics of Multiple Correlation

Multiple-correlation analysis, which is often called multiple regression,[1] provides an analysis of the relations among a single criterion measure and two or more predictor measures. One result of the analysis is an equation for predicting the unknown criterion score of a new subject from his known set of predictor scores. The complete test space in the analysis is m dimensional, with $m - 1$ predictors plus the criterion variable. The criterion is the mth measurement on each subject. As with all the prediction schemes reported in this book, the analysis initially requires *a complete set* of m scores for N subjects in what we may call the sample, or reference, group. On the basis of what is learned about the interrelations (technically, the interdependencies or intercorrelations) among the variables as they occur in this norm group, it becomes possible to take the $m - 1$ predictor scores for new subjects, and compute for each new subject a predicted score on the mth variable, which is the criterion variable. This predicted score is also called a regressed score. It is computed as a linear combination of the $m - 1$ known predictor scores of the subject.

Most of the prediction schemes reported in this book involve linear combinations, also called linear functions, of the predictor variables. Because of this, some discussion of linear combinations may be useful here. The simple slope intercept equation for a straight line, $Y = bX + a$, where b is the slope and a is the Y-axis intercept of the line, may be diagrammed, as in Figure 3.1.

Notice that the equation of a line involves coefficients specifying the location (i.e., intercept, a) and direction (i.e., slope, b) of the line, but no powers of X other than one. Of the infinite number of functional relations that might be established between X and Y, the subset of possible linear relations represents a very simple

---

[1] Although there are important theoretical differences between regression and correlation analysis, in practice both correlation coefficients and regression equations are generally desired in the same problem, and either term is applied to the over-all analysis.

and manageable collection, and statisticians usually elect to restrict their explorations to it. The simplicity resulting from the imposition of the linear restraint can be enhanced by translating the raw scores into deviation or standard scores, so that the fitted line always passes through the origin of the axis system. Then the equation has only to specify the direction of the line (its slope), since the location is fixed (the intercept constant is zero). Thus the regression equation for predicting z_{2i} from z_{1i}, where z_{1i} and z_{2i} are standard scores of subject i on tests 1 and 2, may be written

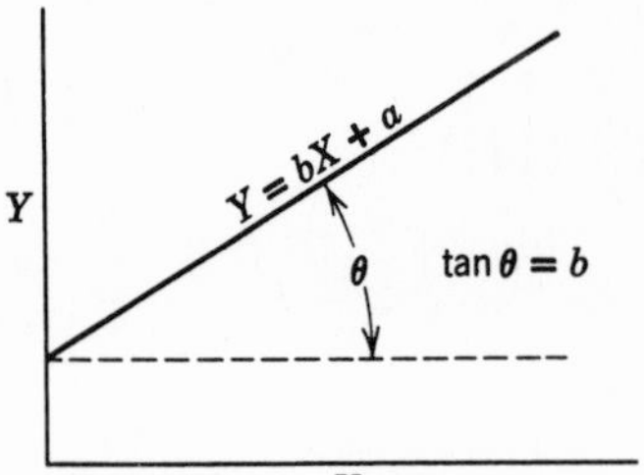

$$\hat{z}_{2i} = r_{12}z_{1i}$$

where r_{12} is the necessary slope coefficient and no intercept constant is required.[2]

When there are two or more predictors, additional terms are required for the regression equation to describe the orientation of a plane in the test space, which is now of higher dimensionality. In the general case of an m-dimensional space, the standard score regression equation has the form

$$\hat{z}_{mi} = \beta_1 z_{1i} + \beta_2 z_{2i} + \beta_3 z_{3i} + \cdots + \beta_{m-1} z_{(m-1)i}.$$

Technically, the general equation locates a hyperplane in the m dimensions from which projections are made to the criterion axis. The beta coefficients, also called beta weights, are not simple correlations of each predictor with the criterion; they are also influenced by the intercorrelations among the predictors. These coefficients have the technical name standard partial regression coefficients. For a given set of predictors, comparison of the absolute values of the beta weights indicates the relative contributions of the corresponding variables to the prediction of the criterion. It is possible to compute a coefficient of multiple correlation $R_{m \cdot 1,2,\ldots,m-1}$ that is similar to a simple product moment correlation coefficient but has the range $0 \leq R \leq +1$. The coefficient R^2 provides an estimate of the proportion of the total variance in the criterion that can be predicted from the known variance in the predictors, and is a measure of the over-all effectiveness of the multiple regression. The standard error of estimate of a regressed score may also be computed. An F test of the statistical significance of R is available.

It is often desirable to compute the regressed deviation score $\hat{x}_{mi}$ or the regressed raw score $\hat{X}_{mi}$ for each new subject, rather than the regressed standard score. The formula for regressed deviation scores is

$$\hat{x}_{mi} = b_1 x_{1i} + b_2 x_{2i} + b_3 x_{3i} + \cdots + b_{m-1} x_{(m-1)i}$$

where the b coefficients are derived from the corresponding beta weights by scaling

Figure 3.1

[2] $z_{1i} = (X_{1i} - \bar{X}_1)/\hat{\sigma}_1$, where $\hat{\sigma}_1$ is the maximum likelihood estimate of the population standard deviation.

each beta weight by the ratio of the standard deviation of the criterion to the standard deviation of that predictor. Thus $b_j = (\hat{\sigma}_m/\hat{\sigma}_j)\beta_j$. The formula for regressed raw scores employs these b weights and is

$$\hat{X}_{mi} = b_1 X_{1i} + b_2 X_{2i} + b_3 X_{3i} + \cdots + b_{m-1} X_{(m-1)i} + C$$

where C is an intercept constant involving the means of the m variables in a way to be shown later in a computing formula.

Differential calculus is used in the derivation of the multiple-regression model to obtain a solution for the weights in the linear function that minimizes the average squared error of prediction. That is, if an error e_i is defined as $e_i = z_{mi} - \hat{z}_{mi}$, which is the discrepancy between the actual and predicted score for the ith individual, the purpose of multiple regression is to minimize the function of e

$$(3.1) \qquad\qquad f(e) = \sum_i (z_{mi} - \hat{z}_{mi})^2/N.$$

If the symbolic linear combination of the predictors that defines $\hat{z}_{mi}$ is substituted in equation 3.1, the function becomes

$$f(e) = \frac{1}{N} \sum_i [z_{mi} - (\beta_1 z_{1i} + \beta_2 z_{2i} + \cdots + \beta_{m-1} z_{(m-1)i})]^2.$$

When the partial derivative of the function with respect to each β_j is taken, a system of $m-1$ normal equations in $m-1$ unknowns is reached. These normal equations have the form

$$
\begin{aligned}
\beta_1 &+ r_{12}\beta_2 &&+ r_{13}\beta_3 &&+ \cdots + r_{1(m-1)}\beta_{m-1} &&= r_{1m} \\
r_{12}\beta_1 &+ \beta_2 &&+ r_{23}\beta_3 &&+ \cdots + r_{2(m-1)}\beta_{m-1} &&= r_{2m} \\
r_{13}\beta_1 &+ r_{23}\beta_2 &&+ \beta_3 &&+ \cdots + r_{3(m-1)}\beta_{m-1} &&= r_{3m} \\
&\ \ \vdots &&\ \ \vdots &&\ \ \vdots \\
r_{1(m-1)}\beta_1 &+ r_{2(m-1)}\beta_2 &&+ r_{3(m-1)}\beta_3 &&+ \cdots + \quad \beta_{m-1} &&= r_{(m-1)m}.
\end{aligned}
$$

Notice that besides the unknown beta weights the normal equations involve all the intercorrelations among the m variables, which are known for the reference group. On the left we see the intercorrelations among the $m-1$ predictors and on the right the correlation of each predictor with the criterion.

There are several useful methods for solving such a system of simultaneous equations, but a very helpful first step is to translate the problem into matrix notation. The collection of all intercorrelations among the m variables forms an m-square symmetric matrix as it is reported by subroutine CORREL (see Section 2.1) and may be called **R**. Matrix **R** must be partitioned into the required segments as follows:

$$R = \begin{bmatrix} r_{11} & r_{12} & r_{13} & \cdots & r_{1(m-1)} & r_{1m} \\ r_{21} & r_{22} & r_{23} & \cdots & r_{2(m-1)} & r_{2m} \\ r_{31} & r_{32} & r_{33} & \cdots & r_{3(m-1)} & r_{3m} \\ \cdot & \cdot & \cdot & \cdots & \cdot & \cdot \\ \cdot & \cdot & \cdot & \cdots & \cdot & \cdot \\ \cdot & \cdot & \cdot & \cdots & \cdot & \cdot \\ r_{(m-1)1} & r_{(m-1)2} & r_{(m-1)3} & \cdots & r_{(m-1)(m-1)} & r_{(m-1)m} \\ r_{m1} & r_{m2} & r_{m3} & \cdots & r_{m(m-1)} & r_{mm} \end{bmatrix} = \begin{bmatrix} \mathbf{R}_{11} & \mathbf{R}_{12} \\ \mathbf{R}_{21} & \mathbf{R}_{22} \end{bmatrix}.$$

Then $\mathbf{R}_{11}$ is the matrix of intercorrelations of the predictors, $\mathbf{R}_{12} = \mathbf{R}_{21}'$ is the column vector of the correlations of the criterion with each of the predictors, and $\mathbf{R}_{22}$ is the scalar 1. The order of $\mathbf{R}_{11}$ is $m - 1$. The required vector of beta weights $\boldsymbol{\beta}$ is computed from the relationship

$$\boldsymbol{\beta} = \mathbf{R}_{21} \cdot \mathbf{R}_{11}^{-1}$$

where $\mathbf{R}_{11}^{-1}$ is the inverse of the matrix $\mathbf{R}_{11}$. This must be computed by means of an appropriate matrix inversion subroutine such as MATINV, which is reported in Section 9.1. Coefficients for the deviation score regression equation are obtained by computing

$$\mathbf{b} = \mathbf{A} \cdot \boldsymbol{\beta}$$

where $\mathbf{A}$ is a diagonal matrix of order $m - 1$. Each element of the diagonal is formed by dividing the standard deviation of the criterion variable by the standard deviation of a predictor variable; for example,

$$a_{11} = s_m / s_1.$$

If the intercept constant C for the raw-score regression equation is desired, it is computed as

$$C = M_m - (\mathbf{b} \cdot \mathbf{M})$$

where $\mathbf{M}$ is the $m - 1$ element vector of the predictor means, and M_m is the mean of the criterion variable.

The multiple correlation coefficient, $R_{m \cdot 1, 2, \ldots, m-1}$, or more simply R, is computed from the relationship

$$R^2 = \boldsymbol{\beta} \cdot \mathbf{R}_{12} = \sum_i \beta_i r_{mi}.$$

The significance of R^2 is tested by the analysis of variance as follows:[3]

$$F_{N-m-2}^{m-1} = \frac{R^2(N - m - 2)}{(1 - R^2)(m - 1)},$$

---

[3] To indicate the two degrees of freedom for variance ratios, n_1 is written as a superscript, and n_2 as a subscript. That is, $F_{n_2}^{n_1}$. This notation avoids the confusion often present when the more frequent F_{n_1, n_2} notation is used with large numbers of degrees of freedom.

where N is the number of subjects in the total sample. The product of each beta coefficient with the corresponding predictor-criterion correlation is that predictor's contribution to the magnitude of R^2, which in turn is the proportion of criterion variance which is predictable. The standard error of estimate for $\hat{z}_m$ is given by $\sqrt{1 - R^2}$ and for $\hat{x}_{mi}$ and $\hat{X}_{mi}$ by $s_m\sqrt{1 - R^2}$.[4]

3.2 Mathematics of Canonical Correlation

The interrelations between two sets of measurements made on the same subjects can be studied by canonical-correlation methods. As developed by Hotelling (1935, 1936), the canonical correlation is the maximum correlation between linear functions of the two sets of variables. Several linear combinations of the two sets are frequently possible. Each pair of functions is so determined as to maximize the correlation between the new pair of canonical variates, subject to the restriction that they be independent of previously derived linear combinations.

The nature of canonical correlation can be best described algebraically. Consider the two sets of N simultaneous equations, with p predictors and q criterion variables, where x_{ij} and y_{ij} represent the two sets of measures:

$$\hat{x}_1 = a_1x_{11} + a_2x_{12} + \cdots + a_px_{1p}; \quad b_1y_{11} + b_2y_{12} + \cdots + b_qy_{1q} = \hat{y}_1$$
$$\hat{x}_2 = a_1x_{21} + a_2x_{22} + \cdots + a_px_{2p}; \quad b_1y_{21} + b_2y_{22} + \cdots + b_qy_{2q} = \hat{y}_2$$

$$\hat{x}_N = a_1x_{N1} + a_2x_{N2} + \cdots + a_px_{Np}; \quad b_1y_{N1} + b_2y_{N2} + \cdots + b_qy_{Nq} = \hat{y}_N.$$

[4] For an alternate treatment of this problem see Chapter 17, "Multiple Regression Analysis," by M. A. Efroymson, in A. Ralston and H. S. Wilf (editors) (1960). *Mathematical Methods for Digital Computers*. New York: John Wiley and Sons, 1960. A stepwise procedure, which adds one variable to the prediction equation at a time and thus provides a number of intermediate regression equations as well as the complete equation, is reported. Variables are added or dropped according to the statistical significance of their contribution to the prediction of the criterion. A flow chart for programming the stepwise procedure is included, and although no program is listed, the IBM 704–709 Users' Organization distributes a FORTRAN-coded program (SHARE distribution 477) of this excellent development by M. A. Efroymson and his colleagues at the Esso Research and Engineering Company.

We have one reservation about the stepwise procedure and the test of significance for a standard partial-regression coefficient it utilizes in selecting the variables to be added or dropped. If we remind ourselves that multiple regression is really a univariate model, since only the criterion variable is treated as subject to errors [see Kendall (1957) pp. 68–69, on this point], it follows that any effort to generalize from sample to population is open to serious danger of capitalization on chance, particularly if it involves selecting some predictors and discarding others. P. O. Johnson and R. W. B. Jackson (1959) have expressed concern for the dangers of interpreting tests of significance of partial-regression coefficients as follows:

"We can, therefore, interpret the partial regression coefficients only in terms of these *fixed values of the predictor variables* or, which amounts to the same thing, in terms of sets of samples in which only these specific X values occur. As we mentioned earlier, to apply the results secured for one set of X's to another, and possibly different, set may not be justified and is in any event a risky procedure. In practice we may have to do just that, but the researcher must be aware of the possibility of securing results that are altogether untrustworthy and invalid." (p. 384)

The problem is to find two sets of weights, **a** and **b**, that maximize the correlation between $\hat{x}$ and $\hat{y}$, the derived canonical variates. For the special case $q = 1$ and $p > 1$, the problem is one of multiple regression. In canonical correlation *both multiple* criteria and *multiple* predictors are involved. The number of possible pairs of linear combinations are p or q, whichever is smaller. Each pair of canonical variates $\hat{x}_i$ and $\hat{y}_i$ is maximally correlated, subject to the restriction that each canonical variate be orthogonal to all other canonical variates on its side of the equation.

Computationally, it is irrelevant whether the variables on the left (x) or on the right (y) are considered as the criterion variables. Geometrically, the canonical correlation can be considered as a measure of the extent to which individuals occupy the same relative positions in the p-dimensional space as they do in the q-dimensional space. For example, different batteries of vocational-interest measures might be compared by canonical correlation. The two batteries might appear dissimilar when compared scale for scale, but canonical-correlation methods would reveal the system of correlation underlying the two batteries. Another example would be the examination of the relations between p somatotype measures and q scores on mental-aptitude tests. Horst (1961a) outlines several other possible applications of these procedures.

The analysis begins with the partitioning of **R**, the matrix of intercorrelations for the $p + q$ variables, into four submatrices:

$\mathbf{R}_{11}$ = intercorrelations among the p predictors.
$\mathbf{R}_{22}$ = intercorrelations among the q criteria.
$\mathbf{R}_{12}$ = intercorrelations of predictors with criteria.
$\mathbf{R}_{21}$ = the transpose of $\mathbf{R}_{12}$.

$$\mathbf{R} = \begin{bmatrix} \mathbf{R}_{11} & \mathbf{R}_{12} \\ \hline \mathbf{R}_{21} & \mathbf{R}_{22} \end{bmatrix}.$$

The matrix **R** is square, symmetric, and of order $(p + q)$.

The partitioned portions of **R** are then substituted into the following canonical equation:[5]

$$(\mathbf{R}_{22}^{-1}\mathbf{R}_{21}\mathbf{R}_{11}^{-1}\mathbf{R}_{12} - \lambda_i\mathbf{I})\mathbf{b}_i = 0.$$

The solution involves finding latent roots λ for which $|\mathbf{R}_{22}^{-1}\mathbf{R}_{21}\mathbf{R}_{11}^{-1}\mathbf{R}_{12} - \lambda\mathbf{I}| = 0$. If $q > p$, there are q possible roots, $q - p$ of them equal to zero. To save computational time, it would be better to define the left and right sets so that $q < p$. The vector of coefficients $\mathbf{b}_i$ for the right-hand set is the characteristic vector associated with λ_i. The vector $\mathbf{a}_i$ is obtained from:[6]

$$\mathbf{a}_i = (\mathbf{R}_{11}^{-1}\mathbf{R}_{12}\mathbf{b}_i)/\sqrt{\lambda_i}.$$

[5] Anderson (1958) shows the derivation of this equation. See p. 296, 300. It can also be written $(\mathbf{R}_{11}^{-1}\mathbf{R}_{12}\mathbf{R}_{22}^{-1}\mathbf{R}_{21} - \lambda_i\mathbf{I})\mathbf{a}_i = 0$.
[6] See Anderson (1958), p. 303.

The vectors $\mathbf{a}_i$ and $\mathbf{b}_i$ are applied to standard score vectors to obtain the canonical variates. The canonical correlation R_c between the ith pair of new composites is $\sqrt{\lambda_i}$. The largest λ_i is the square of the maximum possible correlation between linear combinations of the two sets of measurements $R_{c\cdot\max}^2 = \lambda_1$. If coefficients of observed deviation scores are desirable, they can be obtained by dividing the elements $\mathbf{a}_i$ and $\mathbf{b}_i$ by the standard deviation of the corresponding variables.

In another development, Horst (1961b) has shown that these procedures may also be generalized to m sets of variables, where m may be greater than two. Horst has outlined several ways in which the generalized canonical correlations would be useful in analyzing experimental data.

Bartlett (1941, 1947) has outlined procedures for testing the significance of canonical correlations. He defines lambda (Λ):

$$\Lambda = \prod_{i=1}^{q} (1 - \lambda_i), \qquad q < p.$$

The χ^2 approximation for the distribution of Λ provides a test for the null hypothesis that the p variates are unrelated to the q variates. That is,

$$\chi^2 = -[N - .5(p + q + 1)] \log_e \Lambda$$

with pq degrees of freedom. If the null hypothesis can be rejected, the contribution of the first root to Λ can be removed and the significance of the $q - 1$ roots can be tested

$$\Lambda' = \prod_{i=2}^{q} (1 - \lambda_i),$$

$$\chi^2 = -[N - .5(p + q + 1)] \log_e \Lambda',$$

with $(p - 1)(q - 1)$ degrees of freedom. In general, with r roots removed,

$$\Lambda' = \prod_{i=r+1}^{q} (1 - \lambda_i)$$

and χ^2 is distributed with $(p - r)(q - r)$ degrees of freedom.

Early investigators thought that only λ_1 and the corresponding canonical correlation $R_c = \sqrt{\lambda_1}$ were of interest. Other workers have expanded on this earlier work and have shown that roots other than λ_1 may be relevant, depending on the research question. One or more subsets of the predictor variables may be related to one or more subsets of the criterion variables. The particular combination of variables in set x that are related to a subset in y can be determined by inspecting the elements of the two vectors $\mathbf{a}_i$ and $\mathbf{b}_i$ associated with λ_i. Each $\sqrt{\lambda_i}$ is the correlation between the linear functions of the right and left variables, formed by using $\mathbf{b}_i$ and $\mathbf{a}_i$ respectively. The χ^2 tests we have defined reveal how many of the functions allow statistical interpretation. Programs reported for computing only the largest root $R_{c\cdot\max}$, or all of them, are on pp. 52–57. Examples illustrate both approaches.

3.3 Examples of Multiple Correlation

In the course of evaluating a special summer science program for fifty-five talented high-school students, the question arose whether success in doing independent work in the laboratory was related to a set of temperament variables.[7]

TABLE 3.1

Means and Standard Deviations of Variables

Variable	Mean	S.D.
Success rating	2.11	.74
G-Z temperament survey		
G, general activity, energy	15.89	5.31
R, restraint, seriousness	16.93	5.26
A, ascendance, social boldness	15.85	5.53
S, social interest, sociability	17.31	6.37
E, emotional stability	15.71	6.66
O, objectivity	16.00	6.22
F, friendliness, agreeableness	13.31	5.92
T, thoughtfulness, reflectiveness	20.11	4.31
P, personal relations, cooperativeness	14.58	6.12

TABLE 3.2

Intercorrelations of Variables

G-Z T.S.	G	R	A	S	E	O	F	T	P	Criterion: Success
G		.27	.34	*	*	*	*	*	*	*
R			*	*	*	*	.48	*	.51	*
A				.59	*	*	*	*	*	*
S					*	.28	*	*	*	*
E						.75	.36	−.44	*	*
O							.54	*	.40	*
F								*	.63	*
T									*	*
P										*

* Indicates $r < .27$, $p > .05$.

The success criterion was scaled from ratings of the student projects by supervisors who visited the laboratories and read the students' reports of their research. Nine scales from the Guilford-Zimmerman temperament survey comprised the predictors. Means and standard deviations of the criterion and the nine predictors are given in Table 3.1; significant intercorrelations of the variables are given in Table 3.2. Computation produced the following results:

$$\text{Multiple } R = .284, \qquad F_{45}^{9} = .44$$

[7] Cooley and Bassett (1960).

Since the multiple correlation is not significant, the regression weights are not reported. There is no basis for asserting that temperament variables as scaled by the G-Z temperament survey are capable of predicting judged success in the independent laboratory work of gifted high-school students.

Here the significance of the multiple correlation is the primary concern. The research question was primarily one of determining the extent to which a particular personality domain (temperament) is related to success in independent laboratory work. If the measures are reliable and valid, no significant relation appears to be present. In the next example, the significance of the relationship is not in doubt. Rather, a regression (prediction) equation was desired.

In the second example, the problem is to form a linear regression equation for predicting the final class rank of students who graduated from college-preparatory programs in eastern Massachusetts high schools. A random sample of 175 students was available,[8] and six measures of mental ability were administered 2 years prior to graduation. The means and standard deviations of the six predictors and the normalized rank in class criterion are presented in Table 3.3.

TABLE 3.3
Means and Standard Deviations

	Variable	Mean	S.D.
1	STEP mathematics[1]	14.75	4.38
2	STEP Science	18.91	3.88
3	CTMM spatial[2]	23.70	4.53
4	CTMM logical	22.57	2.81
5	CTMM numerical	15.47	3.91
6	CTMM verbal	20.74	5.65
7	Class rank[3]	52.79	8.54

[1] STEP = *Sequential Tests of Educational Progress*, Princeton: Educational Testing Service (Part I of Form A).
[2] CTMM = *California Test of Mental Maturity*, Los Angeles: California Test Bureau.
[3] Class ranks were converted to proportions (rank/class size), the proportions were converted to normal deviates z, and then $T = 10z + 50$ was used.

The correlation matrix is presented in Table 3.4. Only coefficients greater than .15 ($p < .05$) are reported. As would be expected, most of the relationships among the tests are significant.

The multiple correlation is .516. Analysis of variance yields an F ratio of 10.16, which is significant beyond the .001 level. The fact that $R^2 = .26$ indicates that 26 per cent of the variance in class rank of graduating seniors is predictable from this battery of mental-ability tests administered at the beginning of eleventh grade.

[8] Cooley (1958).

TABLE 3.4

Correlation Matrix: Ability and Class Rank

	1	2	3	4	5	6	7
1	1.00	.46	.32	.34	.62	.47	.44
2		1.00	.28	.29	.29	.35	.19
3			1.00	.33	.40	.15	*
4				1.00	.39	.20	*
5					1.00	.43	.39
6						1.00	.38

The beta coefficients reported in Table 3.5 indicate that the STEP mathematics test is the most useful predictor in the battery, followed by the verbal and numerical scales on the California test.

The regression equation for estimating final rank in class for similar eleventh-grade students who have been administered the same aptitude battery is:

$$\hat{Y} = .570X_1 - .041X_2 - .239X_3 - .131X_4 + .428X_5 + .300X_6 + 40.95.$$

When predicting the class rank from these six achievement and aptitude tests for similar students, the standard error of estimate is $s_7\sqrt{1 - R^2} = 7.34$. This means that the observed class ranks will be in the range ± 7.34 of the predicted class ranks about 68 per cent of the time.

TABLE 3.5

Beta Coefficients

Predictor	β
1	.29
2	−.02
3	−.13
4	−.04
5	.20
6	.20

3.4 Examples of Canonical Correlation

Relations between Early Home Environment and Present Orientation toward People. One application of canonical correlation is to test general hypotheses that relate two *sets* of variables. For instance, Roe and Siegelman (1962) hypothesized that certain variables reflecting early home environment are related to later orientation towards people. In the following example, eight variables from each set were used in testing the general hypothesis. Their sample consisted of 142 college seniors. The variables are briefly described as follows:

Early Home Environment (Predictors)

(Scores based on questionnaire and interview responses)

I_M, I_F Stress in family relations involving either mother I_M or father I_F. High scores indicate high stress.

II_M, II_F Closeness to mother II_M and father II_F in childhood. High scores indicate great closeness.

III   Early experience of social activities. High scores indicate high involvement in social activities.

V_M, V_F The interest and energy which the mother V_M or father V_F devotes to activities other than work or family.

VI   Nature of parental dominance. High scores mean mother dominance, low scores mean father dominance.

Present Orientation towards People (Criteria)

GS IV   The extent of present socializing of subject, based on questionnaire items.

CP   Curiosity about people, based on a person interest inventory. *Low* scores indicate *high* curiosity.

Rel   Desire for close personal relations, also based on person interest inventory. *Low* scores indicate *high* curiosity.

PS   The personal-social scale on the California occupational-interest inventory.

$AEFHQ_2$ A combination of five scales from Cattell's 16 P.F. inventory. High scores mean high interest in and need for interpersonal interaction.

Σ rel.   A composite score which was made up of selected items from questionnaires and inventories. *High* scores indicate orientation toward people.

T-nT   A clinical estimate of over-all person orientation of subject as towards (*low* scores) or not towards (*high* scores) persons.

A   The schizothyme, cyclothyme scale on Cattell's 16 P.F. inventory. High scores indicate warm, sociable.

In Table 3.6 matrix $\mathbf{R}_{11}$, the intercorrelations among the predictors, is presented. Only correlations significant at the .05 level are reported. The matrix of intercorrelations among criteria is reported in Table 3.7. The variables composing $\mathbf{R}_{22}$ seem to have a definite common component, which is assumed to be orientation towards people. The high negative relationships are simply a function of scale directions, which we have described.

When the research questions concern hypothesized relationships between two sets of variables, as in this example, at least three alternative approaches to statistical analysis are possible.

(1) The investigator could move directly to the possible bivariate relations ($\mathbf{R}_{12}$, reported in Table 3.8) and report those proving significant. Twelve of the possible sixty-four correlation coefficients are significant at the .05 in this case. This approach, however, does not tell the investigator the degree of confidence he can place in his over-all hypothesis.

TABLE 3.6

R_{11}: Early Home Environment

	I_M	II_F	II_M	III	V_F	V_M	VI
I_F	*	−.67	*	*	*	*	*
I_M		*	−.59	−.26	*	*	.29
II_F			*	*	.21	*	*
II_M				.24	*	*	*
III					.28	.30	*
V_F						.33	−.32
V_M							*

* Indicates $r < .16$, $p > .05$.

(2) A second approach might be to obtain the principal components of each set (see Chapter 8) and correlate the resulting component scores. Although the principal component of the criterion set may be meaningful, early home environment seems to be multidimensional, and so the principal component would not "cover" the domain of interest. One possibility would be to examine the relation between the eight predictors and the principal component of the criteria by using multiple regression. This approach would be reasonable if the criterion of interest was the factor the eight scales of people orientation measured in common.

(3) Canonical correlation is a third possible technique for analyzing these data. It comes the closest to answering the primary research questions: (a) Is early home

TABLE 3.7

R_{22}: Orientation towards People

	CP	Rel.	PS	AEFHQ$_2$	Σ rel.	T-nT	A
GS IV	−.16	−.50	*	.57	.77	−.43	.29
CP		.30	−.31	*	−.26	.38	*
Rel.			−.36	−.53	−.85	.54	−.42
PS				*	.43	−.59	.31
AEFHQ$_2$					.64	−.42	.67
Σ rel.						−.62	.51
T-nT							−.54
A							

* Indicates $r < .16$, $p > .05$.

TABLE 3.8
R_{12}: Predictors and Criteria

Criteria

Predictors	GS IV	CP	Rel.	PS	AEFHQ-	Σ rel.	T-nT	A
I_F	−.18	*	*	*	*	−.16	*	*
I_M	*	*	*	*	−.18	*	*	*
II_F	*	*	*	*	*	*	*	*
II_M	*	*	*	*	*	*	*	*
III	.36	*	−.31	*	.31	.38	*	.21
V_F	.23	*	*	*	*	.17	*	*
V_M	*	−.17	*	*	.20	*	*	*
VI	*	*	*	*	*	*	*	*

* Indicates $r < .16, p > .05$. Other information: $R_{c1} = .47, \chi^2 = 81.93, p = .05$ $ndf = 64$.

environment significantly related to present orientation toward people? (b) In what ways can the sets be combined to make the correlation between components of the two sets a maximum?

Table 3.9 summarizes the results related to question (a). The maximum canonical correlation is .47, and this is significant at the .05 level. Therefore there is at least one significant way in which the two domains are related. After the first pair of canonical variates are determined, no further significant combinations seem to exist.

The contributions the individual variables make to the significantly related

TABLE 3.9
χ^2 Tests of Successive Latent Roots

Number of Roots Removed	Largest Latent Root Remaining	Corresponding Canonical R	Λ	χ^2	NDF	P
0	.224	.47	.541	81.9	64	=.05
1	.164	.40	.697	48.1	49	>.05
2	.109	.33	.834	24.3	36	>.05
3	.035	.19	.936	8.8	25	>.05
4	.022	.15	.969	4.1	16	>.05
5	.006	.07	.992	1.1	9	>.05
6	.003	.05	.997	.4	4	>.05
7	.000	.00	.999	.0	1	>.05

canonical variates may be seen from Table 3.10. Here the loadings reveal that variables III, V_F, and II_M are the primary environmental antecedents involved, and that the criterion is primarily composed of Σ rel, GS IV and CP.

The investigators were able to conclude that there is a sense in which early home environment is related to orientation towards people. The results indicate that the primary antecedent is early experience of social activities (III).

TABLE 3.10

Canonical Vectors

Predictors	Criteria
.87 III	.73 Σ rel.
.31 V_F	.42 GS IV
.23 II_M	.33 CP
.12 V_M	.29 $AEFHQ_2$
.07 I_M	.21 T-nT
.06 II_F	−.00 Rel.
−.12 VI	−.02 A
−.20 I_F	−.19 PS

Relations between Group and Individually Administered Aptitude Tests. The example of reporting basic matrices and vectors in Chapter 2 is based on aptitude-test scores of 105 male high-school students who attended the St. Paul's School summer program in 1959. The means and standard deviations on the twenty-four scales for this group of subjects are given in Table 2.1 and the significant inter-correlations are given in Table 2.2.

Although all the tests are in the aptitude modality, nine scales are derived from paper-and-pencil group tests and fifteen are based on an individual intelligence test, the Wechsler adult intelligence scale. Psychometricians are interested in the degrees of interrelation between group tests and individual tests to be observed in different situations; the results of a canonical-correlation analysis would seem an appropriate form in which to cast answers to their inquiries. It should be remarked that the relative homogeneity of aptitude variables of this highly selected group of boys (amply demonstrated by their WAIS total score standard deviation of only 6.9, which may be compared to the normal standard deviation of approximately 15 in heterogeneous groups) must be expected to place severe restrictions on the magnitudes of computed canonical correlations. The canonical-correlation analysis, however, was computed using all nine group test scores as the left-hand set of variables and four WAIS scores (Verbal, Performance, Total, V − P) as the right-hand set. Only the maximum R_c is significant, and its value is .62, which seems quite respectable in the light of this consideration. The χ^2 for the test is 82, which with twenty-four degrees of freedom is significant beyond the .01 level. Table 3.11 presents the two vectors of weights. This analysis was computed twice,

TABLE 3.11

Results of Canonical Correlation of Nine Group Aptitude Tests with Four WAIS Scores for 105 St. Paul's Summer Program Boys

Group Test Weights		WAIS Weights	
A.C.E. Q	.26	Verbal	.59
A.C.E. L	.16	Performance	.65
A.C.E. T	.00	Total	−.45
CoopRdg. V	.05	V − P	.15
CoopRdg. S	−.17		
CoopRdg. C	.12		
CoopRdg. T	.20		
Watson-Glaser	.08		
Raven Prog. Matrices	.11		

Here $R_c = .62$, $\Lambda = .44$, $\chi_{24}^2 = 82$, and $p < .01$.

using both the full canonical-correlation program with subroutines DIRNM and HDIAG and the maximum canonical-correlation program with subroutine LROOT. The results were equivalent.

Flow Diagram for Multiple Regression (MULTR Program)

SUBROUTINE

Call subroutine CORREL, which reads data and computes and reports the following results:

T = no. of tests; NG = no. of subjects;

R_{vw} = the complete correlation matrix, in which the last row and column contain the criterion-predictor intercorrelations;

SD_v = vector of standard deviations, the last being for the criterion;

XM_v = vector of means, the last being for the criterion.

Throughout this diagram subscripts have the following ranges: $v = 1, 2, 3, \ldots, T$; $w = 1, 2, 3, \ldots, T$; $x = 1, 2, 3, \ldots, T - 1$; $y = 1, 2, 3, \ldots, T - 1$; $t = T$.

$R11_{xy} = R_{xy}$ Partitioning R into R11, the matrix of intercorrelations among the

$R12_x = R_{xt}$ predictors, and R12, the vector of criterion-predictor intercorrela-

$B_x = R12_x$ tions. Set up B for input to subroutine MATINV.

SUBROUTINE

Call subroutine MATINV, which replaces B with the solutions to the matrix equation $\beta = R12 \cdot R11^{-1}$. Now $B_x = \beta_x$.

RSQ = 0

$RSQ = RSQ + B_x \cdot R12_x$

$RMULT = \sqrt{RSQ}$ computing multiple R.

NDF1 = T − 1   computing F and its degrees of freedom.

NDF2 = NG − T

$F = (RSQ \cdot NDF2)/((1 - RSQ) \cdot NDF1)$

$A_x = SD_t/SD_x$

$B1_x = A_x \cdot B_x$ B1 is the vector of b weights.

C1 = 0

$C1 = C1 + B1_x \cdot XM_x$

$C = XM_t - C1$ C is the intercept constant.

$BSQ_x = B_x \cdot B_x$ BSQ is the squared beta weights.

OUTPUT

Print and punch, with labels, T, NG, RSQ, RMULT, F, NDF1, NDF2, B_x, $B1_x$, C, BSQ_x.

$\boxed{\text{STOP}}$

3.2

Flow Diagram for Complete Canonical-Correlation Analysis (CANON Program)

INPUT
Read M1, M2, N where M1 = no. of variables on the left, M2 = no. of variables on the right, N = no. of subjects. Form M = M1 + M2.
Subscripts in this diagram have the ranges:
$v = 1, 2, 3, \ldots, M1$ $w = 1, 2, 3, \ldots, M1$
$x = 1, 2, 3, \ldots, M2$ $y = 1, 2, 3, \ldots, M2$
$r = M1 + 1, M1 + 2, \ldots, M$ $s = M1 + 1, M1 + 2, \ldots, M$
$p = 1, 2, 3, \ldots, M$ $q = 1, 2, 3, \ldots, M.$

Set $X_p = 0$ and $R_{pq} = 0$ for initialization.
CASES = N

INPUT
Read Y_p the complete score vector of a subject.

$X_p = X_p + Y_p$ accumulating sums.
$R_{pq} = R_{pq} + Y_p \cdot Y_q$ accumulating s.s.c.p.
CASES = CASES − 1

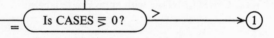

Is CASES $\lesseqgtr$ 0?

$Y_p = X_p/N$ forming means.
$R_{pq} = R_{pq} - X_p \cdot X_q/N$
$Z_p = \sqrt{R_{pp}/(N - 1)}$ forming standard deviations.
$R_{pq} = R_{pq}/(N \cdot Z_p \cdot Z_q)$ forming all correlations among M variables.

OUTPUT
Print and/or punch M1, M2, M, N, Y_p, Z_p, R_{pq}.

SUBROUTINE
Call subroutine MATINV to invert A where $A_{vw} = R_{vw}$; the subroutine replaces A with A^{-1}.

$T_{vx} = 0$ These computations place $R21 \cdot R11^{-1} \cdot R12$ of the notes
$T_{vx} = T_{vx} + A_{vw} \cdot R_{vr}$ in matrix A.
$A_{xy} = 0$
$A_{xy} = A_{xy} + T_{vx} \cdot R_{rx}$

3.2 Flow Diagram for CANON Program (Continued)

SUBROUTINE
Call subroutine DIRNM to compute the latent roots of $B^{-1}A$, placing them in XL, and the latent vectors , placing them as columns in C, where $B_{xy} = R_{rs}$.

$i = M2$
$WL_{i+1} = 1$

$WL_i = WL_{i+1} \cdot (1 - XL_i)$ puts Wilks Λ in WL_1.
$i = i - 1$

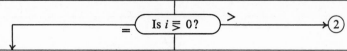
Is $i \lessgtr 0$? $>$
$=$

$CHISQ_x = -(N - (M + 1)/2) \cdot \log_e WL_x$
$NDF_x = (M1 - x) \cdot (M2 - x)$
$CHISQ_1$ is χ^2 for total; $CHISQ_2$, $CHISQ_3$, etc., are χ^2 tests with successive roots removed. NDF are degrees of freedom.
$i = 1$

OUTPUT
Print WL_x, $CHISQ_x$, NDF_x with appropriate labels.

$SROOT = \sqrt{XL_i}$ ith canonical correlation.
$Y_x = C_{xi}$ ith set of right-hand weights.
$X_v = 0$
$X_v = X_v + T_{vx} \cdot Y_x$
$Z_v = (1/SROOT) \cdot X_v$
$SS = 0$
$SS = SS + Z_v^2$
$SS = \sqrt{SS}$ Normalizing vector, ith set of left-hand weights.
$Z_v = Z_v/SS$
$i = i + 1$

OUTPUT
Print and punch SROOT, Y_x, Z_v with labels.

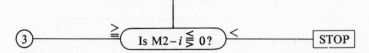
③ — $\gtreqless$ Is $M2 - i \lesseqgtr 0$? $<$ — STOP
$=$

3.3

Flow Diagram for Maximum Canonical-Correlation Analysis (CANON MAX Program)

CANON MAX begins precisely as does CANON; follow CANON flow diagram down to but not including the box which calls for subroutine DIRNM; follow this diagram from that point.

SUBROUTINE
Call subroutine MATINV to invert B where $B_{xy} = R_{rs}$; the subroutine replaces B with B^{-1}.

$C_{xy} = 0$
$C_{xy} = C_{xy} + B_{xz} \cdot A_{zy}$ where $z = 1, 2, 3, \ldots, M2$.
Thus $C = R22^{-1} \cdot R21 \cdot R11^{-1} \cdot R12$ of the notes.

SUBROUTINE
Call subroutine LROOT to compute the maximum latent root and its latent vector of C, placing the root in ROOT and the vector in VECT. VECT now contains the right-hand weights.

$SROOT = \sqrt{ROOT}$ SROOT is canonical R.
$X_v = 0$
$X_v = X_v + T_{vx} \cdot VECT_x$
$Y_v = (1/SROOT) \cdot X_v$
$SS = 0$
$SS = SS + Y_v^2$
$SS = \sqrt{SS}$
$Y_v = Y_v/SS$ Y_v are the normalized left-hand weights.

OUTPUT
Print and punch SROOT, ROOT, $VECT_x$, Y_v with appropriate labels.

$\boxed{\text{STOP}}$

MULTIPLE-REGRESSION ANALYSIS PROGRAM (MULTR)

```
C      MULTR.
C
C          THIS PROGRAM COMPUTES A MULTIPLE-REGRESSION ANALYSIS FOR A
C      SINGLE CRITERION AND A MAXIMUM OF 49 PREDICTOR VARIABLES. THE
C      GAUSS-JORDAN METHOD IS USED IN THE SOLUTION OF THE NORMAL EQUAT-
C      IONS. THERE IS NO RESTRICTION ON THE NUMBER OF SUBJECTS FOR WHOM
C      SCORE VECTORS MAY BE PRESENTED. REQUIRED SUBROUTINES ARE CORREL,
C      MATINV, MPUNCH, AND MPRINT.
C
C      INPUT.
C
C          INPUT IS AS REQUIRED BY CORREL. NOTE
C      THAT THE LAST VARIABLE IS THE CRITERION.
C
C      OUTPUT.
C
C          BASIC ACCUMULATIONS, MEANS, STANDARD DEVIATIONS, DISPERSION
C      MATRIX, AND CORRELATION MATRIX ARE PRINTED AND/OR PUNCHED AS RE-
C      QUIRED OF CORREL. ADDITIONAL PRINTED OUTPUT, APPROPRIATELY
C      LABELED, INCLUDES
C      1) THE MULTIPLE-CORRELATION COEFFICIENT
C      2) THE F TEST CRITERION FOR MULTIPLE R, WITH ITS DEGREES OF FREE-
C      DOM
C      3) THE BETA WEIGHTS
C      4) THE SQUARED BETA WEIGHTS
C      5) THE B WEIGHTS
C      6) THE INTERCEPT CONSTANT.
C      PUNCHED OUTPUT INCLUDES
C      1) THE BETA WEIGHTS
C      2) THE B WEIGHTS
C      3) THE INTERCEPT CONSTANT.
C
       DIMENSION FMT(36), FMR(36), X(50), SX(50), SS(50,50), SSD(50,50),
      1 D(50,50), R(50,50), XM(50), SD(50), R11(50,50), R12(50), B(50),
      2 A(50), B1(50), C1(50), BSQ(50), TITLE(12)
       EQUIVALENCE (SS, R11)
C
       CALL CORREL (T, NG, SX, SS, SSD, D, R, XM, SD)
       M = T - 1.0
       DO 1  I= 1,M
       DO 1  J= 1,M
     1 R11(I,J) = R(I,J)
C      R11 CONTAINS THE INTERCORRELATIONS OF THE PREDICTORS.
C
       DO 2  I= 1,M
     2 R12(I) = R(I,M+1)
C      R12 CONTAINS THE CRITERION-PREDICTOR CORRELATIONS.
       DO 3  I= 1,M
     3 B(I) = R12(I)
C
       CALL MATINV (R11, M, B, 1, DETERM)
C      B CONTAINS THE VECTOR OF BETA WEIGHTS.
C
       RSQ = 0.0
       DO 4  I=1,M
     4 RSQ = RSQ + B(I) * R12(I)
       WRITE OUTPUT TAPE 2, 5, RSQ
     5 FORMAT (21HOMULTIPLE R SQUARE = F14.7)
       RMULT = SQRTF (RSQ)
```

```
      WRITE OUTPUT TAPE 2, 6, RMULT
    6 FORMAT (14HOMULTIPLE R = F14.7)
      XNDF1 = T - 1.0
      WRITE OUTPUT TAPE 2, 7, XNDF1
    7 FORMAT (11HON.D.F.1 = F3.0)
      ENG = NG
      XNDF2 = ENG - T
      WRITE OUTPUT TAPE 2, 8, XNDF2
    8 FORMAT (11HON.D.F.2 = F10.0)
      F = (RSQ * XNDF2) /((1.0 - RSQ) * XNDF1)
      WRITE OUTPUT TAPE 2, 9, F
    9 FORMAT (35HOF FOR ANALYSIS OF VARIANCE ON R = F14.7)
C
      WRITE OUTPUT TAPE 2, 10
   10 FORMAT (13HOBETA WEIGHTS)
      WRITE OUTPUT TAPE 2, 11, (B(I), I= 1,M)
   11 FORMAT (5F14.7)
   12 FORMAT (5E14.7)
      PUNCH 12, (B(I), I= 1,M)
C
      DO 13  I= 1,M
   13 A(I) = SD(M+1) / SD(I)
      DO 14  I= 1,M
   14 B1(I) = A(I) * B(I)
      C1 = 0.0
      DO 15 I = 1,M
   15 C1 = C1 + B1(I) * XM(I)
      C = XM(M+1) - C1
C
      DO 16 I= 1,M
   16 BSQ(I) = B(I) * B(I)
      WRITE OUTPUT TAPE 2, 17
   17 FORMAT (21HOSQUARED BETA WEIGHTS)
      WRITE OUTPUT TAPE 2, 11, (BSQ(I), I= 1,M)
      WRITE OUTPUT TAPE 2, 18
   18 FORMAT (10HOB WEIGHTS)
      WRITE OUTPUT TAPE 2, 11,(B1(I), I= 1,M)
      PUNCH 12, (B1(I), I= 1,M)
      WRITE OUTPUT TAPE 2, 19, C
   19 FORMAT (22HOINTERCEPT CONSTANT = F14.7)
      PUNCH 12, C
C
      CALL EXIT
      END
```

CANONICAL-CORRELATION PROGRAM (CANON)

```
C     CANON.
C
C         THIS PROGRAM COMPUTES A FULL SET OF CANONICAL CORRELATIONS
C     RELATING M1 VARIABLES ON THE LEFT TO M2 VARIABLES ON THE RIGHT,
C     WHERE M1 IS LESS THAN 51, M2 IS LESS THAN 51, AND M1 + M2 IS LESS
C     THAN 81.  TO SAVE COMPUTER TIME, ARRANGE DATA SO THAT  M2 IS LESS
C     THAN M1.  (IT DOES NOT MATTER WHICH SET IS CONSIDERED AS PREDICT-
C     ORS.)  REQUIRED SUBROUTINES ARE MATINV, HDIAG, AND DIRNM.
C
C     INPUT.
C
C         INPUT CARD 1 CONTAINS
C     COL. 1-2    M1 = NO. VARIABLES ON THE LEFT
C     COL. 3-4    M2 = NO. VARIABLES ON THE RIGHT
C     COL. 5-9    N = NO. OF SUBJECTS.
C     CARDS 2-4 CONTAIN THE VARIABLE INPUT FORMAT FOR SCORES (SEE SECT-
C     ION 1.4 OR A FORTRAN MANUAL).  FOLLOWING CARDS CONTAIN  THE SCORE
C     VECTORS OF THE SUBJECTS.
C
C     OUTPUT.
C
C         PRINTED OUTPUT INCLUDES
C     1) PROGRAM TITLE
C     2) M1, M2, N
C     3) MEANS OF ALL VARIABLES
C     4) STANDARD DEVIATIONS OF ALL VARIABLES
C     5) R11 CORRELATION MATRIX
C     6) R22 CORRELATION MATRIX
C     7) R12 CORRELATION MATRIX
C     8) WILKS LAMBDA FOR TOTAL SET OF CANONICAL CORRELATIONS, THE
C     ASSOCIATED CHI-SQUARE,AND ITS DEGREES OF FREEDOM
C     9) THE CHI-SQUARES AND DEGREES OF FREEDOM AFTER REMOVAL OF
C     SUCCESSIVE ROOTS
C     10) THE CANONICAL CORRELATIONS AND LEFT- AND RIGHT-HAND WEIGHTS
C     ASSOCIATED WITH EACH.
C     ALL OUTPUT IS APPROPRIATELY LABELED.
C
      DIMENSION  R(80,80),A(50,50),B(50,50),C(50,50),T1(50,50),
     1 X(80), Y(80), IQ(50), Z(50), FMT(36), VECT(50), XL(50), D(50,50)
C
      PRINT 1
    1 FORMAT(36HOCANONICAL CORRELATION. P. R. LOHNES)
      READ INPUT TAPE 4, 2, M1, M2, N, L
    2 FORMAT (2I2,I5, I1)
      PRINT 3, M1
    3 FORMAT (30HONO. VARIABLES ON LEFT = M1 = I2)
      PRINT 4, M2
    4 FORMAT (31HONO. VARIABLES ON RIGHT = M2 = I2)
      PRINT 5, N
    5 FORMAT (20HONO. SUBJECTS = N = I5)
      READ INPUT TAPE 4, 6, (FMT(I), I = 1,36)
    6 FORMAT (12A6)
      M = M1 + M2
      EM = M
      EN = N
      DO 7  I = 1,M
      X(I) = 0.0
      DO 7  J = 1,M
    7 R(I,J) = 0.0
```

```
    8 READ INPUT TAPE 4, FMT, (Y(I), I = 1,M)
      DO 9   I = 1,M
      X(I) = X(I) + Y(I)
      DO 9   J = I,M
    9 R(I,J) = R(I,J) + Y(I) * Y(J)
      N = N - 1
      IF (N) 10, 10, 8
   10 DO 11   I = 1,M
      Y(I) = X(I)/EN
      DO 11   J = I,M
   11 R(I,J) = (R(I,J) - X(I)*X(J)/EN)
      PRINT 12
   12 FORMAT (24HOMEANS FOR ALL VARIABLES)
      PRINT 13, (Y(I), I = 1,M)
   13 FORMAT (8F10.4)
      DO 14 I = 1,M
   14 Y(I) = SQRTF (R(I,I)/ EN)
      PRINT 15
   15 FORMAT (38HOSTANDARD DEVIATIONS FOR ALL VARIABLES)
      PRINT 13, (Y(I), I = 1,M)
      DO 16   I = 1,M
      DO 16   J = I,M
      R(I,J) = R(I,J) /(EN * Y(I) * Y(J))
   16 R(J,I) = R(I,J)
C
      DO 17   I = 1,M1
      DO 17   J = 1,M1
   17 A(I,J) = R(I,J)
      DO 18   I = 1,M2
      DO 18   J = 1,M2
      IM1 = I + M1
      JM1 = J + M1
   18 B(I,J) = R(IM1,JM1)
      DO 19   I = 1,M1
      DO 19   J = 1,M2
      JM1 = J + M1
   19 C(I,J) = R(I,JM1)
      PRINT 20
   20 FORMAT (11HOR11 MATRIX)
      DO 21   I = 1,M1
   21 PRINT 22, (A(I,J),  J = 1,M1)
   22 FORMAT (8F10.6)
      PRINT 23
   23 FORMAT (11HOR22 MATRIX)
      DO 24   I = 1,M2
   24 PRINT 22, (B(I,J),  J = 1,M2)
      PRINT 25
   25 FORMAT(11HOR12 MATRIX)
      DO 26   I = 1,M1
   26 PRINT 22, (C(I,J),  J = 1,M2)
      GO TO 400
C
  400 CALL MATINV (A, M1, Z, 0, DETERM)
      DO 43   I = 1, M2
      DO 43   J = 1, M1
      T1(I,J) = 0.0
```

```
         DO 43   K = 1,  M1
      43 T1(I,J) = T1(I,J) + C(K,I) * A(K,J)
         DO 44   I = 1,  M2
         DO 44   J = 1,  M2
         D(I,J) = 0.0
         DO 44   K = 1,  M1
      44 D(I,J) = D(I,J) + T1(I,K) * C(K,J)
C        D NOW CONTAINS(R21 * R22 INVERSE * R12)OF THE NOTES
C
         CALL DIRNM(D,M2,B,T1,XL)
         WL = 1.0
         DO 39   I = 1,  M2
      39 WL = WL * (1.0 - XL(I))
         PRINT 40, WL
      40 FORMAT (16HOWILKS LAMBDA = F14.7)
         CHISQ = -(EN - (EM + 1.0)/2.0)*LOGF(WL)
         PRINT 46, CHISQ
      46 FORMAT (14HOCHI SQUARE = F14.7)
         IV = 1
C
     500 ROOT = XL(IV)
         DO 45 I = 1,  M2
      45 VECT(I) = T1(I,IV)
         PRINT 31, ROOT
      31 FORMAT (33HOSQUARED CANONICAL CORRELATION = F14.7)
         SROOT = SQRTF(ROOT)
         PRINT 34, SROOT
      34 FORMAT(25HOCANONICAL CORRELATION = F12.7)
         PRINT 32
      32 FORMAT (19HORIGHT-HAND WEIGHTS)
         DO 33   I = 1,M2
      33 Y(I) = VECT(I)
         PRINT 22, (Y(I),   I = 1,  M2)
C
         DO 36   I = 1,M1
         X(I) = 0.0
         DO 36   J = 1,M2
      36 X(I) = X(I) + C(I,J) * Y(J)
         DO 37   I = 1,  M1
         Z(I) = 0.0
         DO 37   J = 1,  M1
      37 Z(I) = Z(I) + A(I,J) * X(J)
         DO 38   I = 1,  M1
      38 Y(I) = (1.0 / ROOT) * Z(I)
C        Y(I) = LEFT-HAND WEIGHTS.
         PRINT 42
      42 FORMAT(18HOLEFT-HAND WEIGHTS)
         PRINT 22, (Y(I),   I = 1,  M1)
C
         IV = IV + 1
         IF (M2 - IV) 700, 500, 500
     700 CALL EXIT
         END
```

MAXIMUM CANONICAL-CORRELATION COEFFICIENT (CANON MAX)

```
C       CANON MAX.
C
C           THIS PROGRAM COMPUTES THE MAXIMUM CANONICAL CORRELATION
C       RELATING M1 VARIABLES ON THE LEFT TO M2 VARIABLES ON THE RIGHT,
C       WHERE M1 IS LESS THAN 51, M2 IS LESS THAN 51, AND M1 + M2 IS LESS
C       THAN 81.   TO SAVE COMPUTER TIME, ARRANGE DATA SO THAT M2 IS LESS
C       THAN M1.  (IT DOES NOT MATTER WHICH SET IS CONSIDERED AS PREDICT-
C       ORS IN THIS MODEL.)   REQUIRED SUBROUTINES ARE MATINV AND LROOT.
C
C       INPUT.
C
C           INPUT CARD 1 CONTAINS
C       COL. 1-2    M1 = NO. VARIABLES ON THE LEFT
C       COL. 3-4    M2 = NO. VARIABLES ON THE RIGHT
C       COL. 5-9    N = NO. OF SUBJECTS.
C       CARDS 2-4 CONTAIN THE VARIABLE INPUT FORMAT FOR SCORES (SEE SECT-
C       ION 1.4).   FOLLOWING CARDS CONTAIN THE SCORE VECTORS OF SUBJECTS.
C
C       OUTPUT.
C
C           PRINTED OUTPUT INCLUDES
C       1) PROGRAM TITLE
C       2) M1, M2, N
C       3) MEANS OF ALL VARIABLES
C       4) STANDARD DEVIATIONS OF ALL VARIABLES
C       5) R11 CORRELATION MATRIX
C       6) R22 CORRELATION MATRIX
C       7) R12 CORRELATION MATRIX
C       8) SQUARED CANONICAL-CORRELATION COEFFICIENT
C       9) CANONICAL-CORRELATION COEFFICIENT
C       10) RIGHT-HAND WEIGHTS
C       11) LEFT-HAND WEIGHTS
C       ALL OUTPUT IS APPROPRIATELY LABELED.
C
        DIMENSION  R(80,80),A(50,50),B(50,50),C(50,50),T1(50,50),
       1 X(80), Y(80), IQ(50), Z(50), FMT(36), VECT(50), XL(50)
C
        PRINT 1
      1 FORMAT (30HOMAXIMUM CANONICAL CORRELATION)
        READ INPUT TAPE 4, 2, M1, M2, N
      2 FORMAT (2I2,I5)
        PRINT 3, M1
      3 FORMAT (30HONO. VARIABLES ON LEFT = M1 = I2)
        PRINT 4, M2
      4 FORMAT (31HONO. VARIABLES ON RIGHT = M2 = I2)
        PRINT 5, N
      5 FORMAT (20HONO. SUBJECTS = N = I5)
        READ INPUT TAPE 4, 6, (FMT(I), I = 1,36)
      6 FORMAT (12A6)
        M = M1 + M2
        FM = M
        FN = N
        DO 7  I = 1,M
        X(I) = 0.0
        DO 7  J = 1,M
      7 R(I,J) = 0.0
      8 READ INPUT TAPE 4, FMT, (Y(I), I = 1,M)
        DO 9  I = 1,M
        X(I) = X(I) + Y(I)
```

```
      DO 9   J = 1,M
    9 R(I,J) = R(I,J) + Y(I) * Y(J)
      N = N - 1
      IF (N) 10, 10, 8
   10 DO 11   I = 1,M
      Y(I) = X(I)/EN
      DO 11   J = 1,M
   11 R(I,J) = (R(I,J) - X(I)*X(J)/EN)
      PRINT 12
   12 FORMAT (24HOMEANS FOR ALL VARIABLES)
      PRINT 13, (Y(I), I = 1,M)
   13 FORMAT (8F10.4)
      DO 14 I = 1,M
   14 Y(I) = SQRTF (R(I,I)/ EN)
      PRINT 15
   15 FORMAT (38HOSTANDARD DEVIATIONS FOR ALL VARIABLES)
      PRINT 13, (Y(I), I = 1,M)
      DO 16   I = 1,M
      DO 16   J = 1,M
      R(I,J) = R(I,J) /(EN * Y(I) * Y(J))
   16 R(J,I) = R(I,J)
C
      DO 17   I = 1,M1
      DO 17   J = 1,M1
   17 A(I,J) = R(I,J)
      DO 18   I = 1,M2
      DO 18   J = 1,M2
      IM1 = I + M1
      JM1 = J + M1
   18 B(I,J) = R(IM1,JM1)
      DO 19   I = 1,M1
      DO 19   J = 1,M2
      JM1 = J + M1
   19 C(I,J) = R(I,JM1)
      PRINT 20
   20 FORMAT (11HOR11 MATRIX)
      DO 21   I = 1,M1
   21 PRINT 22, (A(I,J),   J = 1,M1)
   22 FORMAT (8F10.6)
      PRINT 23
   23 FORMAT (11HOR22 MATRIX)
      DO 24   I = 1,M2
   24 PRINT 22, (B(I,J),   J = 1,M2)
      PRINT 25
   25 FORMAT(11HOR12 MATRIX)
      DO 26   I = 1,M1
   26 PRINT 22, (C(I,J),   J = 1,M2)
C
      CALL MATINV (B,M2,Z,0,DETERM)
      DO 27   I=1,M2
      DO 27   J = 1,M1
   27 R(I,J) = C(J,I)
      DO 28   I = 1,M2
      DO 28   J = 1,M1
      T1(I,J) = 0.0
      DO 28   K = 1,M2
```

CANON MAX PROGRAM (CONTINUED)

```
   28 T1(I,J) = T1(I,J) + B(I,K) * R(K,J)
      CALL MATINV (A,M1,Z,0,DETERM)
      DO 29   I = 1,M2
      DO 29   J = 1,M1
      B(I,J) = 0.0
      DO 29   K = 1,M1
   29 B(I,J) = B(I,J) + T1(I,K) * A(K,J)
      DO 30   I = 1,M2
      DO 30   J = 1,M2
      T1(I,J) = 0.0
      DO 30   K = 1,M1
   30 T1(I,J) = T1(I,J) + B(I,K) * C(K,J)
C
      CALL LROOT (T1, M2, ROOT, VECT, 0)
C
      PRINT 31, ROOT
   31 FORMAT (33HOSQUARED CANONICAL CORRELATION = F14.7)
      SROOT = SQRF(ROOT)
      PRINT 34, SROOT
   34 FORMAT(25HOCANONICAL CORRELATION = F12.7)
      PRINT 32
   32 FORMAT (19HORIGHT-HAND WEIGHTS)
      DO 33   I = 1,M2
   33 Y(I) = VECT(I)
      PRINT 22, (Y(I),   I = 1, M2)
C
      DO 36   I = 1,M1
      X(I) = 0.0
      DO 36   J = 1,M2
   36 X(I) = X(I) + C(I,J) * Y(J)
      DO 37   I = 1, M1
      Z(I) = 0.0
      DO 37   J = 1, M1
   37 Z(I) = Z(I) + A(I,J) * X(J)
      DO 38   I = 1, M1
   38 Y(I) = (1.0 /SROOT) * Z(I)
C     NORMALIZE Y.
      SS = 0.0
      DO 381  I = 1, M1
  381 SS = SS + Y(I) * Y(I)
      SS = SQRF (SS)
      DO 382  I = 1, M1
  382  Y(I) = Y(I) / SS
      PRINT 42
   42 FORMAT (18HOLEFT-HAND WEIGHTS)
      PRINT 22, (Y(I),   I = 1, M1)
      CALL EXIT
      END
```

ESTIMATED SCORES PROGRAM (EST)

```
C     EST SCORE.
C
C         THIS PROGRAM COMPUTES ESTIMATED SCORES FOR MULTIPLE-REGRESS-
C     ION OR DISCRIMINANT ANALYSIS IN EITHER DEVIATION- OR RAW-SCORE
C     FORM. IF STANDARD SCORE FORM IS DESIRED, USE FACT SCORE PROGRAM.

C
C     INPUT.
C
C         INPUT CARD 1 CONTAINS
C     COL. 1-2    M = NO. OF VARIABLES (LESS THAN 51)
C     COL. 3-16   CONST = INTERCEPT CONSTANT IN FORMAT F14.7
C     COL. 17     INRAW = 0 FOR DEVIATION FORM, INRAW = 1 FOR RAW FORM.
C     CARD 2 IS FORMAT FOR B WEIGHTS.
C     CARDS 3-4 ARE FORMAT FOR RAW SCORES, WHERE ID IS IN F CONVENTION.
C     CARD 5 IS FORMAT FOR MEANS. USE BLANK IF INRAW = 1.
C     CARD 6 BEGINS B WEIGHTS, WHICH ARE FOLLOWED BY MEANS (IF INRAW = 0
C     IN THIS CASE), THEN BY THE SCORE VECTORS FOR SUBJECTS.
C
C     OUTPUT.
C
C         TWO CARDS ARE PUNCHED FOR EACH SUBJECT. THE FIRST IS FOR
C     RECORD PRINTING AND CONTAINS THE ID AND ESTIMATED SCORE WITH
C     APPROPRIATE LABELS.  THE SECOND IS FOR FUTURE COMPUTER INPUT AND
C     CONTAINS THE ID AND ESTIMATED SCORE WITHOUT LABELS.
C
      DIMENSION X(50), B(50), XM(50), FMT(12), FMR(24), FMXM(12)
      READ 11, M,          CONST, INRAW
   11 FORMAT (I2,         F14.7, I1)
      READ 12, (FMT(I), I = 1, 12)
   12 FORMAT (12A6)
      READ 12, (FMR(I), I = 1, 24), (FMXM(I), I = 1,12)
      READ FMT, (B(I), I = 1,M)
      IF (INRAW) 130, 130, 13
  130 READ FMXM, (XM(I), I = 1, M)
   13 READ FMR, XID, (X(I), I = 1,M)
      EST = 0.0
      IF (INRAW) 140, 140, 142
  140 DO 141 I = 1, M
  141 EST = EST+B(I) * (X(I) - XM(I) )
      GO TO 150
  142 DO 14 I = 1, M
   14 EST = EST + B(I) * X(I)
  150 EST = EST + CONST
      PRINT 15, XID, EST
      PUNCH 16, XID, EST
   15 FORMAT (8HOI.D. =  F10.0,5X,  9HEST Y =    F14.7)
   16 FORMAT (F10.0, F14.7)
      GO TO 13
      END
```

3.5 References

Canonical Correlation

Anderson T. W. (1958). *An Introduction to Multivariate Statistical Analysis.* New York: John Wiley and Sons, Chapter 12.

Bartlett, M. S. (1941). "The Statistical Significance of Canonical Correlations," *Biometrika* **32**:29–38.

—— (1947). "Multivariate Analysis," *Supplement to the Journal of the Royal Statistical Society* **9**:176–197.

Horst, Paul (1961a). Generalized Canonical Correlations and Their Applications to Experimental Data. Seattle: University of Washington (mineographed).

—— (1961b). "Relations Among *m* Sets of Measures," *Psychometrika* **26**:129–149.

Hotelling, H. (1935). "The Most Predictable Criterion," *Journal of Educational Psychology* **26**:139–142.

—— (1936), "Relations Between Two Sets of Variates," *Biometrika* **28**:321–377.

Kendall, M. G. (1957). *A Course in Multivariate Analysis.* London: Charles Griffin and Co., Chapter 5.

Thomson, G. (1947). "The Maximum Correlation of Two Weighted Batteries," *British Journal of Psychology, Statistical Section,* Part I, pp. 27–34.

Multiple Correlation and Regression

DuBois, Philip H. (1957). *Multivariate Correlational Analysis.* New York: Harper and Brothers.

Johnson, P. O., and Jackson, R. W. B. (1959). *Modern Statistical Methods: Descriptive and Inductive.* Chicago: Rand McNally and Co.

McNemar, Quinn (1962). *Psychological Statistics.* New York: John Wiley and Sons, Chapter 11.

Williams, E. J. (1959). *Regression Analysis.* New York: John Wiley and Sons.

References for Examples

Cooley, W. W. (1958). Career Development of Scientists. Cooperative Research Project 436, United States Office of Education (mimeographed).

Cooley, W. W. and Bassett, R. D. (1960). *Evaluation and Follow-up Study of a Summer Science and Mathematics Program for Talented Secondary School Students,* Cooperative Research Project 715. United States Office of Education.

Roe, A., and Siegleman, M. (1962). *A Study of the Origin of Interests.* In press.

CHAPTER FOUR

Multivariate analysis of variance and covariance

4.1 Mathematics of Generalized Analysis of Variance

Research workers familiar with the univariate analysis of variance will easily see the usefulness of a generalization of the F test to the problem of testing the significance of differences among groups located in a multidimensional criterion space. The same assumption that occurs in the univariate analysis of variance, namely, that of equality of group variances, is also involved in the generalized analysis of variance. Just as a test of the homogeneity of variances is available in univariate analysis of variance, so a test of the homogeneity of group dispersions is available in the generalized analysis of variance. In multivariate analysis the dispersion of a sample group is the matrix of variances and covariances for the group $\mathbf{D}_g$. The determinant of the dispersion matrix for a group $|\mathbf{D}_g|$ is employed as the scalar representation of the dispersion estimate in the homogeneity test.

The null hypothesis of the test of homogeneity of dispersions, which is called H_1 in this chapter, asserts that the group populations have equal dispersions. Following the convention of representing population parameters by upper-case Greek letters corresponding to the Latin letters used for sample statistics, H_1 asserts that $\mathbf{\Delta}_1 = \mathbf{\Delta}_2 = \cdots = \mathbf{\Delta}_g = \mathbf{\Delta}$, where $\mathbf{\Delta}_j$ is the population dispersion sampled by $\mathbf{D}_j$. The test of H_1 involves the dispersion estimate $\mathbf{D}$, computed from the pooled group deviation sums of squares and cross-products matrices, as well as the $\mathbf{D}_g$ for each of the groups, since on the null hypothesis $\mathbf{D}$ is a best estimate of the population dispersion matrix common to all groups.

Significance tests in multivariate analysis involve more computations than their counterparts in univariate analysis because they involve matrices rather than scalar values, and because matrix algebra is a tremendous generator of laborious arithmetic tasks. We frequently encounter reports of univariate tests of the significance of group mean differences that do not include a testing of the assumed homogeneity of variances, although such a test is usually a desirable safeguard.

60

Research workers will presumably at times desire to bypass the test of H_1 in computing the generalized analysis of variance, and report only the results of the test of the equality of group centroids, called H_2 in this chapter. This is a common practice because H_2 is rather insensitive to moderate departures from homogeneity of dispersions. However, the cost of computing H_1 may be balanced by the value the test's result may have as an important research finding in its own right, particularly if it happens to lead to a rejection of the null hypothesis.

The test of H_2, which asserts the equality of the population centroids $\mathbf{M}_j$, is the multivariate generalization of a one-way univariate analysis of variance. The two program developments reported in this chapter, one providing for tests of H_1 and H_2 on multivariate data, the other providing for the test of H_2 after covariance adjustments, with p criterion variables and c control variables, will be found useful in many research situations.

It should be noted that just as $\mathbf{D}$ and $\mathbf{D}_g$ are matrices representing multivariate dispersions and are logical extensions of the univariate s^2 and $s_g{}^2$, so it is possible to describe matrices that are the logical multivariate extensions of the univariate deviation sums of squares for total and for groups. Thus the test of H_2 involves matrices representing the sums of squares and cross products of deviations from the grand means $\mathbf{T}$, and likewise from group means $\mathbf{W}_g$. The latter are pooled (added together) to form the within-groups estimate $\mathbf{W}$. These matrices are defined precisely later.

The test of the discriminating power of a test battery, which is the test of H_2: $\mu_1 = \mu_2 = \cdots = \mu_g$ assuming H_1: $\mathbf{\Delta}_1 = \mathbf{\Delta}_2 = \cdots = \mathbf{\Delta}_g$, where the μ's are population centroids (i.e., mean vectors) for the g groups and the $\mathbf{\Delta}$'s are population dispersions, is best known in the notation of Rao.[1] He defines Wilks' lambda criterion as follows:

$$\Lambda = |\mathbf{W}|/|\mathbf{T}|$$

where $\mathbf{W}$ is the pooled within-groups deviation score cross-products matrix and $\mathbf{T}$ is the total sample deviation score cross-products matrix. The elements of the $\mathbf{W}$ and $\mathbf{T}$ matrices are defined as follows:

$$w_{ij} = \sum_{k=1}^{g} \left\{ \sum_{n=1}^{N_g} (X_{ikn} - \bar{X}_{ik})(X_{jkn} - \bar{X}_{jk}) \right\}$$

$$t_{ij} = \sum_{n=1}^{N} (X_{in} - \bar{X}_i)(X_{jn} - \bar{X}_j)$$

where g = number of groups, N_g = number of subjects in group g, N = total number of subjects, and i and j run from 1 to p, where p = the number of variables.

As $|\mathbf{T}|$ increases relative to $|\mathbf{W}|$ the ratio decreases in size with an accompanying increase in the confidence with which we reject H_2. In testing the significance of Λ, we can use either the χ^2 approximation of Bartlett (outlined in Section 3.2), or the following F approximation developed by Rao.[1] Monte Carlo methods indicate the latter to be a slightly better approximation.[2]

[1] Rao (1952), pp. 258–272.
[2] Lohnes (1961).

Let
$$s = \sqrt{(p^2q^2 - 4)/(p^2 + q^2 - 5)} \qquad q = g - 1$$
$$m = n - (p + q + 1)/2, \qquad n = N - 1$$
$$\lambda = -(pq - 2)/4,$$
$$r = pq/2,$$

and
$$y = \Lambda^{1/s};$$
then

(4.1)
$$F^{2r}_{ms+2\lambda} = \left(\frac{1 - y}{y}\right)\left(\frac{ms + 2\lambda}{2r}\right).$$

For the one-variate case, this F transformation of Λ is the algebraic equivalent of the familiar univariate F test. This is because $\mathbf{T} = \mathbf{A} + \mathbf{W}$, where $\mathbf{A}$ is the usual among groups sums of squares. The F test can be written

$$F = \left(\frac{\mathbf{A}}{\mathbf{W}}\right)\left(\frac{N - g}{g - 1}\right),$$

which becomes (recalling $\mathbf{A} = \mathbf{T} - \mathbf{W}$)

$$F = \left[\frac{1 - (\mathbf{W}/\mathbf{T})}{\mathbf{W}/\mathbf{T}}\right]\left(\frac{N - g}{g - 1}\right)$$

or

$$F = \left(\frac{1 - \Lambda}{\Lambda}\right)\left(\frac{N - g}{g - 1}\right).$$

Equation 4.1 reduces to this last equation for the univariate case $p = 1$.

A situation frequently encountered in research is that of two groups and a number of variables, where the hypothesis concerns the significance of the difference between the two group mean vectors. Hotelling (1931) devised a test for this case, called T^2. Hotelling's T^2 is a generalization of Student's t test, and is a special case for which Wilks' lambda (H_2) is applicable. Rather than have a special program for the T^2 test, the two-group case can be handled by the program for H_2, reported on pp. 78–81. Actually, there are several equivalent ways of testing the significance of differences for the two-group case; they have been summarized by Rulon and Brooks (1961).

The Λ test of the null hypothesis of the equality of the mean vectors assumes that the g group dispersion matrices are based on samples of g normal populations with a common dispersion. A criterion for testing the null hypothesis H_1 of the equality of g group dispersion matrices, derived from a development by M. S. Bartlett (1937), has been presented by Box (1949).

Box defines the criterion M:

$$M = n \log_e |\mathbf{D}| - \sum_g (n_g \log_e |\mathbf{D}_g|)$$

where $\mathbf{D} = (1/n)\mathbf{W}$ and $\mathbf{D}_g = (1/n_g)\mathbf{W}_g$. Required parameters are:

$$A_1 = \left(\sum_g \frac{1}{n_g} - \frac{1}{n}\right) \frac{2p^2 + 3p - 1}{6(g - 1)(p + 1)},$$

$$A_2 = \left(\sum_g \frac{1}{n_g^2} - \frac{1}{n^2}\right) \frac{(p - 1)(p + 2)}{6(g - 1)}.$$

If $A_2 - A_1^2$ is positive, then

$$f_1 = .5(g - 1)p(p + 1), \qquad f_2 = (f_1 + 2)/(A_2 - A_1^2),$$

$$b = f_1/(1 - A_1 - f_1/f_2),$$

$$F_{f_2}^{f_1} = M/b.$$

If $A_2 - A_1^2$ is negative, use the following:

$$f_1 = .5(g - 1)p(p + 1), \qquad f_2 = (f_1 + 2)/(A_1^2 - A_2),$$

$$b = f_2/(1 - A_1 + 2/f_2),$$

$$F_{f_2}^{f_1} = f_2 M/f_1(b - M).$$

The Λ test of H_2 (the equality of mean vectors) provides a basic tool that should be used in classification studies before the discriminant functions are fitted. If the investigator objects to the expense of evaluating the determinants of $\mathbf{W}$ and $\mathbf{T}$ in addition to the cost of computing discriminant functions, he is reminded that Λ can be derived as a function of the set of latent roots associated with the discriminant vectors, a method covered in Section 6.1. The testing of H_1 involves the expense of computing the determinants of the group dispersion matrices, but Section 7.1 presents a method for computing probabilities of individual membership in groups that utilizes these determinants and is frequently useful when the classification is computed in the original test space. We should also point out that the test of H_1 is often helpful for testing hypotheses concerning the comparative dispersion of groups, and not simply a test of the assumption of H_2. An example would be the hypothesis that the multivariate distribution of aptitude scores for older members of a particular occupational group is more homogeneous than that for groups just entering the occupation. If H_1 is rejected, the variance-covariance matrices and their determinants are compared.

Mathematics of Multiple Convariance Adjustments

Rao[3] has described a method of performing covariance adjustments on the $\mathbf{W}$ and $\mathbf{T}$ matrices prior to forming Λ for any number of control variables, with appropriate adjustment of the degrees of freedom. This model appears to be of great use in exploring the influences of additional variables on a situation previously studied in terms of a set of somewhat related variables, which may now become controls.

[3] Rao, *op. cit.*, p. 264.

This test asks the question: Do the additional (experimental) variables add new information regarding group differences; information not found in the control variables? An analogous test for a continuous criterion has been made available by utilizing the well-known variance ratio test for the difference between two multiple-correlation coefficients, where one R^2 was based on the control variables and the other on the control and experimental variables. A significant increase in the latter R^2 would indicate new information in the experimental variables.[4]

Another application of the generalized covariance procedure is in obtaining an over-all test of treatment differences where several experimental and control variables are used. The procedure we describe would be limited to one-way designs.

The first step in the computations for the generalized covariance analysis is to form the **W** and **T** matrices for all the variables, the p experimental variables and the c control variables, the influence of which is to be removed by regression. These matrices are then partitioned as follows:

$$\mathbf{W} = \begin{bmatrix} \mathbf{W}_{pp} & \mathbf{W}_{pc} \\ \hline \mathbf{W}_{cp} & \mathbf{W}_{cc} \end{bmatrix}, \qquad \mathbf{T} = \begin{bmatrix} \mathbf{T}_{pp} & \mathbf{T}_{pc} \\ \hline \mathbf{T}_{cp} & \mathbf{T}_{cc} \end{bmatrix}.$$

Then two adjusted matrices are formed:

$$\mathbf{W}_{p \cdot c} = \mathbf{W}_{pp} - \mathbf{W}_{pc}\mathbf{W}_{cc}^{-1}\mathbf{W}_{cp}$$
$$\mathbf{T}_{p \cdot c} = \mathbf{T}_{pp} - \mathbf{T}_{pc}\mathbf{T}_{cc}^{-1}\mathbf{T}_{cp}.$$

Then

$$\Lambda = \frac{|\mathbf{W}_{p \cdot c}|}{|\mathbf{T}_{p \cdot c}|}$$

and where p = number of experimental variables, c = number of control variables, $n = N - 1$, and $q = g - 1$. Again, the Rao F transformation applies (equation 4.1) where

$$m = (n - c) - (p + g)/2$$

and s, λ, r, y are defined as for equation 4.1.

To obtain the adjusted means for the experimental variables, the regression coefficients are computed using two partitions of **W**. This involves multiplying $\mathbf{W}_{cc}^{-1}$ times each of the column vectors of $\mathbf{W}_{cp}$. The product vectors are the coefficients b_c used in computing the adjustment for each of the $p \cdot g$ experimental means $\bar{X}_{jg}$. The adjusted mean for group g on experimental variable X is

$$\hat{\bar{X}}_{jg} = \bar{X}_{jg} - [b_1(\bar{Y}_{1g} - \bar{Y}_{1 \cdot}) + b_2(\bar{Y}_{2g} - \bar{Y}_{2 \cdot}) + \cdots + b_c(\bar{Y}_{cg} - \bar{Y}_{c \cdot})]$$

where $\bar{Y}_{cg}$ is the mean of group g on the control variable Y_c and $\bar{Y}_{c \cdot}$ is the grand mean on Y_c.

[4] For a description of this test, see McNemar (1955) p. 279.

4.3 Examples of Generalized Analysis of Variance

Separation of Four Academic-Interest Groups. In a study of gifted male high-school students, Jervis and Congdon[5] administered the American Council on Education Psychological Examination, from which they obtained the Quantitative Q and Language L scale scores. The 105 boys were attending the St. Paul's School summer program in 1959. The boys separated themselves into the four interest groups by their selection of elective subjects in the study program. Table 4.1 reports the means and standard deviations of the four subgroups and the total sample on the quantitative and language scales.

The interesting conclusion is that the four groups are drawn from populations having significantly different dispersions. Inspection of the four determinants in Table 4.1 reveals that the biology group appears to be the most divergent group. This seems to be primarily due to the high negative correlation between Q and L for the biology group, as seen in the off-diagonal elements of D_4. A simple comparison of univariate group variances would not have indicated this difference.

TABLE 4.1

Subgroup and Total Sample Means and Standard Deviations for A.C.E. Q and L Scales on Jervis-Congdon Gifted Boys

Interest Group	A.C.E. Q		A.C.E. L	
	Mean	S.D.	Mean	S.D.
Language and history (30 boys)	31.7	5.3	84.9	13.7
Physical science and mathematics (47 boys)	35.0	6.0	84.2	12.7
Concepts of mathematics (20 boys)	33.9	4.8	80.9	14.7
Biology (8 boys)	31.5	4.8	87.4	13.9
Total Sample (105 boys)	33.6	5.6	84.0	13.4

$$|D_1| = 5066.62 \qquad D_1 = \begin{bmatrix} 27.61 & 11.54 \\ 11.54 & 188.33 \end{bmatrix}$$

$$|D_2| = 5320.87 \qquad D_2 = \begin{bmatrix} 35.61 & 19.80 \\ 19.80 & 160.43 \end{bmatrix}$$

$$|D_3| = 4508.52 \qquad D_3 = \begin{bmatrix} 22.79 & 20.26 \\ 20.26 & 215.84 \end{bmatrix}$$

$$|D_4| = 449.08 \qquad D_4 = \begin{bmatrix} 23.43 & -63.79 \\ -63.79 & 192.84 \end{bmatrix}$$

For H_1, $M = 21.59$; $F_{5200}^9 = 2.26$, $.01 < p < .05$.

For H_2, $\Lambda = .904$; $F_{200}^6 = 1.72$, $p > .05$.

[5] See the footnote on p. 23.

It is also interesting to note that H_2 could not be rejected in this example, whereas H_1 was rejected. This illustrates the insensitivity of H_2 to small departures from homogeneity of dispersions.

Distinguishing Scientists and Science Teachers by Certain Personality Dimensions. Lee (1961) has studied certain personality dimensions that are related to the movement into science teaching. His theoretical model postulated that the more person-oriented college science majors would move out of science and that some of them would become science teachers. Twelve relevant dimensions were obtained from three instruments: (1) the Strong vocational interest blank for men, (2) the Allport-Vernon-Lindzey study of values, and (3) the Guilford-Zimmerman temperament survey.

Two groups of subjects were obtained. One group, from the Scientific Careers Study (SCS), consisted of sixty-one ($N_1 = 61$) males who were tested as college seniors. The SCS group continued toward careers in science following graduation. The science teacher group was obtained by contacting "fifth-year" programs at graduate schools of education, selecting those males who majored in one of the sciences but who were then preparing to enter teaching as a career. Lee called this latter group the Liberal Arts Science Teachers (LAST). Testing was completed for sixty-six of them ($N_2 = 66$).

The sequence of the analyses was as follows:

(1) Test of H_1 for the two groups using all twelve dimensions. (No difference in dispersion was found.)

(2) Test of H_2 using all twelve dimensions (Results in Table 4.3)

Since (2) was rejected:

(3) Test of H_2 using the Strong scales.
(4) Test of H_2 using the A-V-L scales.
(5) Test of H_2 using the G-Z scales.

Rejection of null hypotheses (3), (4), and (5) (see Table 4.4) made it possible to examine the scales within each area (interest, values, and temperament) to determine which particular variables were most significant on an individual basis. The group means for the twelve variables are reported in Table 4.2 and the corresponding t tests are summarized in Table 4.5.

In summary, hypotheses (1) and (2) tested the general model, and (3), (4), and (5) made sure each area was detecting differences and made possible an examination of their relative differences. The univariate t tests made possible the examination of individual variables.[6] The results are shown in Table 4.2.

---

[6] It should be emphasized that the series of hypotheses tested here were all derived from the investigator's theoretical model regarding personality differences between scientists and science teachers. After hypothesis (1) established over-all differences on the variables related to the model, the remaining hypotheses explored the exact nature of those differences to make sure they were consistent with the model. These subsequent tests might be considered more descriptive than inferential.

TABLE 4.2

Subgroup Means and Standard Deviations for Twelve Dimensions of Personality on Subjects in the Lee Science Teachers Study

Personality Scale	SCS Group, 61 Subjects		LAST Group, 66 Subjects	
	Mean	S.D.	Mean	S.D.
Temperament (G-Z)				
Sociability	16.38	6.27	18.91	5.95
Emotional stability	16.77	6.09	19.47	5.66
Objectivity	19.13	5.30	20.36	4.21
Personal relation	16.10	5.63	18.00	5.02
Values (A-V-L)				
Theoretical	53.65	6.08	51.24	7.37
Aesthetic	40.33	8.95	39.03	8.76
Social	32.84	7.77	38.21	7.89
Interests (SVIB)				
Technical worker	48.18	9.80	41.14	10.25
Welfare worker	36.79	9.30	46.47	7.79
Musical performer	41.44	11.82	42.92	11.36
Business detail	23.84	9.76	22.56	9.45
Business contact	30.15	7.49	30.79	8.05

TABLE 4.3

General Analysis

$$H_1 = M = 91.54, \quad F_{48710}^{78} = 1.05, \quad p > .30$$
$$H_2 = \Lambda = .614, \quad F_{114}^{12} = 5.98, \quad p < .001$$

TABLE 4.4

Area Analysis: A Comparison of the F Ratios and Probabilities of the Guilford-Zimmerman, Allport-Vernon, and Strong Areas

Area	F	ndf_1	ndf_2	p
Temperament (4 scales)	2.626	4	122	<.05
Values (3 scales)	5.376	3	123	<.01
Interests (5 scales)	11.719	5	121	<.001

TABLE 4.5

Individual Variable Analysis: A Summary of the Analyses Performed on the Twelve Individual Variables with the Prediction and Outcome of That Prediction

Area Variable	Prediction	t	p	High Group	Outcome of Prediction
Temperament					
Sociability	SCS < LAST	2.373	$p < .01$	LAST	Correct
Emotional stability	SCS < LAST	2.589	$p < .01$	LAST	Correct
Objectivity	SCS < LAST	1.657	$.025 < p < .05$	LAST	Correct
Personal relation	SCS < LAST	2.013	$.01 < p < .025$	LAST	Correct
Values					
Theoretical	SCS > LAST	1.174	Not significant	SCS	No difference
Aesthetic	SCS < LAST	.825	Not significant	SCS	No difference
Social	SCS < LAST	3.865	$p < .0005$	LAST	Correct
Interests					
Technical worker	SCS > LAST	3.946	$p < .0005$	SCS	Correct
Welfare worker	SCS < LAST	6.379	$p < .0005$	LAST	Correct
Musical performer	SCS > LAST	.720	Not significant	LAST	No difference
Business detail	SCS < LAST	.748	Not significant	SCS	No difference
Business contact	SCS < LAST	.454	Not significant	LAST	No difference

The results of Lee's analyses supported the contention that "there are identifiable personality attributes associated with persons choosing science teaching as a career. The science teacher group scored higher on all variables concerned with interpersonal relations. The scientist group scored higher on variables which were 'non-person' oriented, such as the Technical Workers scale."[7]

4.4   Examples of Multiple Covariance Adjustment

Covariance Adjustment of Two Group Aptitude Test Scores by Two Individual Intelligence Test Scores and Test of the Separation of Four Interest Groups. The sample of boys and the two group aptitude test scores (A.C.E. Q and L) are the same as in the example of Section 4.3. The two adjusters are the Verbal and Performance scales of the Wechsler Adult Intelligence Scales (WAIS). As reported in Table 2.2, it has been established that A.C.E. Q and L scores are uncorrelated, and that WAIS V and P are uncorrelated, but that the two A.C.E. scales have low but significant correlations with both the WAIS scales. The analysis reported in Section 4.3 has already established the following result for the test of H_2 on the A.C.E. scales and the four interest groups:

$$\text{for } H_2, \quad \Lambda = .904, \quad F_{200}^6 = 1.72, \quad p > .05.$$

The test of H_2 following covariance adjustment for the two WAIS scales which are correlated with the two A.C.E. experimental scales should produce a larger Λ and

[7] Lee, *op. cit.*, p. xii.

thus a smaller F value and a higher probability. The computed result from the COVAR program is:

$$\text{for } H_2, \qquad \Lambda = .936, \qquad F^6_{196} = 1.08, \qquad p > .05.$$

As expected, the F value, with almost the same ndf as for the previous case, is smaller following covariance adjustment.

To provide a further example of the covariance procedure, the Congdon-Jervis sample was studied again, but this time seven group aptitude test scores, adjusted

TABLE 4.6

Subgroup Means and Total Sample Means and Standard Deviations for Ten Scales on Jervis-Congdon Data

Scales	Total Sample Mean	S.D.	Language and History, Mean	Physical Science and Mathematics, Mean	Concepts of Mathematics, Mean	Biology, Mean
A.C.E. Q	34	6	32	35	34	32
A.C.E. L	84	13	85	84	81	87
Coop Rdg. V	58	8	59	57	56	63
Coop Rdg. S	66	9	67	66	67	64
Coop Rdg. C	62	7	61	62	61	62
Watson-Glaser	70	8	70	70	71	69
Raven Prog. Matrix	25	4	25	25	24	24
WAIS V	131	7	132	131	129	133
WAIS P	118	11	113	120	119	116
WAIS V − P	35	12	40	32	32	38

For H_2, $\Lambda = .786$, $F^{21}_{264.6} = 1.60$, $p < .05$.

by three WAIS scores, were employed in the effort to separate the four interest subgroups. Table 4.6 reports the means and standard deviations for the four groups and ten scales. The intercorrelations of the ten scales have been reported in Table 2.2. The result of this analysis indicates that the residual variances and covariances on the seven experimental scales in the four subgroups following covariance adjustment for the three control scales are such that the null hypothesis of H_2 may be rejected at the 5% level of significance. Thus it may be said that the battery of seven group aptitude tests has the power to discriminate the four interest groups among the 105 gifted boys, even after the removal of the components of determination that the experimental scales have in common with the three individual intelligence test control scales.

An Experimental Study Comparing the Effectiveness of Teaching Deduction in Two Content Areas of Secondary Mathematics. As pointed out earlier, one situation in which the generalized analysis of variance and covariance applies is in

TABLE 4.7

Means and Standard Deviations for the Two Groups

Variable	Geometry Content		Algebra Content	
	Mean	S.D.	Mean	S.D.
Experimental				
1 Shaycoft plane geometry, form Bm	52.70	7.73	46.19	9.40
2 Blyth algebra, form Bm	53.73	8.83	56.03	9.77
3 STEP Mathematics, form 2B	54.88	8.10	56.16	8.89
4 Watson-Glaser deduction	17.19	2.66	17.95	2.99
5 Watson-Glaser critical thinking	64.30	8.62	66.57	10.35
Control				
1 CTMM language aptitude	204.30	19.65	207.84	21.34
2 CTMM nonlanguage aptitude	195.63	23.42	194.66	24.11
3 Shaycoft geometry, form Am	40.57	9.90	40.42	10.41
4 Blyth algebra, form Am	50.10	10.00	52.46	11.25
5 STEP Mathematics, form 2A	50.78	11.55	52.04	10.09
6 Watson-Glaser deduction	16.25	2.31	16.58	2.82
7 Watson-Glaser critical thinking	60.97	7.84	62.15	9.50

$\Lambda = .727$, $F_{121}^5 = 9.06$, $p < .001*$ $\qquad\qquad N_1 = 67 \quad N_2 = 67$

* Significance of the difference between the two treatments on the five experimental variables after adjustment for the seven control variables.

experiments involving several experimental and control variables. A recent experiment by Balomenos (1961) serves to illustrate this application. His general hypothesis was that students who are taught an understanding and appreciation of deduction and deductive systems by two different approaches will not differ significantly on five criterion measures after adjustment has been made for differences in aptitude and initial understanding (pretests of the criterion instruments). Seven control variables were used in all. The resulting lambda criterion was highly significant, indicating that the two treatments produced over-all differences on the five experimental variables.

The investigation next tested the difference between the two groups on each

experimental variable (using all seven controls).[8] Finally, the adjusted means for
the two groups on the only significant experimental variable were computed. The
coefficients for this adjustment are computed within the covariance program. It
involves multiplying $\mathbf{W}_{cc}^{-1}$ by $\mathbf{W}_{cp}$. As can be seen in Table 4.9, the control pretest
of the corresponding experimental variate tended to have the highest loading
among the adjustment coefficients.

TABLE 4.8

Differences on Each of the Experimental Variables

Variable	Λ	F_{125}^1	p
1 Shaycoft plane geometry, form Bm	.7706	36.91	$p < .001$
2 Blyth algebra, form Bm	.9958	.523	—
3 STEP Mathematics, form 2B	.9971	.361	—
4 Watson-Glaser deduction	.9877	1.544	—
5 Watson-Glaser critical thinking	.9936	.799	—

TABLE 4.9

Adjustment Coefficients for the Seven Control Variables

Control Variable	Experimental Variable				
	1	2	3	4	5
1 CTMM language aptitude	.018	−.016	−.017	.011	.021
2 CTMM nonlanguage aptitude	.001	−.012	.045	−.020	−.016
3 Shaycoft geometry, form Am	.412	.067	.016	.036	−.017
4 Blyth algebra, form Am	.149	.517	.020	−.029	.008
5 STEP Mathematics, form 2A'	.046	.158	.496	.059	.190
6 Watson-Glaser deduction	.210	−.069	.221	.426	.572
7 Watson-Glaser critical thinking	.012	.114	.012	.038	.527

Adjusted means for the significant experimental variables	Content Group	
	Geometry	Algebra
Geometry Test	52.95	45.94

[8] The program COVAR given on pp. 82–86 can be used for one-way analysis of covariance
when there is only one experimental or one control variable, as well as for the multivariate case.
A program for two- and three-way experimental designs is described in Chapter 5.

Flow Diagram for Tests of H₁ and H₂ (H1H2 Program)

INPUT
Read K, M where K = no. of groups and M = no. of variables. Note that subscripts have the ranges $v = 1, 2, 3, \ldots, M$ and $w = 1, 2, 3, \ldots, M$.

Set $SUMT_v = 0$, $W_{vw} = 0$, $T_{vw} = 0$, $N = 0$, $H1LOGS = 0$, $GA1S = 0$, $FA1S = 0$, and GROUPS = K for initialization.

①

SUBROUTINE
Call subroutine CORREL, which computes and reports, for each group NG, the number of subjects in the group, SX, the sum of scores vector, SS, the raw s.s.c.p. matrix, SSD, the deviation s.s.c.p. matrix, and D, the dispersion matrix.

$SUMT_v = SUMT_v + SX_v$ accumulating total sums vector.
$W_{vw} = W_{vw} + SSD_{vw}$ accumulating pooled within-groups deviation s.s.c.p. matrix.
$T_{vw} = T_{vw} + SS_{vw}$ accumulating total raw s.s.c.p. matrix.
$N = N + NG$ accumulating total number of cases.

SUBROUTINE
Call subroutine HDIAG, which computes the latent roots of the group D matrix and places them in the diagonal of D.

DETERM = 0
$DETERM = DETERM + \log_e D_{vv}$ forming $\log_e |D_g|$.

OUTPUT
Print DETERM and NG with labels.

$H1LOG = (NG - 1) \cdot DETERM$ accumulating $\Sigma_g n_g \log_e |D_g|$.
H1LOGS = H1LOGS + H1LOG
$FA1 = 1/(NG - 1)$
$FA1S = FA1S + FA1$ accumulating $\Sigma_g 1/n_g$.
$GA1 = 1/((NG - 1) \cdot (NG - 1))$
$GA1S = GA1S + GA1$ accumulating $\Sigma_g 1/n_g^2$.
GROUPS = GROUPS − 1

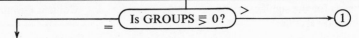

Is GROUPS $\lessgtr$ 0?   >   ①
=

4.1. Flow Diagram for H_1H_2 Program (Continued)

$T_{vw} = T_{vw} - SUMT_v \cdot SUMT_w/N$ forming total sample deviation s.s.c.p.

OUTPUT

Punch W_{vw}, T_{vw} (preserving W and T for possible future multiple-discriminant analysis).

SUBROUTINE

Call subroutine HDIAG, which computes the latent roots of W and places them in the diagonal of W.

DETERM = 0
DETERM = DETERM + $\log_e W_{vv}$ forming $\log_e |W|$.
H1LOG = (DETERM $-$ (($\log_e (N - K)) \cdot M) \cdot (N - K)$
XMM = H1LOG $-$ H1LOGS   Box's m.
F1 = $.5(K - 1) \cdot M \cdot (M + 1)$ Box's f_1.
A1 = (FA1S $-$ (1/(N $-$ K))) $\cdot$ (2M^2 + 3M $-$ 1)/(6(K $-$ 1)(M + 1))
A2 = (GA1S $-$ (1/(N $-$ K)^2)) $\cdot$ ((M $-$ 1)(M + 2))/(6(K $-$ 1))
DIF = A2 $-$ A1^2

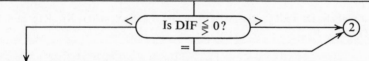

$\langle$ Is DIF $\lessgtr$ 0? $\rangle$ (2)

F2 = (F1 + 2)/(A1^2 $-$ A2)
B = F2/(1 $-$ A1 + (2/F2))
F = (F2 $\cdot$ XMM)/(F1 $\cdot$ (B $-$ XMM)   F for H_1.

   (3)   (2)

F2 = (F1 + 2)/DIF
B = F1/(1 $-$ A1 $-$ (F1/F2))
F = XMM/B   F for H_1.

 (3)

OUTPUT

Print with appropriate labels the results of test of H_1 including DETERM, F, F1, F2, XMM, B, A1, A2.

$D_{vw} = T_{vw}/(N - 1)$ forming total sample D matrix.
$R_{vw} = T_{vw}/\sqrt{T_{vv} \cdot T_{ww}}$ for total sample R matrix.

SUBROUTINE

Call subroutine HDIAG, which computes the latent roots of the T matrix and places them in the diagonal of T.

73

DETERT $= 0$

DETERT $=$ DETERT $+ \log_e T_{vv}$ forming $\log_e |T|$.

XLAMBL $=$ DETERM $-$ DETERT

XLAMBDA $=$ exponential function of XLAMBL, forming Wilks Λ criterion for H_2.

$S = \sqrt{(M^2 \cdot (K-1)^2 - 4)/(M^2 + (K-1)^2 - 5)}$

LY $=$ XLAMBL $\cdot (1/S)$

Y $=$ exponential function of LY.

XM1 $= (N-1) - (M+K)/2$

XL $= -((M \cdot (K-1)) - 2)/4$

R1 $= (M \cdot (K-1))/2$

F1 $= 2 \cdot$ R1   degrees of freedom (numerator).

F2 $= ($XM1 $\cdot$ S$) - (2 \cdot$ XL$)$ degrees of freedom (denominator).

F $= ((1 - Y)/Y) \cdot ($F2$/$F1$)$ F for test of H_2.

$XM_v = SUMT_v/N$ forming total sample means.

$SD_v = \sqrt{D_{vv}}$ forming total sample standard deviations.

OUTPUT

Print, with labels, DETERT, XLAMBDA, F, F1, F2, S, Y, XM1, XL, R1; punch XM_v, SD_v, D_{vw}, R_{vw}.

$\boxed{\text{STOP}}$

Flow Diagram for Test of H_2 with Optional Covariance Controls (COVAR Program)

INPUT
Read K, M, L, where K is the number of groups, M is the number of experimental variables, L is the number of control variables. Form ML = M + L.
In this diagram subscripts have the following ranges:

$r = 1, 2, 3, \ldots, ML$ $s = 1, 2, 3, \ldots, ML$
$v = 1, 2, 3, \ldots, M$ $w = 1, 2, 3, \ldots, M$
$t = 1, 2, 3, \ldots, L$ $u = 1, 2, 3, \ldots, L$
$x = M + 1, M + 2, \ldots, ML$ $y = M + 1, M + 2, \ldots, ML.$

Set $W_{rs} = 0$, $X_{rs} = 0$, $B_r = 0$, NT = 0, GROUPS = K for initialization.

Set $U_{rs} = 0$ and $A_r = 0$.

INPUT
Read KG, KN, where KG is the group identification number and KN is the number of subjects in the group. Set CASES = KN.

INPUT
Read C_r where C is the score vector of a subject.

$A_r = A_r + C_r$ accumulating raw sums.
$U_{rs} = U_{rs} + C_r \cdot C_s$ accumulating raw s.s.c.p.
CASES = CASES $-$ 1

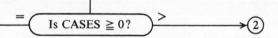

=   Is CASES $\geqq$ 0?   >   ②

$V_{rs} = U_{rs} - A_r \cdot A_s / KN$ forming deviation s.s.c.p., which is $\|W_g\|$.
$D_r = A_r / KN$ forming means.
$E_r = \sqrt{V_{rr}/(KN - 1)}$ forming standard deviations.

OUTPUT
Print and/or punch KG, KN, D_r, E_r, V_{rs}.

$W_{rs} = W_{rs} + U_{rs}$ accumulating raw s.s.c.p. for total sample.
$X_{rs} = X_{rs} + V_{rs}$ accumulating pooled within-groups deviation s.s.c.p. matrix.
$B_r = B_r + A_r$ accumulating total sums of scores.
NT = NT + KN   accumulating total number of subjects.
GROUPS = GROUPS $-$ 1

4.2. Flow Diagram for COVAR Program (Continued)

$$\downarrow$$

$$= \left(\text{Is GROUPS} \geq 0?\right) \xrightarrow{>} \quad \textcircled{1}$$

$Y_{rs} = W_{rs} - B_r \cdot B_s/\text{NT}$ forming $\|T\|$.

$G_r = B_r/\text{NT}$ forming total sample means.

$H_r = \sqrt{Y_{rr}/(\text{NT} - 1)}$ forming total sample standard deviations.

$U_{tu} = X_{xy}$ partitioning off $\|T_{cc}\|$ of notes.

SUBROUTINE

Call subroutine MATINV to compute the inverse of U and place it in U.

$V_{vt} = Y_{vx}$ partitioning off $\|T_{tc}\|$.

$W_{vt} = 0$

$W_{vt} = W_{vt} + V_{vu} \cdot U_{ut}$

$U_{tv} = V_{vt}$ partitioning off $\|T_{ct}\|$.

$V_{vw} = 0$

$V_{vw} = V_{vw} + W_{vt} \cdot U_{tw}$

$W_{vw} = Y_{vw} - V_{vw}$ forming $\|T_{t\cdot c}\|$.

$A_v = \sqrt{W_{vv}/(\text{NT} - 1)}$ forming adjusted total sample standard deviations for the experimental variables.

SUBROUTINE

Call HDIAG, which computes the latent roots of W and places them in the diagonal of W.

DETERT = 0

DETERT = DETERT + $\log_e W_{vv}$ forming $\log_e |W|$, i.e., $\log_e |T_{t\cdot c}|$.

$U_{tu} = X_{xy}$ partitioning off $\|W_{cc}\|$.

SUBROUTINE

Call subroutine MATINV to compute the inverse of U and place it in U.

$V_{vt} = X_{vx}$ partitioning off $\|W_{tc}\|$.

$W_{vt} = 0$

$W_{vt} = W_{vt} + V_{vu} \cdot U_{ut}$

$U_{vw} = 0$

$U_{vw} = U_{vw} + W_{vt} \cdot V_{wt}$

$W_{vw} = X_{vw} - U_{vw}$ forming $\|W_{t\cdot c}\|$.

SUBROUTINE

Call subroutine HDIAG, which computes the latent roots of W and places them in the diagonal of W.

$$\downarrow$$

4.2. Flow Diagram for COVAR Program (Continued)

↓

DETERW $= 0$
DETERW $=$ DETERW $+ \log_e W_{vv}$ forming $\log_e |W|$, i.e., $\log_e |W_{t \cdot c}|$.
XLAMBD $=$ DETERW $-$ DETERT
LAMBDA $=$ exponential function of XLAMBD   forming Λ.
DETERW $=$ exponential function of DETERW
DETERT $=$ exponential function of DETERT
$S = \sqrt{(M^2 \cdot (K - 1)^2 - 4)/(M^2 + (K - 1)^2 - 5)}$
$XL = -(M \cdot (K - 1) - 2)/2$
$XY = $ LAMBDA$^{1/S}$
$XM = (NT - 1 - L) - (M + K)/2$
$F1 = M \cdot (K - 1)$ degrees of freedom for test of H_2.
$F2 = XM \cdot S + XL$
$F = (1 - XY) \cdot F2/(XY \cdot F1)$ F for H_2.
$W_{tv} = 0$
$W_{tv} = W_{tv} - U_{tu} \cdot V_{wt}$ forming coefficients for test of homogeneity of regressions.

OUTPUT
Print and/or punch, with appropriate labels, F, F1, F2, LAMBDA, DETERW, DETERT, S, XL, XY, XM, G_v, H_v, A_v, V_{tv}.

$\boxed{\text{STOP}}$

PROGRAM FOR GENERALIZED ANALYSIS OF VARIANCE WITH TEST OF EQUALITY OF GROUP DISPERSIONS (H1H2)

```
C      H1H2.
C
C          THIS PROGRAM COMPUTES H1 AND H2 FOR UP TO 50 VARIABLES AND
C      ANY NUMBER OF GROUPS.  REQUIRED SUBROUTINES ARE CORREL, HDIAG,
C      MPUNCH, AND MPRINT.
C
C      INPUT.
C
C          INPUT CARD 1 CONTAINS
C      COL. 1-2   K = NO. OF GROUPS
C      COL. 3-4   M = NO. OF VARIABLES.
C      SET UP PARAMETER AND DATA CARDS (AFTER FIRST) AS REQUIRED BY
C      SUBROUTINE CORREL, ONE SET FOR EACH GROUP,
C      USING L1 = 1  TO COMPUTE DISPERSION AND CORRELATION MATRICES.
C
C      OUTPUT.
C
C    ·      PRINTED OUTPUT INCLUDES
C      1) PROGRAM TITLE, AND K
C      2) GROUP MEANS, STANDARD DEVIATIONS, AND DISPERSION MATRIX FROM
C      CORREL, FOR EACH GROUP
C      3) LOG BASE E OF DETERMINANT OF EACH GROUP DISPERSION MATRIX, AND
C      CORRESPONDING DETERMINANT, H1LOG, FA1, AND GA1 FOR EACH GROUP
C      4) LOG BASE E OF DETERMINANT OF POOLED W AND CORRESPONDING DETER-
C      MINANT
C      5) WEIGHT, H1LOG, M, F1, DIF, A1, A2, B, F2, AND F FOR TEST OF H1
C      6) MEANS FOR TOTAL SAMPLE
C      7) STANDARD DEVIATIONS FOR TOTAL SAMPLE
C      8) DISPERSION MATRIX FOR TOTAL SAMPLE
C      9) CORRELATION MATRIX FOR TOTAL SAMPLE
C      10) LOG BASE E OF DETERMINANT OF T MATRIX, WITH DETERMINANT OF T
C      11) WILKS LAMBDA, F1, F2, AND F FOR TEST OF H2.
C      PRINTED OUTPUT IS APPROPRIATELY LABELED.
C      PUNCHED OUTPUT INCLUDES
C      1. MEANS FOR EACH GROUP
C      2) STANDARD DEVIATIONS FOR EACH GROUP
C      3) DISPERSION MATRIX FOR EACH GROUP
C      4) POOLED W MATRIX
C      5) T MATRIX
C      6) DISPERSION MATRIX FOR TOTAL SAMPLE
C      7) CORRELATION MATRIX FOR TOTAL SAMPLE.
C
       DIMENSION FMT(36), FMR(36), X(50), SX(50), SS(50,50), SSD(50,50),
      1 D(50,50), R(50,50), XM(50), SD(50), W(50,50), T(50,50), SUMT(50),
      2 IQ(50), TITLE(12)
       READ INPUT TAPE 4, 1, K, M
     1 FORMAT (2I2)
       WRITE OUTPUT TAPE 2, 2, K
     2 FORMAT(51HOGENERALIZED ANALYSIS OF VARIANCE. NO. OF GROUPS = I2)
       EN = 0.0
       EK = K
       DO 4  I = 1,M
     4 SUMT(I) = 0.0
       DO 5  I = 1,M
       DO 5  J = 1,M
       W(I,J) = 0.0
     5 T(I,J) = 0.0
       H1LOGS = 0.C
       GA1S = 0.0
```

```
      FA1S = 0.0
      GROUPS = K
C
  100 CALL CORREL (TN,NG, SX, SS, SSD, D, R, XM, SD)
      ENG = NG
      EN = EN + ENG
      DO 6  I = 1,M
    6 SUMT(I) = SUMT(I) + SX(I)
      DO 7  I = 1,M
      DO 7  J = 1,M
      W(I,J) = W(I,J) + SSD(I,J)
    7 T(I,J) = T(I,J) + SS(I,J)
C
      CALL HDIAG (D, M, 1, SS, NR)
      DETERM = 0.0
      DO 8  I = 1,M
    8 DETERM = DETERM + LOGF (D(I,I))
      WRITE OUTPUT TAPE 2, 9, DETERM
    9 FORMAT (29HOLOG DETERMINANT OF GROUP D = F14.7)
      DET = EXPF (DETERM)
      PRINT 91, DET
   91 FORMAT (17HODETERMINANT D = F14.7)
C
      H1LOG = (ENG - 1.0) * DETERM
      PRINT 10, H1LOG
   10 FORMAT (24HOH1LOG FOR THIS GROUP = F14.7)
      H1LOGS = H1LOGS + H1LOG
      FA1 = 1.0 / (ENG-1.0)
      PRINT 11, FA1
   11 FORMAT (22HOFA1 FOR THIS GROUP = F14.7)
      FA1S = FA1S + FA1
      GA1 = 1.0 /((ENG-1.0)**2.0)
      PRINT 12, GA1
   12 FORMAT (22HOGA1 FOR THIS GROUP = F14.7)
      GA1S = GA1S + GA1
      GROUPS = GROUPS - 1.0
      IF (GROUPS) 35, 35, 100
C
C     GROUP DISPERSIONS AND TOTAL XX (CALLED T) AND W ARE DONE.
   35 CONTINUE
   25 FORMAT (5F14.7)
   26 FORMAT (5E14.7)
      DO 350  J=1,M
  350 PUNCH 26, (W(I,J), I=1,M)
      DO 36  I=1,M
      DO 36  J=1,M
      SSD(I,J) = W(I,J)
      SS(I,J) = T(I,J)
   36 T(I,J) = SS(I,J) - (SUMT(I) * SUMT(J)/EN)
C     T(I,J) IS NOW THE TOTAL DEVIATION CROSS PRODUCTS MATRIX.
      DO 360  J=1,M
  360 PUNCH 26, (T(I,J), I=1,M)
      CALL HDIAG (SSD, M, 1, D, NR)
      DETERM = 0.0
      DO 38  I=1,M
   38 DETERM = DETERM + LOGF (SSD(I,I))
```

```
        WRITE OUTPUT TAPE 2,381,DETERM
    381 FORMAT (31HOLOG DETERMINANT OF POOLED W = F14.7)
        DET = EXPF (DETERM)
        PRINT 391, DET
    391 FORMAT (17HODETERMINANT W = F14.7)
C
        EM = M
        WATE = LOGF ( EN-EK) * EM
        PRINT 382, WATE
    382 FORMAT (10HOWEIGHT = F14.7)
        H1LOG = ( DETERM - WATE ) * ( EN-EK )
        PRINT 383, H1LOG
    383 FORMAT (9HOH1LOG = F14.7)
        XMM = H1LOG - H1LOGS
        F1 = .5 * (EK-1.0) * EM * (EM+1.0)
        A1A=(FA1S-(1.0/(EN-EK)))*((2.0*(EM**2.0))+(3.0*EM)-1.0)
        A1 = A1A / (6.0 * (EK-1.0)*(EM+1.0))
        A2 =(GA1S-(1.0/(EN-EK)**2.0)) *((EM-1.0)*(EM+2.0))/(6.0*(EK-1.0))
        DIF = A2 - (A1**2.0)
        WRITE OUTPUT TAPE 2, 39, XMM
     39 FORMAT (22HOFOR TEST OF H1    M = F14.7)
        WRITE OUTPUT TAPE 2, 40, F1
     40 FORMAT (6HOF1 = F14.7)
        WRITE OUTPUT TAPE 2, 41, DIF
     41 FORMAT (19HOA2 - A1 SQUARED = F14.7)
        IF (DIF) 42, 42, 442
C
     42 F2 = (F1+2.0) /((A1**2.0) - A2)
        B = F2 / (1.0 - A1 + (2.0/F2))
        F = (F2 * XMM)/(F1 * (B - XMM))
        GO TO 443
    442 F2 = (F1 + 2.0) / DIF
        B = F1 / (1.0 - A1 - (F1/F2))
        F = XMM / B
    443 WRITE OUTPUT TAPE 2, 43, F2
     43 FORMAT (6HOF2 = F14.7)
        WRITE OUTPUT TAPE 2, 143, F
    143 FORMAT (21HOFOR TEST OF H1, F = F14.7)
C       F IS F VALUE FOR TEST OF H1, WITH N.D.F. F1 AND F2.
        PRINT 144, A1
    144 FORMAT (6HOA1 = F14.7)
        PRINT 145, A2
    145 FORMAT (6HOA2 = F14.7)
        PRINT 146, B
    146 FORMAT (5HOB = F14.7)
C
     44 DO 45  I=1,M
        DO 45  J=1,M
     45  D(I,J) = T(I,J) / (EN - 1.0)
C       D(I,J) IS NOW THE TOTAL VARIANCE-COVARIANCE MATRIX.
        DO 450  I=1,M
        DO 450  J=1,M
    450 R(I,J) = T(I,J) / SQRTF (T(I,I) * T(J,J))
C           R(I,J) IS NOW THE TOTAL CORRELATION MATRIX.
        DO 46  I=1,M
        XM(I) = SUMT(I) / EN
```

```
 46 SD(I) = SQRTF (D(I,I))
    WRITE OUTPUT TAPE 2, 47
 47 FORMAT (22HOMEANS OF TOTAL SAMPLE)
    WRITE OUTPUT TAPE 2, 25, (XM(I), I = 1,M)
    WRITE OUTPUT TAPE 2, 48
 48 FORMAT (37HOSTANDARD DEVIATIONS FOR TOTAL SAMPLE)
    WRITE OUTPUT TAPE 2, 25, (SD(I), I = 1,M)
    WRITE OUTPUT TAPE 2, 49
 49 FORMAT(44H1VARIANCE-COVARIANCE MATRIX FOR TOTAL SAMPLE)
    DO 50   J=1,M
 50 WRITE OUTPUT TAPE 2, 25,   (D(I,J),   I=1,M)
    WRITE OUTPUT TAPE 2, 52
 52 FORMAT (36H1CORRELATION MATRIX FOR TOTAL SAMPLE)
    DO 53   J=1,M
 53 WRITE OUTPUT TAPE 2, 25, (R(I,J),   I = 1,M)
C
    DO 150  J = 1,M
150 PUNCH 26,  (D(I,J),   I = 1,M)
    DO 153  J = 1,M
153 PUNCH 26,  (R(I,J),   I = 1,M)
C
    CALL HDIAG (T, M, 1, D, NR)
    DETERT = 0.0
    DO 57   I=1,M
 57 DETERT = DETERT + LOGF  (T(I,I))
    WRITE OUTPUT TAPE 2,571,DETERT
571 FORMAT (24HOLOG DETERMINANT OF T = F14.7)
    DET = EXPF (DETERT)
    PRINT 572, DET
572 FORMAT (17HODETERMINANT T = F14.7)
    XLAMBL = DETERM - DETERT
    XLAMB = EXPF(XLAMBL)
    IF (EM - 2.0) 573, 573, 574
573 F1 = 2.0 * (EK - 1.0)
    F2 = 2.0 * (EN - EK - 1.0)
    Y = SQRTF (XLAMB)
    F = (1.0 - Y) * F2 / (Y * F1)
    GO TO 579
574 S=SQRTF((((EM**2)*((EK-1.0)**2)-4.0)/((EM**2)+((EK-1.0)**2)-5.0)))
    IF (S) 575, 575, 576
575 F1 = EK - 1.0
    F2 = EN - EK
    F =((1.0 - XLAMB) / XLAMB) * (F2 / F1)
    GO TO 579
576 Y = XLAMB**(1.0/S)
    XM1= (EN-1.0)-((EM+EK) / 2.0)
    XL = - ((EM * (EK-1.0)) - 2.0) / 4.0
    R1= (EM * (EK-1.0)) / 2.0
    F1 = 2.0 * R1
    F2 = ( XM1 * S ) + ( 2.0 * XL )
    F = ( ( 1.0 - Y ) / Y ) * ( F2 / F1 )
579 WRITE OUTPUT TAPE 2, 58, XLAMB
 58 FORMAT(9HOLAMBDA= F14.7)
    WRITE OUTPUT TAPE 2, 60, F1
 60 FORMAT (6HOF1 = F14.7)
    WRITE OUTPUT TAPE 2, 61, F2
 61 FORMAT (6HOF2 = F14.7)
    WRITE OUTPUT TAPE 2, 59, F
 59 FORMAT (21HOFOR TEST OF H2, F = F14.7)
    CALL EXIT
    END
```

GENERALIZED ANALYSIS OF VARIANCE WITH COVARIANCE CONTROL (COVAR)

```
C       COVAR.
C
C       THIS PROGRAM COMPUTES THE TEST OF H2 (EQUALITY OF EXPERIMENTAL
C       MEAN VECTORS) WITH COVARIANCE CONTROLS, WHERE THE TOTAL NUMBER OF
C       VARIABLES DOES NOT EXCEED 50.  NOTE THAT THE CONTROL VARIABLES
C       FOLLOW THE EXPERIMENTAL VARIABLES ON THE SCORE CARDS OF SUBJECTS.
C       THE NUMBER OF EXPERIMENTAL (DEPENDENT) VARIABLES MAY BE EQUAL
C       TO ONE.  NOTE THAT ANY NUMBER OF ANALYSES MAY BE COMPUTED WITH
C       ONE LOADING OF THE PROGRAM.
C       REQUIRED SUBROUTINES ARE HDIAG, MATINV, MPUNCH, AND MPRINT.
C
C       INPUT.
C
C           FIRST DATA CARD CONTAINS (IN COLS 1-2) THE NUMBER OF JOBS
C       TO BE RUN.  THE FOLLOWING CARDS ARE PREPARED FOR EACH JOB.
C           INPUT CARD 1 CONTAINS
C       COL. 1-2   K = NO. OF GROUPS
C       COL. 3-4   M = NO. OF EXPERIMENTAL VARIABLES
C       COL. 5-6   L = NO. OF CONTROL VARIABLES.
C       CARDS 2-3 CONTAIN THE VARIABLE INPUT FORMAT FOR SUBJECT SCORE
C       VECTORS.  EACH SET OF SCORE CARDS FOR A GROUP IS PRECEDED BY A
C       CARD CONTAINING
C       COL. 1-2   KG = IDENTIFICATION NUMBER OF THE GROUP
C       COL. 3-7   KN = NO. OF SUBJECTS IN THE GROUP.
C
C       OUTPUT.
C
C           PRINTED OUTPUT INCLUDES
C       1) PROGRAM TITLE, AND K
C       2) M, L
C       3) FOR EACH GROUP, KG, KN, GROUP MEANS, GROUP STANDARD DEVIATIONS
C       4) NT = TOTAL NUMBER OF SUBJECTS
C       5) MEANS FOR TOTAL SAMPLE
C       6) STANDARD DEVIATIONS FOR TOTAL SAMPLE
C       7) CORRELATION MATRIX FOR TOTAL SAMPLE
C       8) ADJUSTED STANDARD DEVIATIONS ON EXPERIMENTAL VARIABLES FOR
C       TOTAL SAMPLE
C       9) LOG BASE E DETERMINANT OF ADJUSTED T MATRIX, AND CORRESPONDING
C       DETERMINANT
C       10) LOG BASE E OF DETERMINANT OF ADJUSTED W MATRIX, AND CORRESPOND-
C       ING DETERMINANT
C       11) WILKS LAMBDA, THE DEGREES OF FREEDOM (F1 AND F2), AND F FOR
C       TEST OF H2
C       12) COEFFICIENTS FOR FORMING THE ADJUSTED MEANS FOR EACH
C       EXPERIMENTAL VARIABLE
C       PRINTED OUTPUT IS APPROPRIATELY LABELED.
C
        DIMENSION  A(50),B(50),C(50),D(50),E(50),G(50),H(50),FMT(24),
       1           U(50,50),V(50,50),W(50,50),X(50,50),Y(50,50),Z(50,50)
        READ 1, JOBS
  111   READ INPUT TAPE 4,1,K,M,L
    1   FORMAT (3I2)
        ML = M+L
        WRITE OUTPUT TAPE 2,2,K
    2   FORMAT (51H1GENERALIZED ANALYSIS OF VARIANCE. NO. OF GROUPS = I2)
        WRITE OUTPUT TAPE 2,3,M
    3   FORMAT(26H0NO. EXPERIMENTAL TESTS = I2)
        WRITE OUTPUT TAPE 2,4,L
    4   FORMAT (21H0NO. CONTROL TESTS = I2)
```

```
      READ INPUT TAPE 4,6,(FMT(I),I=1,24)
    6 FORMAT (12A6)
      DO 8 I=1,ML
    7 B(I) = 0.0
      DO 8 J=1,ML
      W(I,J) = 0.0
    8 X(I,J) = 0.0
      NT = 0
      GROUPS = K
      XM = M
      XL = L
      Q = GROUPS - 1.0
    9 DO 10 I=1,ML
   10 A(I) = 0.0
      DO 11 I=1,ML
      DO 11 J=1,ML
   11 U(I,J) = 0.0
      READ INPUT TAPE 4,12,KG,KN
   12 FORMAT (I2,I5)
      ENK = KN
      WRITE OUTPUT TAPE 2,13,KG,KN
   13 FORMAT(15H1THIS IS GROUP I2,14H NO.SUBJECTS= I5)
      CASES = ENK
   14 READ INPUT TAPE 4, FMT, (C(I), I=1,ML)
      DO 16 I=1,ML
   15 A(I) = A(I)+C(I)
      DO 16 J=1,ML
   16 U(I,J) = U(I,J)+C(I)*C(J)
      CASES = CASES-1.0
      IF (CASES) 17,17,14
   17 DO 18 I=1,ML
      DO 18 J=1,ML
      V(I,J) = U(I,J)-A(I)*A(J)/ENK
      U(J,I) = U(I,J)
   18 V(J,I) = V(I,J)
      DO 19 I=1,ML
      D(I) = A(I)/ENK
   19 E(I) = SQRTF (V(I,I)/(ENK-1.0))
      WRITE OUTPUT TAPE 2,20
   20 FORMAT (20HOMEANS OF THIS GROUP)
      WRITE OUTPUT TAPE 2,21,(D(I), I=1,ML)
   21 FORMAT (5F14.7)
      WRITE OUTPUT TAPE 2,22
   22 FORMAT (34HOSTANDARD DEVIATIONS OF THIS GROUP)
      WRITE OUTPUT TAPE 2,21,(E(I), I=1,ML)
      DO 23 I=1,ML
   23 B(I) = B(I)+A(I)
      DO 24 I=1,ML
      DO 24 J=1,ML
      W(I,J) = W(I,J) + U(I,J)
   24 X(I,J) = X(I,J) + V(I,J)
      NT = NT + KN
      GROUPS = GROUPS-1.0
      IF (GROUPS) 25,25,9
C     X IS NOW RULON W.
   25 WRITE OUTPUT TAPE 2,251,NT
```

```
  251 FORMAT (25H0TOTAL NO. OF SUBJECTS = I5)
      ENT = NT
      DO 26 I=1,ML
      DO 26 J=1,ML
   26 Y(I,J) = W(I,J)-(B(I)*B(J)/ENT)
C     Y IS NOW RULON T.
      DO 27 I=1,ML
      G(I) = B(I)/ENT
   27 H(I) = SQRTF (Y(I,I)/(ENT-1.0))
      WRITE OUTPUT TAPE 2,28
   28 FORMAT (22H0MEANS OF TOTAL SAMPLE)
      WRITE OUTPUT TAPE 2,21,(G(I), I=1,ML)
      WRITE OUTPUT TAPE 2,29
   29 FORMAT (37H0STANDARD DEVIATIONS FOR TOTAL SAMPLE)
      WRITE OUTPUT TAPE 2,21,(H(I), I=1,ML)
      DO 291 I=1,ML
      DO 291 J=1,ML
      Z(I,J) = Y(I,J)/ SQRTF (Y(I,I)*Y(J,J))
  291 Z(J,I) = Z(I,J)
      PRINT 292
  292 FORMAT(36H1CORRELATION MATRIX FOR TOTAL SAMPLE)
      CALL MPRINT (Z,ML,2,6HTOT R )
      DO 30 I=1,L
      DO 30 J=1,L
      IL = I+M
      JL = J+M
   30 U(I,J) = Y(IL,JL)
C     U IS NOW RULON T(C,C).
      CALL MATINV (U,L,B,0,DETERM)
      DO 31 I=1,M
      DO 31 J=1,L
      JL = J+M
   31 V(I,J) = Y(I,JL)
C     V IS NOW RULON T(T,C).
      DO 32 I=1,M
      DO 32 J=1,L
      W(I,J) = 0.0
      DO 32 K=1,L
   32 W(I,J) = W(I,J)+V(I,K)*U(K,J)
      DO 33 I=1,L
      DO 33 J=1,M
   33 U(I,J) = V(J,I)
C     U IS NOW RULON T(C,T).
      DO 34 I=1,M
      DO 34 J=1,M
      V(I,J) = 0.0
      DO 34 K=1,L
   34 V(I,J) = V(I,J)+W(I,K)*U(K,J)
      DO 35 I=1,M
      DO 35 J=1,M
   35 W(I,J) = Y(I,J) - V(I,J)
C     W IS NOW RULON T(T,C).
      DO 355 I=1,M
  355 A(I) = SQRTF(W(I,I)/(ENT-1.0))
      WRITE OUTPUT TAPE 2,48
   48 FORMAT (46H0ADJUSTED STANDARD DEVIATIONS FOR TOTAL SAMPLE)
```

```
      WRITE OUTPUT TAPE 2,21,(A(I), I=1,M)
      CALL HDIAG (W,M,1,V,NR)
      DETERT = 0.0
      DO 36 I=1,M
   36 DETERT = DETERT + LOGF(W(I,I))
      WRITE OUTPUT TAPE 2,47,DETERT
   47 FORMAT (30H1LOG DETERMINANT ADJUSTED T = F14.7)
      DO 37 I=1,L
      DO 37 J=1,L
      IL = I+M
      JL = J+M
   37 U(I,J) = X(IL,JL)
      CALL MATINV (U,L,B,0,DETERM)
      DO 38 I=1,M
      DO 38 J=1,L
      JL = J+M
   38 V(I,J) = X(I,JL)
      DO 39 I=1,M
      DO 39 J=1,L
      W(I,J) = 0.0
      DO 39 K=1,L
   39 W(I,J) = W(I,J) + V(I,K)*U(K,J)
      DO 40  I=1,L
      DO 40 J=1,M
   40 Z(I,J) = V(J,I)
      DO 41 I=1,M
      DO 41 J=1,M
      V(I,J) = 0.0
      DO 41 K=1,L
   41 V(I,J) = V(I,J) + W(I,K)*Z(K,J)
      DO 42 I=1,M
      DO 42 J=1,M
   42 W(I,J) = X(I,J) - V(I,J)
C     W IS NOW RULON W(T.C).
      CALL HDIAG (W,M,1,V,NR)
      DETERW = 0.0
      DO 44 I=1,M
   44 DETERW = DETERW + LOGF(W(I,I))
      WRITE OUTPUT TAPE 2,46,DETERW
   46 FORMAT (30H0LOG DETERMINANT ADJUSTED W = F14.7)
      XLAMBD = DETERW - DETERT
      YLAMBD = EXPF (XLAMBD)
      WRITE OUTPUT TAPE 2, 45, YLAMBD
   45 FORMAT (16H0WILKS LAMBDA = F14.7)
      IF (XM-2.0) 453,451,453
  451 F1 = 2.0* Q
      F2 = 2.0 * (ENT - Q - XL - 2.0)
      XY = SQRTF (YLAMBD)
      F = (1.0 - XY) * F2 / (XY * F1)
      GO TO 52
  453 S = SQRTF(((XM**2)*(Q**2) - 4.0) / (XM**2 + Q**2 - 5.0))
      IF (S) 999,49,51
   49 F1 = Q
      F2 = ENT - XL -(Q + 1.0)
      F = ((1.0 - YLAMBD)/YLAMBD)*(F2/F1)
      GO TO 52
```

```
   51 XLAM = - (XM * Q - 2.0)/2.0
      XY = YLAMBD**(1.0/S)
      XMM=(ENT-1.0-XL)-(XM+Q+1.0)/2.0
      F1 = XM*Q
      F2 = (XMM*S+XLAM)
      F=(1.0-XY) * F2/(XY*F1)
   52 PRINT 53,F1
   53 FORMAT (6HOF1 = F14.7)
      PRINT 54, F2
   54 FORMAT (6HOF2 = F14.7)
      PRINT 55, F
   55 FORMAT(20HOFOR TEST OF H2, F= F14.7)
      DO 60 I=1,L
      DO 60 J=1,M
      V(I,J) = 0.0
      DO 60 K = 1,L
   60 V(I,J)=V(I,J)+U(I,K)*Z(K,J)
      DO 61 J = 1,M
   61 PRINT 64,J,(V(I,J), I = 1,L)
   64 FORMAT (47HOCOEF FOR ADJUSTING MEANS OF DEPENDENT VARIABLE  I2 /
     1   (5F14.7)
  999 JOBS = JOBS - 1
      IF (JOBS) 9999, 9999, 111
 9999 CALL EXIT
      END
```

4.5 References

Anderson, T. W. (1958). *An Introduction to Multivariate Statistical Analysis.* New York: John Wiley and Sons, Chapter 10.

Bartlett, M. S. (1937). "Properties of Sufficiency and Statistical Tests." *Proceedings of the Royal Society, A* **160**: 268–282.

Box, G. E. P. (1949). "A General Distribution Theory for a Class of Likelihood Criteria," *Biometrika* **36**: 317–346.

Hotelling, H. (1931). "The Generalization of Student's Ratio." *Annals of Mathematical Statistics* **2**: 360–378.

Lohnes, P. R. (1961). "Test Space and Discriminant Space Classification Models and Related Significance Tests." *Educational and Psychological Measurement* **21**: 559–574.

McNemar, Quinn (1962). *Psychological Statistics.* New York: John Wiley and Sons.

Rao, C. R. (1952). *Advanced Statistical Methods in Biometric Research.* New York: John Wiley and Sons, Chapter 7.

Rulon, P. J., and Brooks, W. D. (1961). *On Statistical Tests of Group Differences.* Cambridge, Mass: Educational Research Corporation.

Wilks, S. S. (1932). "Certain Generalizations in the Analysis of Variance." *Biometrika* **24**: 471–474.

References for Examples

Balomenos, Richard H. (1961). An Experimental Study Comparing the Effectiveness of Teaching Deduction in Two Content Areas of Secondary Mathematics, Ed.D. Dissertation, Harvard University Graduate School of Education.

Lee, Eugene C. (1961). Career Development of Science Teachers: Personality Determinants at the Exploratory Stage, Ed. D. Dissertation, Harvard University Graduate School of Education.

CHAPTER FIVE

Analysis of variance and covariance for two- and three-way designs

5.1 Brief Description of Analysis of Variance and Covariance

Although the techniques considered in this chapter are not strictly within the domain of multivariate analysis, they are included in this book for several reasons: Multiple variables are involved, the computations are very difficult and time consuming without the aid of a computer, and the procedures would have wider applicability in the behavioral sciences if the computational difficulties were lessened. The computer program presented on pp. 102–114 is probably as general as a single program can be for this type of analysis. The program can compute either two- or three-way factorial designs, with or without covariance control, and up to ten levels are possible for each factor. If covariance adjustment is desired, up to five control variables are possible. The multiple-regression approach to analysis of variance allows greater flexibility than the approach used here, but the preparation for execution of those programs is more complicated.

Numerous discussions of the mathematical basis and computational procedures for analysis of variance are available; therefore these details need not be gone into here.[1] The model that this program is capable of handling, however, is not widely used in current investigations, and its advantages should be described briefly. This model is multiple classification, with multiple covariance control. It is extremely useful in behavioral science investigations since it is often possible to control and stratify certain variables experimentally, although other variables of individual differences can only be measured after the subjects have been selected for the experiment and are assigned to specific treatments. These control variables are then used to adjust statistically for possible differences among the groups of treatments defined by the classification variables. In the factorial design the classification variables are called factors, and the categories of the classification

---

[1] For example, Cox (1958), Edwards (1960), Lindquist (1953), McNemar (1962).

are labeled levels. The number of levels is the number of ways in which a factor is varied. This analysis differs from factor analysis, as described in Chapter 8, in that factorial designs require the factors to be specified in advance, and experiments are devised in which the influence of the factors can be ascertained.

In the usual analysis of variance model, a person's deviation from the population mean μ is considered to be a function of one or more factors and an error term. The equation for a two-way factorial design (i.e., with two factors involved) might be written

(5.1) $$(Y_{sti} - \mu) = A_s + B_t + C_{st} + e_{sti}.$$

If the situation is an experiment in learning, factor A might represent levels of stimulation induced, and B the manner of presenting the materials to be learned. Then Y_{sti} represents the criterion score, which is the amount of learning of individual i, who was exposed to stimulation level s and mode of presentation t. The term C_{st} represents the interaction effect, and e_{sti} is the error, or unexplained variation of Y_{sti} from the mean of Y.

The basic question asked in variance analysis is: Does the presence of a particular factor in equation 5.1 reduce the error term to any substantial degree? If the hypothesis involves the significance of the interaction term, then $C_{st} = 0$ is tested. That is, does a knowledge of the particular combination of row and column treatments received by i yield information regarding the score y_{sti} he is likely to receive? The test of the null hypothesis $C_{st} = 0$ involves summing the squares of equation 5.1 for all individuals in the experiment, then finding the minimum Σe_{sti}^2 with and without the term C_{st}.

To complete the general model covariance terms may be introduced. The hypothesized sources of variation in Y described in equation 5.2 are factors A, B, and C; interaction effects D, E, F, and G; and covariance control variables X_1 and X_2.

(5.2) $$(Y_{stui} - \mu) = A_s + B_t + C_u + D_{st} + E_{su} + F_{tu}$$
$$+ G_{stu} + b_1(X_{1i} - \bar{X}_{1.}) + b_2(X_{2i} - \bar{X}_{2.}) + e_{stui}.$$

The control variables X_1 and X_2, which may be aptitude measures, are present to reduce the experimental error and are generally not of experimental interest themselves, i.e., we are not asking whether the presence of X_1 and X_2 reduces the error term significantly. Rather, it is included because it is known (or believed) to be associated with the dependent variable Y.

Certain of the other factors may be included only for control purposes, also. The factor C, for example, may refer to the sex of individual i. In this case, it may be known that there are sex differences for variable Y, but sex is still included as a factor in the experiment. This reduces the error estimate, thus making the effect of the experimental treatment combinations (defined by factors A and B) more easily detected. The experiment then becomes a type of randomized block design, but the computing procedures are the same. The subjects are randomly assigned to treatment combinations within each sex.

One frequent problem is deciding whether a continuous control variable should be treated as a covariance control (as were X_1 and X_2) or as a stratified control factor (as was C) in a randomized block design.[2] Sometimes the situation will dictate the answer. If the control variable cannot be measured until after the subjects are randomly assigned to the treatments (but before treatment begins), covariance control is preferred. The covariance approach also seems desirable when the sample size is relatively small and the need to maintain proportionality among levels of the factors necessitates discarding subjects.

As many as five covariance control variables are possible in the program provided. They are handled by multiple-regression techniques to adjust the various effect sums of squares. The computational details are completely described in Wert, Neidt, and Ahmann (1954), Chapter 18.

Another problem that is frequently troublesome is the choice of the proper error term. The computer program reports the usual analysis of variance table up through the column of mean squares (or residual mean squares if covariance controls are used). The final variance ratios are left for the investigator to compute, because the within mean square is not always the proper error term. If the categories or levels of all the factors in the experiment are "fixed," the within-mean square is the error term for all interaction and main effects. The term "fixed," as used here, means that only the actual categories used in the experiment are of interest, i.e., that the categories or levels used are not random samples from some population of possible categories for the factor in question. If they are to be considered as random samples, other error terms must be used. Chapter 17 of Edwards (1960) and Chapter 16 of McNemar (1962) are good discussions of the problem of the proper error term and its solution. McNemar (1962), p. 338, also considers the desirability of pooling interaction sums of squares with the within sums of squares under certain conditions to obtain a "better" estimate of the error term.

The general analysis-of-variance model we have presented is too often ignored by research workers because the computational schemes for the most applicable designs are available in the standard texts. It has been reviewed briefly here because it seemed the most efficient way to describe the advantages and flexibility of the computer program provided. The general model also frequently clarifies confusions arising regarding the differences between the two types of independent variables that are possible, factors and covariance controls.

5.2 Example of Analysis of Variance and Covariance

During the academic year 1960–1961 an experiment was conducted that assessed the relative effectiveness of a method of teaching high-school students certain understandings of science and scientists. Called the HOSC Instruction Project,[3] the experimental method used specially prepared cases from the history of science. These cases were developed to produce certain general understandings about

---

[2] Cochran's (1957) discussion of this question is highly recommended.

[3] Klopfer and Cooley (1961).

science and scientists which science educators have for some time proclaimed desirable. Many science teachers claim these same objectives, but few teach for them. A test called TOUS has been developed to measure the extent to which students achieve these understandings.[4] There were several aspects to this project, but the main analysis of variance used serves as an illustration of the techniques described in Section 5.1.

One hundred teachers were selected for participation, and one classroom for each teacher was randomly assigned to one of the treatments. Half the classroom units used the HOSC instruction method, the other half did not. The teachers'

TABLE 5.1

Number of Class Sections in Each Treatment

Subject	HOSC Classes		Control Classes	
	High	Low	High	Low
Biology	6	9	6	9
Chemistry	6	9	6	9
Physics	4	6	4	6

understandings of the concepts involved were tested prior to the treatment by an essay-type test. Each teacher was rated on a ten-point scale, which was then dichotomized high and low. This teacher rating constituted a control variable and was incorporated in the design as the second factor. The third factor was the course being offered, whether biology, chemistry, or physics. Thus this example is a $2 \times 2 \times 3$ design, with the second two factors serving to control certain possible sources of variation.

Two covariance controls were also used. One was a pretest of the TOUS test, and the other was a general test of scholastic aptitude (Otis). Since class sections were randomly assigned to the treatments, class means rather than individual student scores served as the unit of analysis.[5] Table 5.1 summarizes the number of classes in each cell of the design. Eighty classes were randomly selected for inclusion in the analysis. This was necessary to preserve proportionality among cell sizes. In Table 5.2 are presented the observed means for the cells and for all main effects.

Table 5.3 presents the analysis-of-variance table. The F ratios are computed using the within-mean square as the denominator, since this is a fixed design. Only the HOSC main effect produced significant differences ($p < .001$). To determine the nature of these significant differences, the adjusted means are computed, since covariance control was involved. The means for the unadjusted

[4] Cooley and Klopfer (1961).
[5] See Lindquist (1953) for a discussion of the groups-within-treatments design (Chapter 7).

TABLE 5.2

Observed Cell and Main Effect Means

	HOSC Classes		Control Classes		Means for Course Type Effects
	High	Low	High	Low	
Biology					
TOUS-Post	35.61	32.58	28.01	31.71	32.01
TOUS-Pre	30.92	28.00	27.20	29.63	28.91
Otis	49.87	46.76	44.56	50.32	48.01
Chemistry					
TOUS-Post	41.50	36.61	33.97	34.00	36.28
TOUS-Pre	35.04	31.68	31.78	31.69	32.37
Otis	58.95	54.09	51.89	54.08	54.61
Physics					
TOUS-Post	39.37	40.23	39.52	36.18	38.70
TOUS-Pre	34.05	35.20	35.88	34.16	34.80
Otis	57.42	60.17	58.17	56.48	58.11

	Experimental	Control
Means for treatment effects		
TOUS-Post	37.10	33.46
TOUS-Pre	32.01	31.36
Otis	53.78	52.25

	High	Low	Grand Means	S.D.
Means for teacher rating effects				
TOUS-Post	35.94	34.84	35.28	5.07
TOUS-Pre	32.17	31.36	31.68	4.43
Otis	52.94	53.06	53.01	7.42

TABLE 5.3

Analysis-of-Variance Table

Source	ndf	Residual Sums of Squares	Mean Square	F Ratios
HOSC method, I	1	170.45	170.45	102.9
Teacher rating, J	1	5.16	5.16	3.1
Course type, K	2	9.19	4.59	2.8
$I \times J$ interaction	1	2.77	2.77	1.7
$I \times K$	2	4.03	2.02	1.2
$J \times K$	2	8.27	4.13	2.5
$I \times J \times K$	2	7.60	3.80	2.3
Within	66	109.33	1.66	
Total	77	316.80		

dependent variables, the adjusted means, and the control variable means are printed out for all effects. Table 5.4 summarizes these means for the significant main effect.

The investigators were therefore able to conclude that, taking into account initial differences in understanding and aptitude, the HOSC method produced significantly greater understanding of science and scientists as measured by TOUS.

TABLE 5.4

Means For Significant Main Effect

	Otis	TOUS-Pre	TOUS-Post	TOUS-Adjusted
HOSC classes	53.78	32.01	37.10	36.76
Control classes	52.25	31.36	33.46	33.81

Flow Diagram for Complex Analysis of Variance, Two- or Three-Way Design, with or without Covariance Adjustors (ANOVA Program), with Subroutines READIN, DEVMAT, ANOVA, and MEANS

INPUT-OUTPUT
Read JOBS where JOBS is the number of analyses to be computed.
Print program title.

SUBROUTINE
Call subroutine READIN, which reads data and performs the basic reduction to raw accumulations.

SUBROUTINE
Call subroutine DEVMAT, which computes the required deviation sums and s.s.c.p.

SUBROUTINE
Call subroutine ANOVA, which makes regression adjustments (if any) and forms analysis of variance table.

SUBROUTINE
Call subroutine MEANS, which computes means for the different effects and adjusted means (if any).

JOBS = JOBS − 1

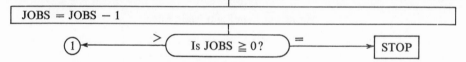

Flow Diagram for READIN Subroutine

Read NI, NJ, NK, LV, NE, SEM, EM_{ijk} where
NI = no. I effect categories
NJ = no. J effect categories
NK = no. K effect categories (NK = 1 if two-way design)
LV = no. of variables, criterion plus up to 5 covariance adjustors
NE = no. of effects (4 for two-way design, 8 for three-way design)
SEM = total no. of observations
EM_{ijk} = no. of observations in cell ijk.
Throughout this diagram, subscript ranges are: $i = 1, 2, 3, \ldots, NI$;
$j = 1, 2, 3, \ldots, NJ$; $k = 1, 2, 3, \ldots, NK$; $v = 1, 2, 3, \ldots, LV$;
$w = 1, 2, 3, \ldots, LV$.

5.1. Flow Diagram for ANOVA Program (Continued)

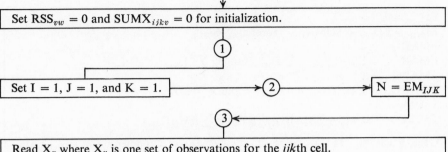

Set $RSS_{vw} = 0$ and $SUMX_{ijkv} = 0$ for initialization.

①

Set I = 1, J = 1, and K = 1. ——————→ ② ——————→ $N = EM_{IJK}$

③

Read X_v where X_v is one set of observations for the ijkth cell.

$RSS_{vw} = RSS_{vw} + X_v \cdot X_w$ accumulating raw s.s.c.p. for total.
$SUMX_{IJKv} = SUMX_{IJKv} + X_v$ recording basic cell entries.
$N = N - 1$

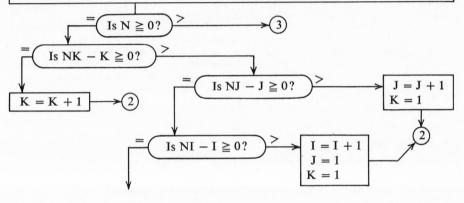

Is N ≧ 0?   ——→ ③

Is NK − K ≧ 0?

K = K + 1 ——→ ②

Is NJ − J ≧ 0?   ——→   J = J + 1
K = 1

Is NI − I ≧ 0?   ——→   I = I + 1
J = 1
K = 1

②

5.1. Flow Diagram for ANOVA Program (Continued)

$\text{EIJ}_{ijv} = 0$

$\text{EIJ}_{ijv} = \text{EIJ}_{ijv} + \text{SUMX}_{ijkv}$ forming $\sum_k \text{X}_{ijkv}$.

$\text{EMAIN}_{1iv} = 0$

$\text{EMAIN}_{1iv} = \text{EMAIN}_{1iv} + \text{EIJ}_{ijv}$ forming $\sum_j \text{EIJ}_{ijv}$.

$\text{EMAIN}_{2jv} = 0$

$\text{EMAIN}_{2jv} = \text{EMAIN}_{2jv} + \text{EIJ}_{ijv}$ forming $\sum_i \text{EIJ}_{ijv}$.

$\text{TSUM}_v = 0$

$\text{TSUM}_v = \text{TSUM}_v + \text{EMAIN}_{1iv}$ forming $\sum_i \text{EMAIN}_{1iv}$.

$\text{CT}_{vw} = \text{TSUM}_v \cdot \text{TSUM}_w / \text{SEM}$ forming the correction term for any s.s.c.p.

$\text{EMIJ}_{ij} = 0$ matrix vwth element.

$\text{EMIJ}_{ij} = \text{EMIJ}_{ij} + \text{EM}_{ijk}$ forming N's for the I × J interaction cells.

$\text{EMI}_i = 0$

$\text{EMI}_i = \text{EMI}_i + \text{EMIJ}_{ij}$ forming N's for I effect cells.

$\text{EMJ}_j = 0$

$\text{EMJ}_j = \text{EMJ}_j + \text{EMIJ}_{ij}$ forming N's for J effect cells.

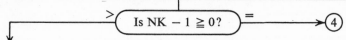

>   Is NK − 1 ≧ 0?   =   ④

$\text{EIK}_{ikv} = 0$

$\text{EIK}_{ikv} = \text{EIK}_{ikv} + \text{SUMX}_{ijkv}$ forming $\sum_j \text{X}_{ijkv}$.

$\text{EJK}_{jkv} = 0$

$\text{EJK}_{jkv} = \text{EJK}_{jkv} + \text{SUMX}_{ijkv}$ forming $\sum_i \text{X}_{ijkv}$.

$\text{EMAIN}_{3kv} = 0$

$\text{EMAIN}_{3kv} = \text{EMAIN}_{3kv} + \text{EJK}_{jkv}$ forming $\sum_j \text{EJK}_{jkv}$.

$\text{EMIK}_{ik} = 0$

$\text{EMIK}_{ik} = \text{EMIK}_{ik} + \text{EM}_{ijk}$ forming N's for the I × K interaction cells.

$\text{EMJK}_{jk} = 0$

$\text{EMJK}_{jk} = \text{EMJK}_{jk} + \text{EM}_{ijk}$ forming N's for the J × K interaction cells.

$\text{EMK}_k = 0$

$\text{EMK}_k = \text{EMK}_k + \text{EMJK}_{jk}$ forming N's for the K effect cells.

(Report all these accumulations to the main or calling program and return control to it.)

④ ——————→ RETURN

5.1. Flow Diagram for ANOVA Program (Continued)

Flow Diagram for DEVMAT Subroutine

$\text{SSCP}_{vw1} = \text{RSS}_{vw1} - \text{CT}_{vw}$ deviation s.s.c.p. for total sample.
$\text{SUM} = 0$
$\text{SUM} = \text{SUM} + (\text{EMAIN}_{1iv} \cdot \text{EMAIN}_{1iw})/\text{EMI}_i$
$\text{SSCP}_{vw2} = \text{SUM} - \text{CT}_{vw}$ deviation s.s.c.p. for the I effect.
$\text{SUM} = 0$
$\text{SUM} = \text{SUM} + (\text{EMAIN}_{2jv} \cdot \text{EMAIN}_{2jw})/\text{EMJ}_j$
$\text{SSCP}_{vw3} = \text{SUM} - \text{CT}_{vw}$ deviation s.s.c.p. for the J effect.
$\text{SUM} = 0$
$\text{SUM} = \text{SUM} + (\text{EIJ}_{ijv} \cdot \text{EIJ}_{ijw})/\text{EMIJ}_{ij}$
$\text{SSCP}_{vw4} = \text{SUM} - \text{CT}_{vw} - \text{SSCP}_{vw2} - \text{SSCP}_{vw3}$ deviation s.s.c.p. for the
$\text{SSCP}_{vw8} = 0$ I×J interaction.
$\text{SSCP}_{vw8} = \text{SSCP}_{vw8} + (\text{SUMX}_{ijkv} \cdot \text{SUMX}_{ijkw})/\text{EM}_{ijk}$
$\text{SSCP}_{vw9} = \text{SSCP}_{vw8}$ steps toward the I×J×K interaction s.s.c.p. (if any) and
the within s.s.c.p.

$>$ Is NK $- 1 \geqq 0$? $=$ ——→ ①

$\text{SUM} = 0$
$\text{SUM} = \text{SUM} + (\text{EMAIN}_{3kv} \cdot \text{EMAIN}_{3kw})/\text{EMK}_k$
$\text{SSCP}_{vw5} = \text{SUM} - \text{CT}_{vw}$ deviation s.s.c.p. for the K effect.
$\text{SUM} = 0$
$\text{SUM} = \text{SUM} + (\text{EIK}_{ikv} \cdot \text{EIK}_{ikw})/\text{EMIK}_{ik}$
$\text{SSCP}_{vw6} = \text{SUM} - \text{CT}_{vw} - \text{SSCP}_{vw2} - \text{SSCP}_{vw5}$ for the I×K interaction.
$\text{SUM} = 0$
$\text{SUM} = \text{SUM} + (\text{EJK}_{jkv} \cdot \text{EJK}_{jkw})/\text{EMJK}_{jk}$
$\text{SSCP}_{vw7} = \text{SUM} - \text{CT}_{vw} - \text{SSCP}_{vw3} - \text{SSCP}_{vw5}$ for the J×K interaction.
$\text{SSCP}_{vw8} = \text{SSCP}_{vw8} - \text{SSCP}_{vwm}$ where $m = 2, 3, \ldots, 7$; for the I×J×K
$\text{SSCP}_{vw8} = \text{SSCP}_{vw8} - \text{CT}_{vw}$ interaction.
$\text{SSCP}_{vwx} = \text{RSS}_{vw} - \text{SSCP}_{vw9}$ where $x = \text{NE} + 1$; deviation s.s.c.p. for within.

①

OUTPUT
Print and/or punch, with appropriate labels, SSCP_{vw1}, $\text{SSCP}_{vw2}, \ldots, \text{SSCP}_{vwx}$
where $x = \text{NE} + 1$.

RETURN

5.1. Flow Diagram for ANOVA Program (Continued)

Flow Diagram for Subroutine ANOVA

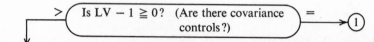

> Is LV $- 1 \geqq 0$? (Are there covariance controls?) $=$ →①

$\text{SSCP}_{vwm} = \text{SSCP}_{vwm} + \text{SSCP}_{vwx}$ where $m = 2, 3, 4, \ldots, \text{NE}$ and $x = \text{NE} + 1$; adds within s.s.c.p. to each effect s.s.c.p.
$M = 1$

②

$A_{x-1, y-1} = \text{SSCP}_{xym}$ where $m = M + 1$; $x = 2, 3, 4, \ldots, \text{LV}$; and $y = 2, 3, 4, \ldots, \text{LV}$; partitioning matrix for entry to MATINV.
$B_{x-1} = \text{SSCP}_{1xm}$

SUBROUTINE
Call subroutine MATINV to replace A by A^{-1} and B by the vector of solution coefficients (see Chapter 9).

$C_{x-1, m} = B_{x-1}$ where $x = 2, 3, 4, \ldots, \text{LV}$ and $m = M$; loading the regression
$D_m = 0$ coefficients in C.
$D_m = D_m + B_{x-1} \cdot \text{SSCP}_{1, x, m+1}$ forming the residuals due to covariance
$M = M + 1$ controls.

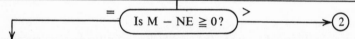

$=$ Is $M - \text{NE} \geqq 0$? $>$ →②

$D_m = \text{SSCP}_{1,1, m+1} - D_m$ where $m = 1, 2, 3, \ldots, \text{NE}$; forming adjusted sums of squares-within.

OUTPUT
Print and/or punch, with labels, D_m, C_{xm} where $m = 1, 2, 3, \ldots, \text{NE}$ and $x = 1, 2, 3, \ldots, \text{LV} - 1$.

$D_m = D_m - D_{NE}$ where $m = 1, 2, 3, \ldots, \text{NE} - 1$; forming adjusted sums of squares.

③

$D_m = \text{SSCP}_{1,1, m+1}$ where $m = 1, 2, 3, \ldots, \text{NE}$; forming sums of squares.

③

5.1. Flow Diagram for ANOVA Program (Continued)

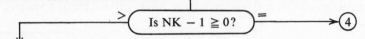

$D_8 = D_{NE}$, $N = SEM$, $DF_1 = NI - 1$, $DF_2 = NJ - 1$, $DF_3 = DF_1 \cdot DF_2$, $DF_4 = NK - 1$, $DF_5 = DF_1 \cdot DF_4$, $DF_6 = DF_2 \cdot DF_4$, $DF_7 = DF_1 \cdot DF_6$, $DF_8 = N - (NI \cdot NJ \cdot (NK + LV - 1))$ forming degrees of freedom.
$SQ_p = D_p/DF_p$ where $p = 1, 2, 3, \ldots, 8$ forming mean squares.

OUTPUT
Print and/or punch, with labels, DF_1, D_1, SQ_1; DF_2, D_2, SQ_2; DF_3, D_3, SQ_3 (starts output of analysis-of-variance table).

$>$ Is $NK - 1 \geq 0$? $=$ → ④

OUTPUT
Print and/or punch DF_4, D_4, SQ_4; DF_5, D_5, SQ_5; DF_6, D_6, SQ_6; DF_7, D_7, SQ_7 (continues analysis-of-variance table, if three-way design).

④

OUTPUT
Print and/or punch DF_8, D_8, SQ_8 (within line completes table).

$DFT = N - LV$
$DT = 0$
$DT = DT + D_m$ where $m = 1, 2, 3, \ldots, NE$ forming degrees of freedom and sums of squares for total.

OUTPUT
Print and/or punch, with labels, DFT and DT.

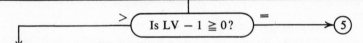

$>$ Is $LV - 1 \geq 0$? $=$ → ⑤

$B_v = \sqrt{SSCP_{vv1}}$ forming standard deviations for total sample times $N - 1$.
$SSCP_{vw1} = SSCP_{vw1}/(B_v \cdot B_w)$ forming correlation matrix for total sample.
$B_v = B_v/\sqrt{SEM - 1}$

OUTPUT
Print and/or punch, with labels, B_v, $SSCP_{vw1}$.

⑤ ─────────→ RETURN

99

5.1. Flow Diagram for ANOVA Program (Continued)

Flow Diagram for Subroutine MEANS

$\text{SUMX}_{ijkv} = \text{SUMX}_{ijkv}/\text{EM}_{ijk}$ forming cell means.
$\text{EIJ}_{ijv} = \text{EIJ}_{ijv}/\text{EMIJ}_{ij}$ I × J interaction means.
$\text{EMAIN}_{1iv} = \text{EMAIN}_{1iv}/\text{EMI}_i$ I effect means.
$\text{EMAIN}_{2jv} = \text{EMAIN}_{2jv}/\text{EMJ}_j$ J effect means.
$\text{TSUM}_v = \text{TSUM}_v/\text{SEM}$ grand means.

OUTPUT
Print and/or punch, with labels, SUMX_{ijkv}, EIJ_{ijv}, EMAIN_{1iv}, EMAIN_{2jv}, TSUM_v.

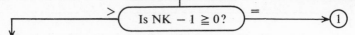
> / =   Is NK − 1 ≧ 0?   → ①

$\text{EIK}_{ikv} = \text{EIK}_{ikv}/\text{EMIK}_{ik}$ forming I × K interaction means.
$\text{EJK}_{jkv} = \text{EJK}_{jkv}/\text{EMJK}_{jk}$ J × K interaction means.
$\text{EMAIN}_{3kv} = \text{EMAIN}_{3kv}/\text{EMK}_k$ K effect means.

OUTPUT
Print and/or punch EMAIN_{3kv}, EIK_{ikv}, EJK_{jkv}.

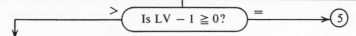
> / =   Is LV − 1 ≧ 0?   → ⑤

$\text{SUM} = 0$ Note: range of x hereafter is $x = 1, 2, \ldots, \text{LV} - 1$, and $y = \text{NE}$.
$\text{SUM} = \text{SUM} + C_{xy} \cdot (\text{EMAIN}_{1ix+1} - \text{TSUM}_{x+1})$
$\text{EMAIN}_{1i1} = \text{EMAIN}_{1i1} - \text{SUM}$ forming adjusted I effect means.
$\text{SUM} = 0$
$\text{SUM} = \text{SUM} + C_{xy} \cdot (\text{EMAIN}_{2jx+1} - \text{TSUM}_{x+1})$
$\text{EMAIN}_{2j1} = \text{EMAIN}_{2j1} - \text{SUM}$ forming adjusted J effect means.
$\text{SUM} = 0$
$\text{SUM} = \text{SUM} + C_{xy} \cdot (\text{EIJ}_{ijx+1} - \text{TSUM}_{x+1})$
$\text{EIJ}_{ij1} = \text{EIJ}_{ij1} - \text{SUM}$ forming adjusted I × J effect means.

OUTPUT
Print and/or punch, with labels, EMAIN_{1i1}, EMAIN_{2j1}, EIJ_{ij1}.

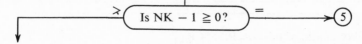
> / =   Is NK − 1 ≧ 0?   → ⑤

5.1. Flow Diagram for ANOVA Program (Continued)

SUM $= 0$
SUM $=$ SUM $+ C_{xy} \cdot (\text{EMAIN}_{3kx+1} - \text{TSUM}_{x+1})$
$\text{EMAIN}_{3k1} = \text{EMAIN}_{3k1} - \text{SUM}$ forming adjusted K effect means.
SUM $= 0$
SUM $=$ SUM $+ C_{xy} \cdot (\text{EIK}_{ikx+1} - \text{TSUM}_{x+1})$
$\text{EIK}_{ik1} = \text{EIK}_{ik1} - \text{SUM}$ forming adjusted $I \times K$ effect means.
SUM $= 0$
SUM $=$ SUM $+ C_{xy} \cdot (\text{EJK}_{jkx+1} - \text{TSUM}_{x+1})$
$\text{EJK}_{jk1} = \text{EJK}_{jk1} - \text{SUM}$ forming adjusted $J \times K$ effect means.
SUM $= 0$
SUM $=$ SUM $+ C_{xy} \cdot (\text{SUMX}_{ijkx+1} - \text{TSUM}_{x+1})$
$\text{SUMX}_{ijk1} = \text{SUMX}_{ijk1} - \text{SUM}$ forming adjusted cell means.

OUTPUT
Print and/or punch, with labels, EMAIN_{3k1}, EIK_{ik1}, EJK_{jk1}, SUMX_{ijk1}.

RETURN

PROGRAM FOR ANALYSIS OF VARIANCE AND COVARIANCE FOR TWO- AND THREE-WAY FACTORIAL DESIGNS (ANOVA), INCLUDING SUBROUTINES READIN, DEVMAT, ANOVA, AND MEANS

```
C     ANOVA.

C         THIS PROGRAM PERFORMS TWO- OR THREE-WAY ANALYSIS OF VARIANCE WITH
C     COVARIANCE ADJUSTMENT.  THE NUMBER OF CATEGORIES (LEVELS) FOR EACH
C     FACTOR IS LIMITED TO TEN.   THE MAXIMUM NUMBER OF COVARIANCE
C     CONTROLS IS FIVE. THE NUMBER OF OBSERVATIONS PER CELL MUST BE
C     PROPORTIONAL ACROSS ROWS AND ACROSS COLUMNS.

C     INPUT.
C         THE FIRST CONTROL CARD CONTAINS THE NUMBER OF ANALYSES (JOBS)
C     TO BE RUN AT ONE TIME.   THIS IS PUNCHED IN COLUMNS 1 AND 2.
C     THEN THE FOLLOWING THREE CONTROL CARDS PRECEDE THE DATA CARDS FOR
C     EACH ANALYSIS.   THE FIRST CARD CONTAINS THE JOB TITLE (COL 1-72).
C     THE NEXT CONTROL CARD CONTAINS THE FOLLOWING INFORMATION.
C         COLS 1-2  NI= NUMBER OF LEVELS IN THE FIRST MAIN EFFECT
C         COLS 3-4  NJ = NUMBER OF LEVELS IN THE SECOND MAIN EFFECT
C         COLS 5-6  NK = NUMBER OF LEVELS IN THE THIRD MAIN EFFECT
C            (IF THE ANALYSIS IS A TWO-WAY DESIGN, SET NK = 1)
C         COL 7  LV = TOTAL NUMBER OF VARIABLES.  THIS INCLUDES ONLY
C            THE DEPENDENT VARIABLE (CRITERION) PLUS THE NUMBER OF
C            COVARIANCE CONTROLS.   THE CRITERION MUST PRECEDE THE
C            CONTROL VARIABLES IN THE DATA CARDS.
C         COL 8  NE = 4 IF A TWO-WAY DESIGN
C                NE = 8 IF A THREE-WAY DESIGN
C         COL 9-13  SEM = TOTAL NUMBER OF OBSERVATIONS.
C     THE THIRD CONTROL CARD PRECEDING EACH ANALYSIS CONTAINS THE SCORE
C     CARD FORMAT.
C         FOLLOWING THE THREE CONTROL CARDS ARE CARDS WHICH CONTAIN
C     THE NUMBER OF OBSERVATIONS PER CELL.  IF IT IS A THREE-WAY DESIGN,
C     THERE ARE NI TIMES NJ OF THESE CARDS, WITH NK CELL SIZES DEFINED
C     ON EACH CARD.  THE FORMAT IS (10X 10F3.0).  THE FIRST TEN COLUMNS
C     MAY BE USED TO DESIGNATE THE COMBINATIONS OF I AND J WHICH EACH
C     CARD REPRESENTS.  IF THE ANALYSIS IS A TWO-WAY DESIGN, PUT NJ
C     CELL SIZES PER CARD USING NI CARDS.
C         THE INDIVIDUAL SCORE CARDS FOLLOW CELL SIZE CARDS.  PUT
C     SCORE CARDS IN ORDER BY CELL, WHERE CELL ORDER IS NUMERICAL
C     SEQUENCE OF IJK VALUES.  THE IJK VALUES NEED NOT BE IN THE SCORE
C     CARDS, BUT IF THEY ARE, SEQUENCING IS FACILITATED.
C     SUBROUTINE MATINV, READIN, DEVMAT, ANOVA, AND MEANS ARE REQUIRED.

C     OUTPUT.
C         ALL OUTPUT IS PRINTED AND INCLUDES THE FOLLOWING.  DEVIATION
C     SUMS OF SQUARES AND CROSS PRODUCTS MATRICES FOR MAIN EFFECTS,
C     INTERACTIONS, WITHIN AND TOTAL.  ALSO WITHIN-PLUS RESIDUALS,
C     REGRESSION COEFFICIENTS AND CORRELATION MATRIX IF COVARIANCE,
C     USED.  COMPLETE ANALYSIS OF VARIANCE TABLE IS PRINTED, USING
C     ADJUSTED SUMS OF SQUARES IF APPROPRIATE.  FINALLY, ALL OBSERVED
C     CELL AND ARRAY MEANS AND ADJUSTED MEANS ARE PRINTED, WHETHER OR
C     NOT EFFECTS ARE SIGNIFICANT.

      DIMENSION RSS(6,6), CT(6,6), SUMY(10,10,10), SUMX1(10,10,10) ,
     1  SUMX2(10,10,10),SUMX3(10,10,10),SUMX4(10,10,10),SUMX5(10,10,10),
     2  EMAIN(3,10,6), SSCP(6,6,9), EMI(10,10,10), EMI(10), EMJ(10),
     3  EMK(10), X(6), TSUM(6), FMT(12), EIJ(10,10,6), EIK(10,10,6),
     4  EJK(10,10,6), EMIJ(10,10), EMIK(10,10), EMJK(10,10), A(50,50),
     5  B(50), C(6,8), D(8), DF(8), SQ(8),TITLE(12)
 1001 FORMAT (I2)
 1002 FORMAT(12A6)
 1004 FORMAT (40H1ANALYSIS OF VARIANCE AND COVARIANCE OF , 12A6)
```

```
        READ 1001, JOB
   10   READ 1002, (TITLE(I),I=1,12)
        PRINT 1004, (TITLE(I), I=1,12)
        CALL READIN       (RSS,CT,SUMY,SUMX1,SUMX2,SUMX3,SUMX4,SUMX5,
   2      EMAIN,EM,EMI,EMJ,EMK,TSUM,FMT,EIJ,EIK,EJK,EMIJ,EMIK,EMJK,
   3      NI,NJ,NK,NE,LV,SEM,LC,NW )
        CALL DEVMAT        (RSS,CT,SUMY,SUMX1,SUMX2,SUMX3,SUMX4,SUMX5,
   2      EM,EIJ,EIK,EJK,EMIJ,EMIK,EMJK,
   3      EMAIN,SSCP,EMI,EMJ,EMK,NI,NJ,NK,NE,LV,SEM,LC,NW)
        CALL ANOVA          (SSCP,NI,NJ,NK,NE,LV,SEM,LC,NW,C)
        CALL MEANS         (SUMX1,SUMX2,SUMX3,SUMX4,SUMX5,EM,EMI,EMJ,EMK,SUMY
   2   ,EMAIN,TSUM,EIJ,EIK,EJK,EMIJ,EMIK,EMJK,NI,NJ,NK,NE,LV,SEM,LC,NW,C)
        JOB = JOB - 1
        IF (JOB) 9999, 9999, 10
 9999   CALL EXIT
        END




C      SUBROUTINE READIN

C      THIS SUBROUTINE READS IN THE SCORES AND FORMS THE RAW SUMS OF
C      SQUARES AND CROSS PRODUCTS.

        SUBROUTINE READIN(RSS,CT,SUMY,SUMX1,SUMX2,SUMX3,SUMX4,SUMX5,
   2      EMAIN,EM,EMI,EMJ,EMK,TSUM,FMT,EIJ,EIK,EJK,EMIJ,EMIK,EMJK,
   3      NI,NJ,NK,NE,LV,SEM,LC,NW )
        DIMENSION RSS(6,6), CT(6,6), SUMY(10,10,10), SUMX1(10,10,10) ,
   1      SUMX2(10,10,10),SUMX3(10,10,10),SUMX4(10,10,10),SUMX5(10,10,10),
   2      EMAIN(3,10,6),                 EM(10,10,10), EMI(10), EMJ(10),
   3      EMK(10), X(6), TSUM(6), FMT(12), EIJ(10,10,6), EIK(10,10,6),
   4      EJK(10,10,6), EMIJ(10,10), EMIK(10,10), EMJK(10,10)
 1001   FORMAT (3I2, 2I1, F5.0, I2)
 1002   FORMAT (10X, 10F3.0)
 1003   FORMAT (12A6)
 1005   FORMAT (33HONUMBER OF I EFFECT CATEGORIES = I4)
 1006   FORMAT (33HONUMBER OF J EFFECT CATEGORIES = I4)
 1007   FORMAT (33HONUMBER OF K EFFECT CATEGORIES = I4)
        READ 1001, NI, NJ, NK, LV, NE, SEM, JOB
        PRINT 1005, NI
        PRINT 1006, NJ
        PRINT 1007, NK
        READ 1003, (FMT(I), I=1,12)
        IF (NK-1) 9999, 13, 11
   11   DO 12 I=1,NI
        DO 12 J=1,NJ
   12   READ 1002, (EM(I,J,K), K=1,NK)
        GO TO 15
   13   DO 14 I=1,NI
   14   READ 1002, (EM(I,J,1), J=1,NJ)
   15   DO 16 I=1,LV
        DO 16 J=1, LV
   16   RSS (I,J) =0.0
        LC=LV-1
        DO 20 I=1,NI
        DO 20 J=1,NJ
```

103

```
      DO 20 K=1, NK
      SUMY   (I,J,K) = 0.0
      SUMX1  (I,J,K) = 0.0
      SUMX2  (I,J,K) = 0.0
      SUMX3  (I,J,K) = 0.0
      SUMX4  (I,J,K) = 0.0
      SUMX5  (I,J,K) = 0.0
   20 CONTINUE
      I=1
      J=1
      K=1
   21 N=EM(I,J,K)
   22 READ FMT, (X(L1), L1=1,LV)
      DO 23 L1=1,LV
      DO 23 L2=L1,LV
      RSS(L1,L2)= RSS(L1,L2) + X(L1)*X(L2)
   23 RSS (L2,L1) = RSS(L1,L2)
      SUMY   (I,J,K) = SUMY   (I,J,K) + X (1)
      SUMX1  (I,J,K) = SUMX1  (I,J,K) + X (2)
      SUMX2  (I,J,K) = SUMX2  (I,J,K) + X (3)
      SUMX3  (I,J,K) = SUMX3  (I,J,K) + X (4)
      SUMX4  (I,J,K) = SUMX4  (I,J,K) + X (5)
      SUMX5  (I,J,K) = SUMX5  (I,J,K) + X (6)
      N = N-1
      IF (N) 9999, 24, 22
   24 IF (NK-K) 9999, 26, 25
   25 K = K+1
      GO TO 21
   26 IF (NJ-J) 9999, 28, 27
   27 J = J+1
      K=1
      GO TO 21
   28 IF (NI-I) 9999, 30, 29
   29 I = I+1
      K=1
      J=1
      GO TO 21
   30 DO 44 L=1,LV
      DO 44 I=1,NI
      DO 44 J=1,NJ
      EIJ(I,J,L) =0.0
      DO 44 K=1,NK
      GO TO (32,34,36,38,40,42), L
   32 EIJ(I,J,L)=EIJ(I,J,L)+SUMY(I,J,K)
      GO TO 44
   34 EIJ(I,J,L) = EIJ(I,J,L) + SUMX1 (I,J,K)
      GO TO 44
   36 EIJ(I,J,L) = EIJ(I,J,L) + SUMX2 (I,J,K)
      GO TO 44
   38 EIJ(I,J,L) = EIJ(I,J,L) + SUMX3 (I,J,K)
      GO TO 44
   40 EIJ(I,J,L) = EIJ(I,J,L) + SUMX4 (I,J,K)
      GO TO 44
   42 EIJ(I,J,L) = EIJ(I,J,L) + SUMX5 (I,J,K)
   44 CONTINUE
      IF (NK-1) 9999, 75, 45
```

```
45 DO 60 L=1,LV
   DO 60 I=1,NI
   DO 60 K=1,NK
   EIK(I,K,L) =0.0
   DO 60 J=1,NJ
   GO TO (46,48,50,52,54,56),L
46 EIK(I,K,L) = EIK(I,K,L) + SUMY   (I,J,K)
   GO TO 60
48 EIK(I,K,L) = EIK(I,K,L) + SUMX1  (I,J,K)
   GO TO 60
50 EIK(I,K,L) = EIK(I,K,L) + SUMX2  (I,J,K)
   GO TO 60
52 EIK(I,K,L) = EIK(I,K,L) + SUMX3  (I,J,K)
   GO TO 60
54 EIK(I,K,L) = EIK(I,K,L) + SUMX4  (I,J,K)
   GO TO 60
56 EIK(I,K,L) = EIK(I,K,L) + SUMX5  (I,J,K)
60 CONTINUE
   DO 74 L = 1,LV
   DO 74 J=1,NJ
   DO 74 K=1,NK
   EJK(J,K,L) =0.0
   DO 74 I =1,NI
   GO TO (62,64,66,68,70,72),L
62 EJK(J,K,L) = EJK(J,K,L) + SUMY   (I,J,K)
   GO TO 74
64 EJK(J,K,L) = EJK(J,K,L) + SUMX1  (I,J,K)
   GO TO 74
66 EJK(J,K,L) = EJK(J,K,L) + SUMX2  (I,J,K)
   GO TO 74
68 EJK(J,K,L) = EJK(J,K,L) + SUMX3  (I,J,K)
   GO TO 74
70 EJK(J,K,L) = EJK(J,K,L) + SUMX4  (I,J,K)
   GO TO 74
72 EJK(J,K,L) = EJK(J,K,L) + SUMX5  (I,J,K)
74 CONTINUE
75 DO 80 L=1,LV
   DO 80 I=1,NI
   EMAIN (1,I,L) =0.0
   DO 80 J=1,NJ
80 EMAIN (1,I,L) = EMAIN (1,I,L) + EIJ(I,J,L)
   DO 82 L=1,LV
   DO 82 J=1,NJ
   EMAIN (2,J,L) =0.0
   DO 82 I=1,NI
82 EMAIN(2,J,L)=EMAIN(2,J,L)+EIJ(I,J,L)
   IF (NK-1) 9999, 85, 83
83 DO 84 L = 1, LV
   DO 84 K =1,NK
   EMAIN (3,K,L) =0.0
   DO 84 J=1,NJ
84 EMAIN (3,K,L) = EMAIN(3,K,L) + EJK(J,K,L)
85 DO 86 L=1,LV
   TSUM(L) = 0.0
   DO 86 I=1,NI
86 TSUM(L) = TSUM(L) + EMAIN(1,I,L)
```

```
       DO 88 L1=1,LV
       DO 88 L2=L1,LV
       CT(L1,L2) = TSUM(L1)*TSUM(L2)
   88 CT(L2,L1) = CT(L1,L2)
       DO 90 L1=1,LV
       DO 90 L2=L1,LV
       CT(L1,L2) = CT(L1,L2)/SEM
   90 CT(L2,L1) = CT(L1,L2)
       DO 91 I=1,NI
       DO 91 J=1,NJ
       EMIJ(I,J) = 0.0
       DO 91 K=1,NK
   91 EMIJ(I,J)= EMIJ(I,J)+EM(I,J,K)
       IF (NK-1) 9999, 95, 89
   89 DO 92 I=1,NI
       DO 92 K=1,NK
       EMIK(I,K) =0.0
       DO 92 J=1,NJ
   92 EMIK(I,K)=EMIK(I,K)+EM(I,J,K)
       DO 93 J=1,NJ
       DO 93 K=1,NK
       EMJK(J,K) =0.0
       DO 93 I=1,NI
   93 EMJK(J,K) = EMJK(J,K) + EM(I,J,K)
   95 DO 94 I=1,NI
       EMI(I) = 0.0
       DO 94 J=1,NJ
   94 EMI(I) = EMI(I) + EMIJ(I,J)
       DO 96 J=1,NJ
       EMJ(J) =0.0
       DO 96 I=1,NI
   96 EMJ(J) = EMJ(J) + EMIJ(I,J)
       DO 98 K=1,NK
       EMK(K) = 0.0
       DO 98 J=1,NJ
   98 EMK(K) = EMK(K) + EMJK(J,K)
 9999 RETURN
       END




C      SUBROUTINE DEVMAT

C      THIS SUBROUTINE COMPUTES THE DEVIATION SUMS OF SQUARES AND CROSS-
C      PRODUCTS MATRICES (SSCP) FOR ALL SOURCES OF VARIATION.

       SUBROUTINE DEVMAT (RSS,CT,SUMY,SUMX1,SUMX2,SUMX3,SUMX4,SUMX5,
     2    EM,EIJ,EIK,EJK,EMIJ,EMIK,EMJK,
     3    EMAIN,SSCP,EMI,EMJ,EMK,NI,NJ,NK,NE,LV,SEM,LC,NW)
       DIMENSION RSS(6,6), CT(6,6), SUMY(10,10,10), SUMX1(10,10,10) ,
     1    SUMX2(10,10,10),SUMX3(10,10,10),SUMX4(10,10,10),SUMX5(10,10,10),
     2    EMAIN(3,10,6), SSCP(6,6,9),                    EMI(10), EMJ(10),
     3    EJK(10,10,6), EMIJ(10,10), EMIK(10,10), EMJK(10,10),EMK(10),
     4    EM(10,10,10 ),EIJ(10,10,6),EIK(10,10,6)
 1008 FORMAT (26HOSS AND CP FOR ALL SOURCES)
 1009 FORMAT (6HOTOTAL)
```

```
1010 FORMAT (9HOI EFFECT)
1011 FORMAT (9HOJ EFFECT)
1012 FORMAT(9HOK EFFECT)
1013 FORMAT (18HOI X J INTERACTION)
1014 FORMAT (18HOI X K INTERACTION)
1015 FORMAT (18HOJ X K INTERACTION)
1016 FORMAT (22HOI X J X K INTERACTION)
1017 FORMAT (7HOWITHIN)
1018 FORMAT (6F14.6)
     DO 100 L=1,LV
     DO 100 LL=L,LV
     SSCP(L,LL,1) = RSS(L,LL) - CT(L,LL)
 100 SSCP(LL,L,1) = SSCP(L,LL,1)
     DO 104 L=1,LV
     DO 104 LL= L,LV
     SUM = 0.0
     DO 102 I=1,NI
 102 SUM=SUM+(EMAIN(1,I,L)*EMAIN(1,I,LL)/EMI(I))
     SSCP(L,LL,2) = SUM-CT(L,LL)
 104 SSCP(LL,L,2) = SSCP(L,LL,2)
     DO 108 L=1,LV
     DO 108 LL=L,LV
     SUM=0.0
     DO 106 J=1,NJ
 106 SUM=SUM+(EMAIN(2,J,L)*EMAIN(2,J,LL)/EMJ(J))
     SSCP(L,LL,3) = SUM-CT(L,LL)
 108 SSCP(LL,L,3) = SSCP(L,LL,3)
     IF (NK-1) 9999,116,110
 110 DO 114 L=1,LV
     DO 114 LL=L,LV
     SUM = 0.0
     DO 112 K=1,NK
 112 SUM=SUM+(EMAIN(3,K,L)*EMAIN(3,K,LL)/EMK(K))
     SSCP(L,LL,5) = SUM-CT(L,LL)
 114 SSCP(LL,L,5) = SSCP(L,LL,5)
 116 DO 120 L=1,LV
     DO 120 LL=L,LV
     SUM=0.0
     DO 118 I=1,NI
     DO 118 J=1,NJ
 118 SUM=SUM+(EIJ(I,J,L)*EIJ(I,J,LL)/EMIJ(I,J))
     SSCP(L,LL,4)=SUM-CT(L,LL)-SSCP(L,LL,2)-SSCP(L,LL,3)
 120 SSCP(LL,L,4)=SSCP(L,LL,4)
     IF (NK-1)9999,131,122
 122 DO 126 L=1,LV
     DO 126 LL=L,LV
     SUM=0.0
     DO 124 I=1,NI
     DO 124 K=1,NK
 124 SUM=SUM+(EIK(I,K,L)*EIK(I,K,LL)/EMIK(I,K))
     SSCP(L,LL,6)=SUM-CT(L,LL)-SSCP(L,LL,2)-SSCP(L,LL,5)
 126 SSCP(LL,L,6) = SSCP(L,LL,6)
     DO 130 L=1,LV
     DO 130 LL= L,LV
     SUM = 0.0
     DO 128 J=1,NJ
```

```
      DO 128 K=1,NK
128 SUM=SUM+(EJK(J,K,L)*EJK(J,K,LL)/EMJK(J,K))
    SSCP(L,LL,7)=SUM-CT(L,LL)-SSCP(L,LL,3)-SSCP(L,LL,5)
130 SSCP(LL,L,7) = SSCP(L,LL,7)
131 DO 132 L=1,LV
    DO 132 LL=L,LV
132 SSCP(L,LL,8) = 0.0
    DO 134 K = 1,NK
    DO 134 J = 1,NJ
    DO 134 I = 1,NI
    SSCP(1,1,8) = SSCP(1,1,8)+SUMY(I,J,K)**2/EM(I,J,K)
    IF ( LC) 9999, 134, 1
  1 SSCP(1,2,8) = SSCP(1,2,8) + SUMY   (I,J,K) * SUMX1(I,J,K)/EM(I,J,K)
    SSCP(1,3,8) = SSCP(1,3,8) + SUMY   (I,J,K) * SUMX2(I,J,K)/EM(I,J,K)
    SSCP(1,4,8) = SSCP(1,4,8) + SUMY   (I,J,K) * SUMX3(I,J,K)/EM(I,J,K)
    SSCP(1,5,8) = SSCP(1,5,8) + SUMY   (I,J,K) * SUMX4(I,J,K)/EM(I,J,K)
    SSCP(1,6,8) = SSCP(1,6,8) + SUMY   (I,J,K) * SUMX5(I,J,K)/EM(I,J,K)
    SSCP(2,2,8) = SSCP(2,2,8) + SUMX1  (I,J,K) * SUMX1(I,J,K)/EM(I,J,K)
    SSCP(2,3,8) = SSCP(2,3,8) + SUMX1  (I,J,K) * SUMX2(I,J,K)/EM(I,J,K)
    SSCP(2,4,8) = SSCP(2,4,8) + SUMX1  (I,J,K) * SUMX3(I,J,K)/EM(I,J,K)
    SSCP(2,5,8) = SSCP(2,5,8) + SUMX1  (I,J,K) * SUMX4(I,J,K)/EM(I,J,K)
    SSCP(2,6,8) = SSCP(2,6,8) + SUMX1  (I,J,K) * SUMX5(I,J,K)/EM(I,J,K)
    IF(LC-1) 9999, 134, 2
  2 SSCP(3,3,8) = SSCP(3,3,8) + SUMX2  (I,J,K) * SUMX2(I,J,K)/EM(I,J,K)
    SSCP(3,4,8) = SSCP(3,4,8) + SUMX2  (I,J,K) * SUMX3(I,J,K)/EM(I,J,K)
    SSCP(3,5,8) = SSCP(3,5,8) + SUMX2  (I,J,K) * SUMX4(I,J,K)/EM(I,J,K)
    SSCP(3,6,8) = SSCP(3,6,8) + SUMX2  (I,J,K) * SUMX5(I,J,K)/EM(I,J,K)
    IF(LC-2) 9999, 134, 3
  3 SSCP(4,4,8) = SSCP(4,4,8) + SUMX3  (I,J,K) * SUMX3(I,J,K)/EM(I,J,K)
    SSCP(4,5,8) = SSCP(4,5,8) + SUMX3  (I,J,K) * SUMX4(I,J,K)/EM(I,J,K)
    SSCP(4,6,8) = SSCP(4,6,8) + SUMX3  (I,J,K) * SUMX5(I,J,K)/EM(I,J,K)
    SSCP(5,5,8) = SSCP(5,5,8) + SUMX4  (I,J,K) * SUMX4(I,J,K)/EM(I,J,K)
    SSCP(5,6,8) = SSCP(5,6,8) + SUMX4  (I,J,K) * SUMX5(I,J,K)/EM(I,J,K)
    SSCP(6,6,8) = SSCP(6,6,8) + SUMX5  (I,J,K) * SUMX5(I,J,K)/EM(I,J,K)
134 CONTINUE
    DO 136 L = 1,LV
    DO 136 LL = L,LV
136 SSCP(LL,L,8) = SSCP(L,LL,8)
    DO 138 L = 1,LV
    DO 138 LL = 1,LV
138 SSCP(L,LL,9) = SSCP(L,LL,8)
    NW=NE+1
    IF(NK-1) 9999,146,140
140 DO 144 L = 1,LV
    DO 144 LL=L,LV
    DO 142 M=2,7
142 SSCP(L,LL,8) = SSCP(L,LL,8)-SSCP(L,LL,M)
    SSCP(L,LL,8) = SSCP(L,LL,8)-CT(L,LL)
144 SSCP(LL,L,8)=SSCP(L,LL,8)
146 DO 148 L = 1,LV
    DO 148 LL = 1,LV
148 SSCP(L,LL,NW) = RSS(L,LL)-SSCP(L,LL,9)
    PRINT 1008
    PRINT 1009
    DO 150 L = 1,LV
150 PRINT 1018, (SSCP(L,LL,1), LL=1,LV)
```

```
          PRINT 1010
          DO 152 L=1,LV
      152 PRINT 1018, (SSCP(L,LL,2), LL = 1,LV)
          PRINT 1011
          DO 154 L = 1,LV
      154 PRINT 1018, (SSCP(L,LL,3), LL = 1,LV)
          IF(NK-1) 9999,160,156
      156 PRINT 1012
          DO 158 L = 1,LV
      158 PRINT 1018, (SSCP(L,LL,5) , LL = 1,LV)
      160 PRINT 1013
          DO 162 L = 1,LV
      162 PRINT 1018, (SSCP(L,LL,4), LL = 1,LV)
          IF (NK-1) 9999,172,164
      164 PRINT 1014
          DO 166 L = 1,LV
      166 PRINT 1018, (SSCP(L,LL,6), LL = 1,LV)
          PRINT 1015
          DO 168 L =1,LV
      168 PRINT 1018, (SSCP(L,LL,7), LL = 1,LV)
          PRINT 1016
          DO 170 L = 1,LV
      170 PRINT 1018, (SSCP(L,LL,8), LL = 1,LV)
      172 PRINT 1017
          DO 174 L=1,LV
      174 PRINT 1018, (SSCP(L,LL,NW), LL = 1,LV)
     9999 RETURN
          END




    C     SUBROUTINE ANOVA

    C     THIS SUBROUTINE FORMS THE REGRESSION COEFFICIENTS FOR COVARIANCE
    C     ADJUSTMENT, THE ANALYSIS OF VARIANCE TABLE, AND THE CORRELATIONS
    C     AMONG INDEPENDENT AND DEPENDENT VARIABLES.

          SUBROUTINE ANOVA (SSCP,NI,NJ,NK,NE,LV,SEM,LC,NW,C)
          DIMENSION        SSCP(6,6,9),                       A(50,50),
         2 B(50), C(6,8), D(8), DF(8), SQ(8)
     1018 FORMAT (6F14.6)
     1019 FORMAT (22HOWITHIN-PLUS RESIDUALS / 8F14.6)
     1020 FORMAT (24HOREGRESSION COEFFICIENTS)
     1021 FORMAT (27H1ANALYSIS OF VARIANCE TABLE)
     1022 FORMAT (7HOSOURCE,12X, 3HNDF, 14X, 2HSS, 12X, 7HMEAN SQ)
     1023 FORMAT (10HOI EFFECT ,3F14.4)
     1024 FORMAT (10HOJ EFFECT ,3F14.4)
     1025 FORMAT (10HOK EFFECT ,3F14.4)
     1026 FORMAT (10HOI X J    , 3F14.4)
     1027 FORMAT (10HOI X K    , 3F14.4)
     1028 FORMAT (10HOJ X K    , 3F14.4)
     1029 FORMAT (10HOI X J X K, 3F14.4)
     1030 FORMAT (10HOWITHIN    , 3F14.4)
     1031 FORMAT (19H2CORRELATION MATRIX)
     1032 FORMAT (6F14.4)
```

```
1050 FORMAT(10HOTOTAL      .2F14.4)
1051 FORMAT(20HOSTANDARD DEVIATIONS/6F14.4)
     IF (LC) 9999,188,175
 175 DO 176 M = 2,NE
     DO 176 L = 1,LV
     DO 176 LL = 1,LV
 176 SSCP(L,LL,M) = SSCP(L,LL,M)+SSCP(L,LL,NW)
     DO 184 M = 2,NW
     DO 178 L = 2,LV
     DO 178 LL = 2,LV
 178 A(L-1,LL-1) = SSCP(L,LL,M)
     DO 180 L = 2,LV
 180 B(L-1) = SSCP(1,L,M)
     CALL MATINV (A,LC,B,1,DETERM)
     DO 182 L = 1,LC
 182 C(L,M-1) = B(L)
     D(M-1) = 0.0
     DO 184 L = 1,LC
 184 D(M-1) = D(M-1)+B(L)*SSCP(1,L+1,M)
     DO 185 M=2,NW
 185 D(M-1) = SSCP(1,1,M) -D(M-1)
     PRINT 1019, (D(M), M=1,NE)
     PRINT 1020
     DO 186 M = 1,NE
 186 PRINT 1018, (C(L,M), L = 1,LC)
     N = NE-1
     DO 187 M = 1,N
 187 D(M)=D(M)-D(NE)
     GO TO 190
 188 DO 189 M = 2,NW
 189 D(M-1) = SSCP(1,1,M)
 190 D(8)=D(NE)
     PRINT 1021
     PRINT 1022
     N = SEM
     DF(1) = NI-1
     DF(2) = NJ-1
     DF(3) = DF(1)*DF(2)
     DF(4) = NK-1
     DF(5) = DF(1)*DF(4)
     DF(6) = DF(2)*DF(4)
     DF(7) = DF(1)*DF(6)
     DF(8) = N-(NI*NJ*NK+LC)
     DO 191 I=1,8
 191 SQ(I)=D(I)/DF(I)
     PRINT 1023, DF(1), D(1), SQ(1)
     PRINT 1024, DF(2), D(2), SQ(2)
     IF(NK-1) 9999,194,192
 192 PRINT 1025, DF(4), D(4), SQ(4)
 194 PRINT 1026, DF(3), D(3), SQ(3)
     IF(NK-1) 9999,198,196
 196 PRINT 1027, DF(5), D(5), SQ(5)
     PRINT 1028, DF(6), D(6), SQ(6)
     PRINT 1029, DF(7), D(7), SQ(7)
 198 PRINT 1030, DF(8), D(8), SQ(8)
     DFT=N-1-LC
```

```
      DT=0.0
      DO 199 M= 1,NE
  199 DT=DT+D(M)
      PRINT 1050, DFT, DT
      IF (LC) 9999,9999, 200
  200 PRINT 1031
      DO 202 L = 1,LV
  202 B(L) = SQRTF(SSCP(L,L,1))
      DO 204 L = 1,LV
      DO 204 LL = L,LV
      SSCP(L,LL,1)=SSCP(L,LL,1)/(B(L)*B(LL))
  204 SSCP (LL,L,1) = SSCP (L,LL,1)
      DO 206 L = 1,LV
  206 PRINT 1032, (SSCP(L,LL,1), LL = 1,LV)
      DO 205 L=1,LV
  205 B(L)=B(L)/SQRTF(SEM)
      PRINT 1051,(B(L),L=1,LV)
 9999 RETURN
      END



C     SUBROUTINE MEANS

C     THIS SUBROUTINE FORMS ALL THE OBSERVED CELL MEANS AND EFFECT
C     MEANS AND ALL ADJUSTED MEANS.

      SUBROUTINE MEANS(SUMX1,SUMX2,SUMX3,SUMX4,SUMX5,EM,EMI,EMJ,EMK,SUMY
     2,EMAIN,TSUM,EIJ,EIK,EJK,EMIJ,EMIK,EMJK,NI,NJ,NK,NE,LV,SEM,LC,NW,C)
      DIMENSION                   SUMY(10,10,10), SUMX1(10,10,10) ,
     1   SUMX2(10,10,10),SUMX3(10,10,10),SUMX4(10,10,10),SUMX5(10,10,10),
     2   EMAIN(3,10,6),              EM(10,10,10), EMI(10), EMJ(10),
     3   EMK(10), X(6), TSUM(6),          EIJ(10,10,6), EIK(10,10,6),
     4   EJK(10,10,6), EMIJ(10,10), EMIK(10,10), EMJK(10,10) ,
     5   C(6,8)
 1033 FORMAT (11H1CELL MEANS)
 1034 FORMAT (2I2, 10F10.2)
 1035 FORMAT (12H0I X J MEANS)
 1036 FORMAT (12H0I X K MEANS)
 1037 FORMAT (12H0J X K MEANS)
 1038 FORMAT (8H1I MEANS)
 1039 FORMAT (8H0J MEANS)
 1040 FORMAT (8H0K MEANS)
 1041 FORMAT (I2, 10F10.2)
 1042 FORMAT (12H0GRAND MEANS/6F10.2)
 1043 FORMAT (15H0ADJ. I EFFECTS/10F10.2)
 1044 FORMAT (15H0ADJ. J EFFECTS/10F10.2)
 1045 FORMAT (15H0ADJ. K EFFECTS/10F10.2)
 1046 FORMAT (19H0ADJ. I X J EFFECTS)
 1047 FORMAT (19H0ADJ. I X K EFFECTS)
 1048 FORMAT (19H0ADJ. J X K EFFECTS)
 1049 FORMAT (16H0ADJ. CELL MEANS)
 1070 FORMAT (24H1CELL MEANS FOR CONTROLS)
 1080 FORMAT (10H0ADJMT SUM/5F10.2)
  207 PRINT 1033
      DO 208 I = 1,NI
```

```
      DO 208 J = 1,NJ
      DO 208 K = 1,NK
208 SUMY(I,J,K) = SUMY(I,J,K)/EM(I,J,K)
      DO 210 I = 1,NI
      DO 210 J = 1,NJ
210 PRINT 1034, I, J, (SJMY(I,J,K), K = 1,NK)
212 DO 214 I=1,NI
      DO 214 J = 1,NJ
      DO 214 L = 1,LV
214 EIJ(I,J,L) = EIJ (I,J,L)/EMIJ(I,J)
      IF(NK-1) 9999, 219, 215
215 DO 216 I = 1,NI
      DO 216 K = 1,NK
      DO 216 L = 1,LV
216 EIK(I,K,L) = EIK(I,K,L)/EMIK(I,K)
      DO 218 J = 1,NJ
      DO 218 K = 1,NK
      DO 218 L = 1,LV
218 EJK(J,K,L) = EJK(J,K,L)/EMJK(J,K)
219 DO 220 I = 1,NI
      DO 220 L = 1,LV
220 EMAIN (1,I,L)= EMAIN (1,I,L)/EMI(I)
      DO 222 J = 1,NJ
      DO 222 L = 1,LV
222 EMAIN(2,J,L) = EMAIN(2,J,L)/EMJ(J)
      IF(NK-1) 9999,229,223
223 DO 224 K = 1,NK
      DO 224 L = 1,LV
224 EMAIN(3,K,L) = EMAIN(3,K,L)/EMK(K)
      PRINT 1035
      DO 226 I = 1,NI
      DO 226 J = 1,NJ
226 PRINT 1034,I,J,(EIJ(I,J,L), L = 1,LV)
      PRINT 1036
      DO 227 I = 1,NI
      DO 227 K = 1,NK
227 PRINT 1034,I,K,(EIK(I,K,L),L=1,LV)
      PRINT 1037
      DO 228 J = 1,NJ
      DO 228 K = 1,NK
228 PRINT 1034, J,K, (EJK(J,K,L), L = 1,LV)
229 PRINT 1038
      DO 230 I = 1,NI
230 PRINT 1041,I,(EMAIN(1,I,L), L = 1,LV)
      PRINT 1039
      DO 232 J = 1,NJ
232 PRINT 1041,J, (EMAIN(2,J,L), L = 1,LV)
      IF(NK-1) 9999, 235, 231
231 PRINT 1040
      DO 234 K = 1,NK
234 PRINT 1041, K, (EMAIN(3,K,L), L = 1,LV)
235 DO 236 L=1,LV
236 TSUM(L) = TSUM(L)/SEM
      PRINT 1042, (TSUM(L), L = 1,LV)
      IF (LC) 9999, 9999, 237
237 DO 240 I = 1,NI
```

```
        SUM = 0.0
        DO 238 L = 1,LC
238 SUM=SUM+C(L,NE)*(EMAIN(1,I,L+1)-TSUM(L+1))
240 EMAIN(1,I,1) = EMAIN(1,I,1)-SUM
        PRINT 1043, (EMAIN(1,I,1), I = 1,NI)
        DO 244 J = 1,NJ
        SUM = 0.0
        DO 242 L = 1,LC
242 SUM=SUM+C(L,NE)*(EMAIN(2,J,L+1)-TSUM(L+1))
244 EMAIN(2,J,1)=EMAIN(2,J,1)-SUM
        PRINT 1044, (EMAIN(2,J,1), J = 1,NJ)
        IF (NK-1) 9999, 250, 245
245 DO 248 K=1,NK
        SUM = 0.0
        DO 246 L = 1,LC
246 SUM=SUM+C(L,NE)*(EMAIN(3,K,L+1)-TSUM(L+1))
248 EMAIN(3,K,1)=EMAIN(3,K,1)-SUM
        PRINT 1045, (EMAIN(3,K,1), K = 1,NK)
250 PRINT 1046
        DO 260 J=1,NJ
        DO 260 I=1,NI
        SUM=0.0
        DO 255 L=1,LC
255 SUM=SUM+C(L,NE)*(EIJ(I,J,L+1)-TSUM(L+1))
260 EIJ(I,J,1)=EIJ(I,J,1)-SUM
        DO 265  I=1,NI
265 PRINT 1041,I,(EIJ(I,J,1), J=1,NJ)
        IF (NK-1) 9999, 9999, 270
270 PRINT 1047
        DO 280 I=1,NI
        DO 280 K=1,NK
        SUM=0.0
        DO 275 L=1,LC
275 SUM=SUM+C(L,NE)*(EIK(I,K,L+1)-TSUM(L+1))
280 EIK(I,K,1)=EIK(I,K,1)-SUM
        DO 285 I=1,NI
285 PRINT 1041,I,(EIK(I,K,1), K=1,NK)
290 PRINT 1048
        DO 300 J=1,NJ
        DO 300 K=1,NK
        SUM=0.0
        DO 295 L=1,LC
295 SUM=SUM+C(L,NE)*(EJK(J,K,L+1)-TSUM(L+1))
300 EJK(J,K,1)=EJK(J,K,1)-SUM
        DO 305 J=1,NJ
305 PRINT 1041, J,(EJK(J,K,1),K=1,NK)
        PRINT 1070
        DO 360 L=1,LC
        DO 360 I=1,NI
        DO 360 J=1,NJ
        DO 360 K=1,NK
        GO TO (351, 352, 353, 354, 355),L
351 SUMX1 (I,J,K)=SUMX1 (I,J,K)/EM(I,J,K)
410 PRINT 1034,I,J, SUMX1(I,J,K)
        GO TO 360
352 SUMX2 (I,J,K)=SUMX2 (I,J,K)/EM(I,J,K)
```

```
420 PRINT 1034,I,J, SUMX2(I,J,K)
    GO TO 360
353 SUMX3 (I,J,K)=SUMX3 (I,J,K)/EM(I,J,K)
430 PRINT 1034,I,J, SUMX3(I,J,K)
    GO TO 360
354 SUMX4 (I,J,K)=SUMX4 (I,J,K)/EM(I,J,K)
440 PRINT 1034,I,J, SUMX4(I,J,K)
    GO TO 360
355 SUMX5 (I,J,K)=SUMX5 (I,J,K)/EM(I,J,K)
450 PRINT 1034,I,J, SUMX5(I,J,K)
360 CONTINUE
    DO 401 I=1,NI
    DO 401 J=1,NJ
    DO 401 K=1,NK
    SUM=0.0
    SUM=SUM+C(1,NE)*(SUMX1(I,J,K)-TSUM(2))
    IF(LC-1) 9999, 400, 380
380 SUM=SUM+C(2,NE)*(SUMX2(I,J,K)-TSUM(3))
    IF(LC-2) 9999, 400, 385
385 SUM=SUM+C(3,NE)*(SUMX3(I,J,K)-TSUM(4))
    IF(LC-3) 9999, 400, 390
390 SUM=SUM+C(4,NE)*(SUMX4(I,J,K)-TSUM(5))
    IF(LC-4) 9999, 400, 395
395 SUM=SUM+C(5,NE)*(SUMX5(I,J,K)-TSUM(6))
400 PRINT 1080,SUM,C(1,NE),SUMX1(I,J,K),TSUM(2)
401 SUMY(I,J,K)=SUMY(I,J,K)-SUM
    PRINT 1049
    DO 405 I=1,NI
    DO 405 J=1,NJ
405 PRINT 1034,I,J,(SUMY(I,J,K), K=1,NK)
9999 RETURN
    END
```

114

5.3 References

Cochran, W. G. (1957). "Analysis of Covariance: Its Nature and Uses," *Biometrics* **13**:261–281.

Cox, D. R. (1958). *Planning of Experiments*. New York, John Wiley and Sons.

Edwards, Allen L. (1960). *Experimental Design in Psychological Research*. New York: Holt, Rinehart and Winston.

Jackson, R. W. B. (1940). *Application of the Analysis of Variance and Covariance Method to Educational Problems*. Toronto: University of Toronto Press.

Johnson, P. O., and Neyman, J. (1936). "Tests of Certain Linear Hypotheses and Their Application to Some Educational Problems," *Statistical Research Memoirs* **1**:57–93 (Department of Applied Statistics, University College, London).

Lindquist, E. F. (1953). *Design and Analysis of Experiments in Psychology and Education*. Boston: Houghton Mifflin Co.

McNemar, Quinn (1962). *Psychological Statistics*. New York: John Wiley and Sons.

Wert, J. E., Neidt, C. D., and Ahmann, J. S. (1954). *Statistical Methods in Educational and Psychological Research*. New York: Appleton-Century-Crofts.

References for Example

Cooley, W. W., and Klopfer, L. E. (1961). *Test on Understanding Science*. Princeton: Educational Testing Service.

Klopfer, L. E. and Cooley, W. W. (1961). Use of Case Histories in the Development of Student Understanding of Science and Scientists. Cooperative Research Project Number 896, United States Office of Education (mimeographed).

CHAPTER SIX

Multiple-discriminant analysis

6.1 Mathematics of Multiple-Discriminant Analysis

Discriminant analysis is a procedure for estimating the position of an individual on a line that best separates classes or groups. The estimated position is obtained as a linear function of the individual's m test scores. Since one "best" line may not exhaust the predictive power of the test battery in distinguishing among the classes, additional discriminant functions, all mutually orthogonal,[1] may be fitted. The maximum number of discriminants is indicated by the lesser of the two numbers $g - 1$ and m.

Although it is possible to treat the classification problem directly in the m-dimensional test space by the methods described in Chapter 7, the multiple-discriminant analysis has the advantage that it often leads to a dramatic reduction in the predictor space's dimensionality without substantial loss of information. In addition, since by the Central Limit Theorem linear functions of variates are more likely to be normal than are the component variates, multiple-discriminant scores may satisfy the important assumption of a multivariate normal distribution better than the original test scores. An approximate test of the statistical significance of the separation of groups on a particular discriminant function is available, and the relative contributions of the original variables to a discriminant function can be shown. It is useful to compute the centroids and dispersions of the groups in the discriminant space, especially when group classification is the primary objective.

The geometric interpretation of discriminant analysis can best be seen for the case of two groups and two variates. The bivariate plot for groups A and B is shown in Figure 6.1. The two tests X and Y are slightly positively correlated, as illustrated. Each ellipse in the diagram is the locus of points of equal density (or frequency) for a particular group. For example, the outer ellipse for group A might define the region within which 90 per cent of group A lies. These ellipses are called centours (*cen*tile con*tours*). They are discussed in detail in Section 7.1.

---

[1] Orthogonal in the sense that discriminant scores are uncorrelated. Discriminant scores are defined below.

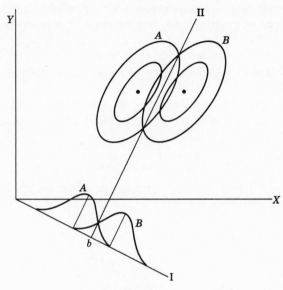

Figure 6.1

The two points at which corresponding centours intersect define a straight line II. If a second line I is constructed perpendicular to line II, and if the points in the two-dimensional space are projected onto I, the overlap between the two groups will be smaller than for any other possible line. The discriminant function therefore transforms the individual test scores to a single discriminant score, and that score is the individual's location along line I. The point b where II intersects I would divide the one-dimensional discriminant space into two regions, one indicating probable membership in group A and the other region for group B.

Multiple-discriminant functions are computed as the vectors associated with the latent roots of the determinantal equation

$$(6.1) \qquad\qquad |\mathbf{W}^{-1}\mathbf{A} - \lambda\mathbf{I}| = 0$$

where $\mathbf{I}$ is an identity matrix and $\mathbf{W}$ is the pooled within-groups deviation scores cross-products matrix defined in Chapter 4. In addition,

$$\mathbf{A} = \mathbf{T} - \mathbf{W}$$

where $\mathbf{T}$ is the total sample deviation score cross-products matrix defined in Chapter 4. The matrix $\mathbf{A}$ is thus the among-groups cross products of deviations of group from grand means weighted by group sizes:

$$a_{ij} = \sum_{k=1}^{g} N_g(\overline{X}_{ik} - \overline{X}_i)(\overline{X}_{jk} - \overline{X}_j).$$

The matrix equation $(\mathbf{W}^{-1}\mathbf{A} - \lambda\mathbf{I})\mathbf{v} = \mathbf{0}$ is derived from the partial derivatives of the ratio

$$\lambda_i = \frac{\mathbf{v}_i'\mathbf{A}\mathbf{v}_i}{\mathbf{v}_i'\mathbf{W}\mathbf{v}_i}, \qquad i = 1, 2, 3, \ldots, r,$$

(where r is the lesser of $g - 1$ and m) which is to be maximized in order that the among-groups sums of squares $\mathbf{v}_i'\mathbf{A}\mathbf{v}_i$ may be large relative to the within-groups sums of squares $\mathbf{v}_i'\mathbf{W}\mathbf{v}_i$ on the discriminant functions represented by the roots λ_i (eigenvalues) and their associated vectors $\mathbf{v}_i$ (eigenvectors). The relative sizes of λ_i indicate the extent to which the associated discriminant functions distinguish among the groups.

Wilks' lambda criterion for the discriminating power of the test battery, described in Chapter 4, may be derived as a function of the roots of $\mathbf{W}^{-1}\mathbf{A}$ as follows:

$$\Lambda = \prod_{i=1}^{r} \left[\frac{1}{(1 + \lambda_i)} \right].$$

The percentage of the total discriminating power of the battery contained in the ith discriminant function is represented by

$$100 \cdot \left(\frac{\lambda_j}{\sum\limits_{i=1}^{r} \lambda_i} \right).$$

One problem in discriminant analysis is deciding how many discriminant functions to use in subsequent analyses or in the interpretation of group differences. Two approximate tests of the significance of a particular discriminant function which may be applied to large-sample studies are available.[2] It is also possible simply to select a subset of the computed functions that accounts for a major portion of the discriminating power of the test battery, say approximately 80 or 90 per cent of it.

The computed latent vectors $\mathbf{v}_i$ are the coefficients of the discriminant functions. To show the relative contributions of the variables to the discriminant function, these normalized vectors may be adjusted by multiplying corresponding elements by the square roots of the diagonal elements of the $\mathbf{W}$ matrix.

The matrix $\mathbf{C}$ of the centroids of the groups in the reduced discriminant space may be computed by applying the $r \times m$ matrix of discriminant vectors $\mathbf{V}$ to the $m \times g$ matrix $\mathbf{M}$ of g group means on the m original variables as follows:[3]

$$\mathbf{C}_{(r,g)} = \mathbf{V}'_{(r,m)} \cdot \mathbf{M}_{(m,g)}.$$

The $r \times r$ dispersion matrix $\mathbf{DD}_g$ in the discriminant space for group g may be obtained by pre- and post-multiplying the test space dispersion matrix $\mathbf{D}_g$ for group g by the matrix $\mathbf{V}$ containing the discriminant function vectors, as follows:

$$\mathbf{DD}_{g(r,r)} = \mathbf{V}'_{(r,m)} \cdot \mathbf{D}_{g(m,m)} \cdot \mathbf{V}_{(m,r)}.$$

In Chapter 7 a scheme is described for computing classification probabilities for individuals in groups. These computations require $\mathbf{DD}_g$.

[2] See Rao (1952), pp. 370–378.

[3] Individuals' discriminant scores are computed by multiplying $\mathbf{V}$ times the score vector. The flow chart and program for computing discriminant scores are identical to those for computing estimated scores in multiple regression. See Flow Chart 3.4 and p. 58.

6.2   Discriminating among Three Career-Plan Groups

One objective of the Scientific Careers Study (Cooley, 1958) currently in progress is the determination of personality dimensions associated with different post-college career decisions of college science majors. Over two hundred sophomore and senior males were selected from among the science and engineering majors at six colleges in eastern Massachusetts. At the time they were selected (fall, 1958), they were administered the Study of Values test[4] and several other personality instruments. Follow-up information is being collected to determine the educational and career decisions made by these young men over a 5-year period.

After 3 years of follow-up, three interesting and distinct groups were found when the postcollege decisions and plans of the sample of seniors were examined. The groups are as follows:

(1) Research group. Those who enter graduate work to conduct fundamental research as part of their future work.

(2) Applied Science Group. Those who continue in science and engineering but do not plan a research career.

(3) Nonscience Group. Those who leave science work and enter fields having more direct involvement with people.

The Study of Values measured six attributes that were hypothesized as related to membership in the three groups. A discriminant analysis was therefore conducted to test the significance of the group separations, provide an efficient basis for examining the nature of any differences found, and provide equations for predicting the decisions of a check sample (the group of sophomores who are now making similar decisions). The use of the results with the check sample is described in Chapter 7.

The computer program for discriminant analysis computes Wilks' lambda criterion by obtaining the roots of $\mathbf{W}^{-1}\mathbf{A}$ and then computing $\Pi[1/(1 + \lambda_i)]$. The Λ for the three groups was .576, which was significant at the .001 level. Thus the chance of producing group differences this large or larger by drawing three random samples from a six-dimensional multivariate swarm is less than one in one thousand.

The generalized, multivariate, null hypothesis was that the three groups had similar value orientations; it can now be regarded as not tenable. Therefore we may proceed to examine the group differences obtained, by examining the group mean vectors (Table 6.1), the scaled discriminant vectors (Table 6.2), and the group centroids (Figure 6.1).

The scaled vectors (Table 6.2) indicate that the large contributors to group separation along the first discriminant function are the theoretical, religious, and aesthetic scales, high scores on these scales resulting in high scores on function I. Table 6.1 shows that the research group has high means on the theoretical and aesthetic scales, which partially explains the location of that group's centroid in Figure 6.2.

[4] Allport, G. W., Vernon, P. E., and Lindzey, G. (1951). *Study of Values*. Boston: Houghton Mifflin Co.

TABLE 6.1
Study of Values: Means and Standard Deviations

Values Scale	Research, $N = 33$	Applied, $N = 25$	Nonscience, $N = 38$	Total Sample, $N = 96$
	Group Means			
1 Theoretical	56.73	51.56	48.95	52.30
2 Economic	33.24	41.52	38.21	37.36
3 Aesthetic	41.55	38.60	34.95	38.17
4 Social	34.58	29.84	36.58	34.14
5 Political	37.24	41.76	41.53	40.11
6 Religious	36.82	36.96	39.89	38.07
	S.D.			
1 Theoretical	3.73	6.79	6.97	6.84
2 Economic	7.15	7.14	7.77	8.02
3 Aesthetic	9.12	10.11	8.83	9.61
4 Social	8.28	7.08	7.06	7.91
5 Political	5.20	7.39	6.00	6.43
6 Religious	10.71	10.54	9.85	10.33

TABLE 6.2
Study of Values Discriminant Analysis: Root and Vectors of $W^{-1}A$

Values	Normalized Vectors		Scaled Vectors	
	I	II	I	II
1 Theoretical	.917	.416	.972	.423
2 Economic	−.120	.439	−.156	.551
3 Aesthetic	.246	.425	.407	.667
4 Social	.109	.356	.147	.452
5 Political	−.076	.402	−.081	.419
6 Religious	.257	.408	.470	.714

Latent Roots	Per Cent of Trace
$\lambda_1 = .4887$	74.62
$\lambda_2 = .1661$	25.36

The $\lambda_i = .000$, where $i = 3, 4, 5, 6$; trace of $W^{-1}A = .6549$. The $\Sigma\lambda_i = .6548$, $\Lambda = .576$, $F_{176}^{12} = 4.66, p < .001$.

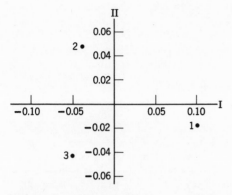

Figure 6.2. Group centroids in the discriminant space. Group centroids and dispersions in the reduced discriminant space are computed by the program R SPACE.

Figure 6.3

The high weighting for religious values on discriminant I is difficult to explain, but it illustrates one of the advantages of multivariate analysis. If these data had been analyzed by the conventional univariate procedures, the importance of religion might have been lost. Table 6.4 summarizes the six F tests for the significance of group differences on each of the six values scales. The religious scale, by itself, appears insignificant. However, religious values do appear relevant to this particular career choice process when the total profile is considered, as revealed by the foregoing. The reason for this can perhaps best be seen in Figure 6.3.

If two variables A and B are used in a discriminant analysis involving groups I and II, the following situation might prevail. Group I mean is higher than group II on variable A. There is no difference between groups I and II on variable B. Variables A and B are negatively correlated. The resulting discriminant function would be oriented as illustrated in Figure 6.3, utilizing the relation between A and B to produce minimum overlap between the groups, thus resulting in a high loading for variable B. For people of average A values, as can be seen in the diagram, the B score is quite useful in predicting group membership, even though the group means on B do not differ.

TABLE 6.3

Standard Deviations Along Discriminant Axes

Group	Function	
	I	II
1 Research	.068	.115
2 Applied	.124	.028
3 Nonscience	.114	.101

TABLE 6.4
Univariate F Tests

Values Scale	Sums of Squares		Mean Squares		F ratio	p
	W	A	W	A	$n_1 = 2;\ n_2 = 93$	
1 Theoretical	3350.	1087.	36.0	543.5	15.1	<.001
2 Economic	5096.	1019.	54.8	509.5	9.3	<.001
3 Aesthetic	8000.	775.	86.0	387.5	4.5	<.05
4 Social	5242.	694.	56.4	347.0	6.2	<.001
5 Political	3508.	415.	37.7	207.5	5.5	<.01
6 Religious	9929.	209.	106.7	104.5	.98	—
$ndf =$	93	2				

TABLE 6.5
Significance of the Discriminant Functions χ^2 Approximations*

Function		ndf	χ^2	p
I	.4887	7	36.51	<.001
II	.1661	5	14.37	<.02

* Rao (1952), pp. 370–378.

TABLE 6.6

Variance-Covariance Matrix for Each Group

Research Group

	1 Theoretical	2 Economic	3 Aesthetic	4 Social	5 Political	6 Religious
1	13.89	−2.31	10.03	−.74	1.00	−22.24
2		51.19	−11.79	−33.43	.35	−4.61
3			83.26	−14.64	−6.61	−58.59
4				68.63	−6.08	−13.95
5					27.06	−15.67
6						114.72

Applied Group

	1	2	3	4	5	6
1	46.17	−1.80	8.11	−23.53	−11.78	−17.73
2		51.01	−29.70	−13.12	13.30	19.85
3			102.17	−23.23	−8.72	−49.81
4				50.14	−6.12	−17.20
5					54.61	−40.63
6						111.12

Nonscience Group

	1	2	3	4	5	6
1	48.59	−6.02	12.56	−8.51	.33	−46.49
2		60.39	−32.12	−30.99	20.45	−11.71
3			77.94	−2.78	−21.43	−33.98
4				49.82	−19.23	11.39
5					35.99	−16.29
6						97.07

Flow Diagram for Multiple-Discriminant Analysis (DISCRIM Program)

INPUT
Read L, K, M where L $= 0$ if W and T matrices are to be computed from subjects' score vectors, L $= 1$ if W and T are to be read in. K is the number of groups, and M is the number of variables.

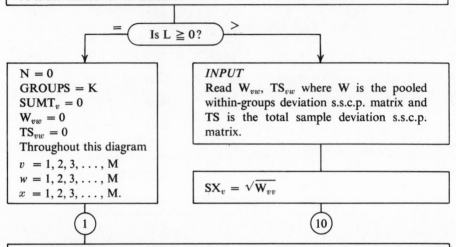

Is L $\geqq$ 0? $=$ $>$

N $= 0$
GROUPS $=$ K
SUMT$_v = 0$
W$_{vw} = 0$
TS$_{vw} = 0$
Throughout this diagram
$v = 1, 2, 3, \ldots, M$
$w = 1, 2, 3, \ldots, M$
$x = 1, 2, 3, \ldots, M$.

INPUT
Read W$_{vw}$, TS$_{vw}$ where W is the pooled within-groups deviation s.s.c.p. matrix and TS is the total sample deviation s.s.c.p. matrix.

$$SX_v = \sqrt{W_{vv}}$$

(1)   (10)

SUBROUTINE
Call subroutine CORREL, which computes and reports number of subjects in group (NG), sums of scores (SX), raw s.s.c.p. (SS), and deviation s.s.c.p. (SSD).

N $=$ N $+$ NG   accumulating total sample size in N.
SUMT$_v =$ SUMT$_v +$ SX$_v$ accumulating total sums of scores.
W$_{vw} =$ W$_{vw} +$ SSD$_{vw}$ accumulating pooled within-groups deviation s.s.c.p. matrix.
TS$_{vw} =$ TS$_{vw} +$ SS$_{vw}$ accumulating total sample raw s.s.c.p. matrix. Set GROUPS $=$ GROUPS $- 1$.

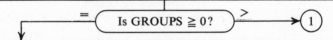

Is GROUPS $\geqq$ 0? $=$ $>$ (1)

TS$_{vw} =$ TS$_{vw} -$ SUMT$_v \cdot$ SUMT$_w$/N   forming the total sample deviation
SX$_v = \sqrt{W_{vv}}$ s.s.c.p. matrix.
XM$_v =$ SUMT$_v$/N   forming total sample means.
SD$_v = \sqrt{TS_{vv}/(N - 1)}$ forming total sample standard deviations.
A$_{vw} =$ TS$_{vw} -$ W$_{vw}$ forming the among-groups deviation s.s.c.p. matrix.

6.1. Flow Diagram for DISCRIM Program (Continued)

OUTPUT
Print and/or punch, with labels, N, XM_v, SD_v, W_{vw}, TS_{vw}, A_{vw}.

SUBROUTINE
Call subroutine DIRNM to compute the eigenvalues and eigenvectors of the problem $A \cdot X = W \cdot X \cdot \Lambda$ where A and W are the symmetric matrices previously formed and the columns of X contain the eigenvectors. (DIRNM places the eigenvalues from the diagonal of Λ in the vector L.)

TRACE $= 0$
TRACE $=$ TRACE $+ L_v$
$XM_v = 100 \cdot (L_v/\text{TRACE})$ computing the percentage of the trace of $W^{-1} \cdot A$ contained in each root.
$TS_{vw} = SX_v \cdot X_{vw}$ computing scaled vectors to show the relative contributions of the variables to each of the discriminant functions.

OUTPUT
Print and/or punch, with labels, L_v, TRACE, XM_v, TS_{vw}, X_{vw}.

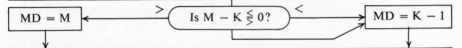

| MD = M | $\xrightarrow{>}$ | Is $M - K \lessgtr 0$? | $\xleftarrow{<}$ | MD = K − 1 |

LAMBDA $= 1$
LAMBDA $=$ LAMBDA $\cdot (1/(1 + L_v))$ forming Wilks lambda.
$S = \sqrt{(M^2 \cdot (K - 1)^2 - 4)/(M^2 + (K - 1)^2 - 5)}$
$Y = \text{LAMBDA}^{1/S}$
$XM1 = (N - 1) - ((M + K)/2)$
$XL = - ((M(K - 1)) - 2)/4$
$F1 = M \cdot (K - 1)$
$F2 = (XM1 \cdot S) + 2 \cdot XL$
$F = ((1 - Y)/Y) \cdot (F2/F1)$ forming F for test of H_2, with degrees of freedom F1, F2.

OUTPUT
Print, with labels, LAMBDA, F, F1, F2, S, Y, XM1, XL.

STOP

125

Flow Diagram for Centroids and Dispersions in a Discriminant or Factor Space (or Other Reduced Space) (RSPACE Program)

INPUT

Read KG, M, N, V_{vw}, $XBAR_{kv}$, where KG is the number of groups, M is the number of test variables in the original space, N is the number of variables in the reduced space, V is the M $\times$ N matrix of weights (discriminant vectors or factor loadings), and XBAR is the KG $\times$ M matrix of group means in the original test space. In this flow diagram subscripts have the following ranges: $y = 1, 2, 3, \ldots, M$; $k = 1, 2, 3, \ldots, KG$; $v = 1, 2, 3, \ldots, M$; $w = 1, 2, 3, \ldots, N$; $x = 1, 2, 3, \ldots, N$.

$CENT_{kw} = 0$
$CENT_{kw} = CENT_{kw} + XBAR_{kv} \cdot V_{vw}$ forming centroids in the reduced space.
$L = 0$

OUTPUT
Punch $CENT_{kw}$.

---

①

INPUT
Read D_{vy} where D is the M $\times$ M dispersion matrix in the original test space for a group.

$L = L + 1$ forming group identification number.
$CENT_{wy} = 0$
$CENT_{wy} = CENT_{wy} - V_{vw} \cdot D_{vy}$
$RD_{wx} = 0$
$RD_{wx} = RD_{wx} - CENT_{wy} \cdot V_{yx}$ forming the N $\times$ N dispersion matrix for group
$KG = KG - 1$ L in the reduced space.

OUTPUT
Punch L, RD_{wx}

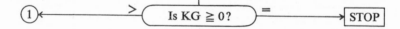

① $\xleftarrow{\quad > \quad}$ (Is KG $\geqq$ 0?) $\xrightarrow{\quad = \quad}$ STOP

MULTIPLE-DISCRIMINANT ANALYSIS (DISCRIM)

```
C      DISCRIM.
C
C          THIS PROGRAM COMPUTES MULTIPLE-DISCRIMINANT FUNCTIONS FOR UP
C      TO 50 VARIABLES AND ANY NUMBER OF GROUPS.  INPUT MAY BE RAW SCORE
C      VECTORS OF SUBJECTS (IN WHICH CASE SET L = 0) OR PREVIOUSLY COM-
C      PUTED W AND T MATRICES (IN WHICH CASE SET L = 1).  WILKS LAMBDA
C      TEST OF THE SIGNIFICANCE OF THE DISCRIMINATION IS ALSO COMPUTED.
C      REQUIRED SUBROUTINES ARE CORREL, DIRNM, AND HDIAG, MPRINT, AND
C      MPUNCH.
C
C      INPUT.
C
C          INPUT CARD 1 CONTAINS
C      COL. 1     L
C      COL. 2-3   K = NO. OF GROUPS
C      COL. 4-5   M = NO. OF VARIABLES.
C      IF L = 0, FOLLOW WITH DATA CARDS FOR EACH GROUP, PRECEDING SUBJECT
C      SCORE VECTORS WITH CONTROL CARD FOR SUBROUTINE CORREL AND FORMAT
C      CARDS.  INSTRUCT CORREL TO PUNCH OUT GROUP MEANS AND DISPERSION
C      MATRICES, AS THESE WILL BE NEEDED FOR LATER COMPUTATION OF
C      CENTROIDS AND DISPERSIONS OF GROUPS IN THE DISCRIMINANT SPACE.
C      IF L = 1, FOLLOW FIRST CARD WITH W AND T MATRICES, PUNCHED TO
C      FORMAT 5E14.7 (I.E., AS PUNCHED BY CORREL).
C
C      OUTPUT.
C
C          PRINTED OUTPUT INCLUDES
C      1) PROGRAM TITLE, K, M
C      2) FROM CORREL, FOR EACH GROUP, NUMBER CF GROUP, NUMBER IN GROUP,
C      GROUP MEANS, GROUP STANDARD DEVIATIONS, GROUP DISPERSION, GROUP
C      CORRELATION MATRIX IF REQUESTED
C      3) POOLED W MATRIX
C      4) T MATRIX
C      5) MEANS FOR TOTAL SAMPLE
C      6) STANDARD DEVIATIONS FOR TOTAL SAMPLE
C      7) A MATRIX
C      8) EIGENVALUES OF W-INVERSE * A
C      9) TRACE OF W-INVERSE * A , AND SUM OF EIGENVALUES
C      10) PERCENTAGE WHICH EACH EIGENVALUE IS OF TRACE
C      11) VECTORS OF W-INVERSE * A
C      12) SCALED VECTORS TO SHOW THE RELATIVE CONTRIBUTIONS OF THE
C      VARIABLES TO EACH FUNCTION
C      13) TOTAL SAMPLE SIZE, WILKS LAMBDA, F1, F2,  AND F FOR TEST OF H2
C      PRINTED OUTPUT IS APPROPRIATELY LABELED.
C      PUNCHED OUTPUT CONTAINS THE EIGENVECTORS OF W-INVERSE * A, WHICH
C      ARE THE DISCRIMINANT FUNCTION WEIGHTS. THESE ARE PUNCHED IN ROWS.
C      INSTRUCT CORREL TO PUNCH OUT GROUP MEANS AND DISPERSIONS IN E CON-
C      VENTION FOR INPUT TO RSPACE.
C
C
       DIMENSION   TS(50,50),    X(50),SX(50),SS(50,50),SSD(50,50),
      1 D(50,50),R(50,50),XM(50),SD(50),IQ(50),SUMT(50),W(50,50)
       READ INPUT TAPE 4, 1, L, K, M
     1 FORMAT (I1,2I2)
       PRINT 2
     2 FORMAT (31HOMULTIPLE-DISCRIMINANT ANALYSIS)
       PRINT 4, K
     4 FORMAT (17HONO. OF GROUPS = I2)
       PRINT 5, M
```

```
      5 FORMAT  (20HONO. OF VARIABLES = I2)
        IF (L) 999, 100, 300
    100 N = 0
        DO 6  I = 1,M
        SUMT(I) = 0.0
        DO 6  J = 1,M
        W(I,J) = 0.0
      6 TS(I,J) = 0.0
        DO 8 II = 1, K
    200 CALL CORREL (T, NG, SX, SS, SSD, D, R, XM, SD)
        N = N + NG
        DO 8  I = 1,M
        SUMT(I) = SUMT(I) + SX(I)
        DO 8  J = 1,M
        W(I,J) = W(I,J) + SSD(I,J)
      8 TS(I,J) = TS(I,J) + SS(I,J)
      9 EN = N
        DO 10  I = 1, M
        SX(I) = SQRTF (W(I,I))
C       SQUARE ROOTS OF DIAGONALS OF W ARE PRESERVED IN SX(I).
        X(I) = SUMT(I) / EN
C       TOTAL SAMPLE MEANS ARE NOW IN X(I).
        DO 10  J = 1, M
        SS(I,J) = TS(I,J)
     10 TS(I,J) = SS(I,J) - (SUMT(I)*SUMT(J)/EN)
C       TS(I,J) IS NOW THE TOTAL SAMPLE DEVIATION CROSS PRODUCTS MATRIX.
        DO 11  I = 1, M
     11 SD(I) = SQRTF (TS(I,I)/(EN-1.0))
C       TOTAL SAMPLE STANDARD DEVIATIONS ARE NOW IN SD(I).
        PRINT 12
     12 FORMAT (16H1POOLED W MATRIX)
        CALL MPRINT (W, M, 2, 6HW MAT )
     14 FORMAT (8F15.4)
        PRINT 16
     16 FORMAT (51H1TOTAL DEVIATION SUMS OF SQUARES AND CROSS PRODUCTS)
        CALL MPRINT (TS, M, 2, 6HT MAT )
        PRINT 17, N
     17 FORMAT (25H0TOTAL NO. OF SUBJECTS = I5)
        PRINT 18
     18 FORMAT (23H0MEANS FOR TOTAL SAMPLE)
        PRINT 14, (X(I), I = 1,M)
        PRINT 19
     19 FORMAT (37H0STANDARD DEVIATIONS FOR TOTAL SAMPLE)
        PRINT 14, (SD(I), I = 1,M)
        DO 191 I = 1,M
        DO 191 J = 1,M
        R(I,J) = TS(I,J) / ((EN - 1.0) * SD(I) * SD(J))
    191 R(J,I) = R(I,J)
C       R(I,J) NOW CONTAINS THE TOTAL R MATRIX.
        PRINT 192
    192 FORMAT (25H1TOTAL CORRELATION MATRIX)
        CALL MPRINT (R, M, 2, 6HTOT R )
        CALL MPUNCH (R,IPROB, 1HR, M, 1)
        GO TO 400
C
    300 DO 21  J = 1, M
```

DISCRIM PROGRAM (CONTINUED)

```
   21 READ INPUT TAPE 4, 20, (W(I,J), I = 1,M)
   20 FORMAT (5E14.7)
      PRINT 12
      CALL MPRINT (W, M, 2, 6HW MAT )
      DO 23  J = 1, M
   23 READ INPUT TAPE 4, 20, (TS(I,J), I = 1,M)
      PRINT 16
      CALL MPRINT (TS, M, 2, 6HT MAT )
C
  400 DO 25  I = 1, M
      DO 25  J = 1, M
   25 D(I,J) = TS(I,J) - W(I,J)
C     D(I,J) NOW CONTAINS THE A MATRIX.
      PRINT 26
   26 FORMAT (9H1A MATRIX)
      CALL MPRINT (D, M, 2, 6HA MAT )
      CALL DIRNM(D, M, W, SSD, SD)
C     ROOTS OF W-A ARE NOW IN SD AND VECTORS ARE COLUMNS OF SSD
C
      PRINT 34
   34 FORMAT (21HOROOTS OF W-INVERSE*A)
      PRINT 14, (SD(I), I = 1,M )
      TRACE = 0.0
      DO 35  I = 1, M
   35 TRACE = TRACE + SD(I)
      DO 36  I = 1, M
   36 XM(I) = 100.0 * (SD(I)    / TRACE)
      PRINT 37, TRACE
   37 FORMAT (24HOTRACE OF W-INVERSE*A = F15.5)
      PRINT 38
   38 FORMAT(39HOPERCENTAGE WHICH EACH ROOT IS OF TRACE)
      PRINT 39, (XM(I), I = 1,M)
   39 FORMAT (10F8.4)
      PRINT 42
   42 FORMAT (35H1VECTORS OF W-INVERSE A, AS COLUMNS )
      CALL MPRINT (SSD, M, 2, 6HVECTOR)
      CALL MPUNCH(SSD, IPROB, 1HV, M, 2)
      DO 44  I = 1, M
      DO 44  J = 1, M
   44 TS(I,J) = SX(I) * SSD(I,J)
C     TS(I,J) NOW CONTAINS THE SCALED VECTORS TO SHOW THE RELATIVE
C     CONTRIBUTIONS OF THE VARIABLES TO A FUNCTION.
      PRINT 46
   46 FORMAT (15H1SCALED VECTORS)
      CALL MPRINT (TS, M, 2, 6HSCALED)
      CALL MPUNCH(TS, IPROB, 1HS, M, 1)
      IF (M - K) 47, 48, 48
   47 MD = M
      GO TO 49
   48 MD = K - 1
   49 IF (L) 50, 50, 500
   50 XLAMB = 1.0
      DO 51  I = 1, MD
   51 XLAMB = XLAMB * (1.0/(1.0 + SD(I)))
      PRINT 52, XLAMB
   52 FORMAT (25H1LAMBDA FOR TEST OF H2 = F14.7)
```

DISCRIM PROGRAM (CONTINUED)

```
      EM = M
      EK = K
      S=SQRTF((((EM**2)*((EK-1.0)**2)-4.0)/((EM**2)+((EK-1.0)**2)-5.0)))
      Y = XLAMB**(1.0/S)
      XM1 = (EN - 1.0) - ((EM + EK)/2.0)
      XL = - ((EM * (EK-1.0)) - 2.0)/4.0
      R1 = (EM * (EK-1.0))/2.0
      F1 = 2.0 * R1
      F2 = (XM1 * S) +(2.0*XL)
      F = ((1.0 - Y)/ Y) * (F2/F1)
      PRINT 53, F1
   53 FORMAT (6HOF1 = F14.7)
      PRINT 54, F2
   54 FORMAT (6HOF2 = F14.7)
      PRINT 55, F
   55 FORMAT (21HOFOR TEST OF H2, F = F14.7)
C
  500 PRINT 56
   56 FORMAT(43HOTHIS COMPLETES MAIN DISCRIMINANT ANALYSIS.)
      PRINT 57
   57 FORMAT(37HOREMEMBER TO USE RSPACE PROGRAM NEXT.)
  999 CALL EXIT
      END
```

CENTROIDS AND DISPERSIONS IN DISCRIMINANT OR FACTOR SPACE (RSPACE)

```
C      RSPACE.
C
C          THIS PROGRAM COMPUTES GROUP MEAN VECTORS (CENTROIDS) AND
C      DISPERSION MATRICES IN A REDUCED SPACE BASED UPON LINEAR COMBINA-
C      TIONS OF THE VARIABLES IN AN ORIGINAL TEST SPACE. OFTEN THE RE-
C      DUCED SPACE WILL BE A DISCRIMINANT FUNCTION OR FACTOR SPACE.
C      THE BASIS OF THE ORIGINAL SPACE OR THE REDUCED SPACE MAY NOT
C      EXCEED 50 VARIABLES. THERE IS NO LIMIT ON THE NUMBER OF GROUPS.
C      NOTE THAT CENTROIDS IN A FACTOR SPACE ARE BEST COMPUTED BY THE
C      FACTOR SCORE PROGRAM (CHAPTER 8).
C      SUBROUTINE MPUNCH IS REQUIRED.
C
C      INPUT.
C
C          INPUT CARD 1 CONTAINS
C      COL. 1-2   KG = NO. OF GROUPS
C      COL. 3-4   M = NO. OF TEST OR ORIGINAL VARIABLES
C      COL. 5-6   N = NO. OF DISCRIMINANT FUNCTIONS OR FACTORS (I. E.,
C      THE DIMENSIONALITY OF THE REDUCED SPACE)
C      FOLLOWING CARDS PRESENT
C      1) VECTORS OF DISCRIMINANT OR FACTOR WEIGHTS, AS COLUMNS
C      2) VECTORS OF GROUP MEANS
C      3) GROUP DISPERSION MATRICES
C      (THESE VALUES ARE PUNCHED TO FORMAT 5E14.7, AS PUNCHED BY CORREL
C      AND OTHER PROGRAMS IN THIS SYSTEM.)
C
C      OUTPUT.
C
C          PRINTED OUTPUT INCLUDES
C      1) PROGRAM TITLE, KG, M, N
C      2) VECTORS OF WEIGHTS
C      3) ORIGINAL MEAN VECTORS FOR GROUPS
C      4) CENTROIDS OF GROUPS IN REDUCED SPACE
C      5) DISPERSIONS OF GROUPS IN REDUCED SPACE
C      PRINTED OUTPUT IS APPROPRIATELY LABELED.
C      PUNCHED OUTPUT INCLUDES
C      1) CENTROIDS OF GROUPS IN REDUCED SPACE
C      2) DISPERSION MATRICES OF GROUPS IN REDUCED SPACE.
C      PUNCHED CENTROIDS (REDUCED SPACE) ARE PRECEDED BY A LABEL CARD.
C      PUNCHED DISPERSION MATRICES (REDUCED SPACE) HAVE THE LETTER D
C      PUNCHED IN COLUMN 5.
C
C
       DIMENSION XBAR(50,50),CENT(50,50),D(50,50),DD(50,50),V(50,50)
       PRINT 1
     1 FORMAT(43H0CENTROIDS AND DISPERSIONS IN REDUCED SPACE)
       READ INPUT TAPE 4, 2, KG, M, N
     2 FORMAT (3I2)
       PRINT 3, KG
     3 FORMAT (17H0NO. OF GROUPS = I2)
       PRINT 4, M
     4 FORMAT (25H0NO. OF TEST VARIABLES = I2)
       PRINT 5, N
     5 FORMAT (30H0NO. OF LINEAR COMBINATIONS = I2)
       DO 6 I = 1,M
     6 READ 70, (V(I,J), J = 1,N)
     7 FORMAT (5E14.7)
    70 FORMAT (10X 5E14.7)
       PRINT 8
```

```
    8 FORMAT (28H0VECTORS OF WEIGHTS, AS ROWS)
      DO 9   J = 1, N
    9 PRINT 10, (V(I,J), I = 1,M)
   10 FORMAT (8F15.7)
      DO 11  I = 1, KG
   11 READ INPUT TAPE 4, 7, (XBAR(I,J), J = 1,M)
      PRINT 12
   12 FORMAT (30H0MEANS OF GROUPS IN TEST SPACE)
      DO 13  I = 1, KG
   13 PRINT 10, (XBAR(I,J),   J = 1,M)
      DO 14  I = 1, KG
      DO 14  J = 1, N
      CENT(I,J) = 0.0
      DO 14  K = 1, M
   14 CENT(I,J) = CENT(I,J) + XBAR(I,K) * V(K,J)
      PRINT 15
   15 FORMAT(47H0CENTROIDS OF GROUPS IN REDUCED SPACE, ROW-WISE)
      DO 16  I = 1, KG
   16 PRINT 10, (CENT(I,J),   J = 1,N)
      PUNCH 15
      DO 17  I = 1, KG
   17 PUNCH 7, (CENT(I,J),   J = 1,N)
      DO 23 L = 1, KG
      PRINT 18,L
   18 FORMAT (39H0DISPERSION IN REDUCED SPACE FOR GROUP I2)
      DO 19  I = 1, M
   19 READ 70, (D(I,J), J = 1,M)
      DO 20  I = 1, N
      DO 20  J = 1,  M
      CENT (I,J) = 0.0
      DO 20  K = 1,  M
   20 CENT(I,J) = CENT(I,J) + V(K,I) * D(K,J)
      DO 21  I = 1, N
      DO 21  J = 1, N
      DD(I,J) = 0.0
      DO 21  K = 1, M
   21 DD(I,J) = DD(I,J) + CENT(I,K) * V(K,J)
      CALL MPUNCH (DD, L, 1HD, N, 2)
      DO 23  I = 1, N
   23 PRINT 10, (DD(I,J),   J = 1,N)
  200 CALL EXIT
      END
```

6.3 References

Mathematical Treatments of Discriminant Analysis
Anderson, T. W. (1958). *An Introduction to Multivariate Statistical Analysis*. John Wiley and Sons, Chapter 6.
Bryan, J. G. (1951). "The Generalized Discriminant Function: Mathematical Foundation and Computational Routine." *Harvard Educational Review* 21: 2, 90–95.
Rao, C. R. (1952). *Advanced Statistical Methods in Biometric Research*. John Wiley and Sons, Chapter 8.

Historical Development
Kendall, M. G. (1957). *A Course in Multivariate Analysis*. London: Charles Griffin and Co., pp. 105–116.

Comparisons of Discriminant and Regression Analysis
Rulon, P. J. (1951). "The Stanine and Separile: A Fable." *Personnel Psychology* 4: 99–114.
——— (1951). "Distinctions Between Discriminant and Regression Analysis and a Geometric Interpretation of the Discriminant Function." *Harvard Educational Review.* 21: 80–90.

Applications of Discriminant Analysis
Cooley, W. W. (1958). Career Development of Scientists: An Overlapping Longitudinal Study, Cambridge, Mass. (mimeographed).
Tatsuoka, Maurice M., and Tiedeman, David V. (1954). "Discriminant Analysis." *Review of Educational Research*, Washington, D.C.: American Educational Research Association.
Tiedeman, David V., and Bryan, Joseph G. (1954). "Prediction of College Field of Concentration." *Harvard Educational Review* 24: 122–139.
Tiedeman, David V., Bryan, Joseph G., and Rulon, Phillip J. (1951). *The Utility of the Airman Classification Battery for Assignment of Airmen to Eight Air Force Specialties*. Cambridge, Mass.: Educational Research Corporation, p. 328.

CHAPTER SEVEN

Classification procedures

7.1 Mathematics of Centour Scores and Probability of Group Membership

In the three previous chapters our primary concern has been with testing null hypotheses and exploring group differences, in terms of group mean vectors, group dispersions, adjusted group means, or configuration of group centroids in the discriminant space. In such cases the null hypothesis is either provisionally accepted or rejected, and if rejected the alternatives are not clearly defined. This chapter is concerned with a different type of problem. Here we have a set of hypotheses regarding the group membership of an individual, one of which is to be accepted and the others rejected. The general form for the likelihood of such an hypothesis might be written

$$P(H_j \mid \mathbf{X}_i), \quad i = 1, 2, \ldots, N \text{ and } j = 1, 2, \ldots, g,$$

which reads: The probability of hypothesis j, given the score vector of individual i. Hypothesis j states that individual i is a member of group j. There would be g such hypotheses for each individual, and the hypothesis which is most probable is selected. This is the maximum likelihood method of classification.[1]

More specifically, this chapter is concerned with the general problem of discrimination, with emphasis on the problem of comparing the profile of an individual with that of a group. The problem is fundamental in taxonomy, career guidance, and the selection and assignment of manpower. The approach to the profile problem described here is also potentially useful to the psychologist who finds the idiographic approach necessary but who sees that only nomothetic procedures are sufficiently rigorous for statistical treatment. For some time psychologists have emphasized the importance of considering the individual's entire profile, rather than focusing on a particular variable, but few reliable procedures have been available for this task.

Renewed efforts on the profile comparison problem began with the work of DuMas (1949) and Cattell (1949), who developed coefficients of profile similarity; Cronbach and Gleser (1953) focused on general distance measures. All these

---

[1] A more rigorous treatment of the following discussion can be found in Rao (1952), Chapter 8.

efforts were primarily concerned with comparing one individual's profile with another's.

A thorough consideration of the problem of inferring an individual's group membership from multivariate data can be found in the extensive work of Rulon et al. (1954). They demonstrated the shortcomings of earlier approaches and proposed the centour score for assessing "the degree to which an individual resembles each of several groups in terms of certain antecedent variables that are known or believed to be important in distinguishing among these several groups."[2]

To introduce the centour concept, consider a hypothetical bivariate distribution of test scores for a sample of N graduate students in history. Let X_{1i} and X_{2i} represent the verbal and quantitative scores on the Graduate Record Exam (GRE) for individual i. One way to describe such a bivariate distribution is in terms of ellipses, each of which is the locus of points of a specified frequency.[3] In a multivariate normal distribution, the size of the ellipse is determined by the value of the quadratic

$$(7.1) \qquad\qquad \chi^2 = \mathbf{x}_i' \mathbf{D}^{-1} \mathbf{x}_i,$$

where $\mathbf{D}^{-1}$ is the inverse of the dispersion (variance-covariance) matrix and $\mathbf{x}_i$ is an m-element vector of deviation scores;

$$\mathbf{x}_i' = [X_{1i} - \bar{X}_1. \quad X_{2i} - \bar{X}_2. \quad \cdots \quad X_{mi} - \bar{X}_m.].$$

The larger the values of χ^2 the lesser the density at that point $[X_{1i} \quad X_{2i} \quad \cdots \quad X_{mi}]$.

Each student is represented as a point in the test space, and each point can be located on a particular ellipse by substituting the student's test scores in equation 7.1. Unless the means and dispersion matrix for the population of graduate students of history is known, the sample estimates are used. This example assumes that we have a random sample from that population.

If points are selected at random from the bivariate normal distribution, the resulting values for χ^2, using equation 7.1, would be distributed as χ^2. The χ^2 tables are entered with two degrees of freedom, the degrees of freedom associated with the choice of any point in a two-dimensional test space. Since the tabled probability of a given χ^2 is the likelihood of obtaining a larger value, the probability is also the proportion of sample points that would be expected to lie beyond the ellipse on which $[X_{1i} \quad X_{2i}]$ lies.

For example, the ellipses in Figure 7.1 represent the locus of points for three different densities in the bivariate swarm of history students. Here the ellipse A defines the points beyond which 90 per cent of graduate students in history are expected to lie. The value of χ^2 for ellipse A is 0.21. The ellipse C defines the points beyond which 10 per cent of the population is expected to lie ($\chi^2 = 4.60$). Here S is the location of a history student whose scores are X_{1s} and X_{2s}. When these values are substituted into equation 7.1, the resulting χ^2 is 2.41. Entering the χ^2 table

---

[2] See Tatsuoka (1957), p. 3.

[3] Or, more generally, a specified density.

with two degrees of freedom we find that the probability of lying further from the centroid than S is .30 (i.e., the probability of obtaining $\chi^2 > 2.41$ is .30).

The ellipse, when used in this way, is called a centour, because it can be thought of as a *cent*ile cont*our*. It is a good index of the extent to which an individual resembles a particular group, where the group means and dispersion are known. If they were actually known for the hypothetical example we have given, it would be possible to tell a college senior the extent to which his GRE scores resemble those of other students before him who have entered graduate work in history. If the groups on which means and dispersions are based consist of students who successfully complete their advanced degree program, a centour based on that data would be even more useful.

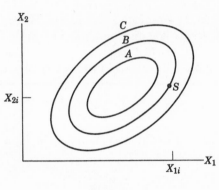

Figure 7.1

The centour method has been generalized for any number of variables. In the three-dimensional test space, the ellipses (centours) become ellipsoids, and in the m-dimensional space, where $m > 3$, hyperellipsoids. Equation 7.1 is completely general as it stands, **x** being an m-element vector of deviation scores and **D** the variance-covariance matrix of order m. The centour still defines the proportion of sample points that is expected to lie outside the region enclosed by the corresponding hyperellipsoid.

To gain consistency with the centile concept, the probability of obtaining a larger value of χ^2 is multiplied by 100. The higher the centour of an individual, the greater is his similarity to that group, i.e., the smaller the sum of squared distances from his point to all other points in the group.

The problem of considering more than one group can be most easily seen for the two-group, bivariate case. Let us add graduate students in physics to the GRE test space defined above. The 90 and 10 centours for the two groups might appear as in Figure 7.2. Two classification χ^2's could be computed for student S, one based on the means and dispersion for history students (χ_1^2), and the other based on the means and dispersion for physics students (χ_2^2). If S is the same student represented in Figure 7.1, his centour for history students is 30. Then substituting S's scores into equation 7.1 and using the means and dispersion matrix for physics students, χ_2^2 is 6.9. Again entering the χ^2 table with two degrees of freedom (since $m = 2$), we find that S lies beyond the ellipse within which 99 per cent of the physics students lie. That is, S's physics centour is less than one. The fact that S resembles successful history students more than successful physics students might be useful to S as he makes decisions regarding graduate study.

If we were interested in classifying students into one of two groups, using only GRE scores, one decision rule might be to assign each student to that group for

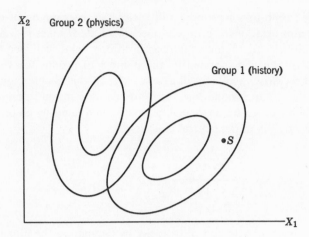

Figure 7.2

which his centour is highest or, in other words, for whichever χ^2 is smallest.[4] Symbolically, such a rule can be expressed as follows:

Decision Rule I: $R_1 \cap \chi_1^{\,2} \leq \chi_2^{\,2}$
$\qquad\qquad\qquad R_2 \cap \chi_2^{\,2} \leq \chi_1^{\,2}.$

The rule is read: The region of the test space for group 1 (R_1) is defined as ($\cap$) the space for which the group 1 χ_2 is smaller than the group 2 χ^2. The region for group 2 is defined as the space for which the group 2 χ^2 is smaller than the group 1 χ^2. For g groups Rule I becomes

$$R_j \cap \chi_j^{\,2} \leq \chi_k^{\,2}, \qquad j, k = 1, 2, \ldots, g;\ j \neq k.$$

If the two dispersion matrices are equal ($\mathbf{D}_1 = \mathbf{D}_2$) and if the sizes of the two groups are equal, Decision Rule I will result in the minimum number of misclassifications. A more general rule can be written, however:

Decision Rule II: $R_j \cap \chi_j^{\,2} \leq \chi_k^{\,2} - \log \dfrac{|\mathbf{D}_j|}{|\mathbf{D}_k|} + 2 \log \dfrac{p_j}{p_k}$

where p_j is the *a priori* probability of membership in group j.

By comparing Decision Rules I and II, the following generalizations can be made. If $\mathbf{D}_1 = \mathbf{D}_2$ and $p_1 = p_2$, both rules will result in the same proportion of misclassifications. But if $p_1 > p_2$ (i.e., if membership in group 1 occurs more frequently than membership in group 2, Rule I will tend to overassign students to group 2. Rule I assumes that membership in group 2 occurs as frequently as membership in group 1. If $|\mathbf{D}_1| > |\mathbf{D}_2|$, group 1 will tend to be overassigned

---

[4] In this two-group hypothetical example it must be assumed that the individual to be classified is drawn from a mixed population containing only two groups, history and physics students. The examples of Section 7.2 illustrate how this assumption is dealt with in practice.

because a given centour for group 1 will enclose a larger region of the test space than will the same centour for group 2. Decision Rule II takes into account these possible inequalities and minimizes misclassification even if such inequalities occur. Both decision rules can be applied to any number of groups for any number of dimensions. Of course, here as well as elsewhere in this chapter, the assumption is made that the group samples are from multivariate normal populations.

The probability of group membership can be computed by employing Bayes's theorem, which results in the general equation[5]

$$(7.2) \qquad P_{ij}(H_j \mid X_i) = \frac{\dfrac{p_j}{|D_j|^{1/2}} e^{-\frac{x_j^2}{2}}}{\sum_k \dfrac{p_k}{|D_k|^{1/2}} e^{-\frac{x_k^2}{2}}}, \qquad \begin{aligned} &k = 1, 2, \ldots, j, \ldots, g \\ &i = 1, 2, \ldots, N, \end{aligned}$$

Equation 7.2 can be understood most easily by comparing the numerator on the right with the equation for the density or height (y) of the normal curve:

$$y = \frac{N}{\sigma\sqrt{2\pi}} e^{-\frac{x_i^2}{2\sigma^2}}$$

For the one variable case, the exponent of e in equation 7.2 is equal to the exponent in the normal curve equation. Reference to equation 7.1 should help the reader see this equivalence if it is not immediately obvious. In addition, the coefficients of e in both equations involve the ratio of group size to group dispersion. Just as the normal curve equation gives the density at a particular point along a single dimension, the equation for the multivariate normal distribution gives the density in an m-dimensional test space. Equation 7.2 is therefore a ratio between the density of group j and the combined density of all groups at a certain point in the test space.

This probability function utilizes the information regarding both differences in frequency of occurrence of membership in the g groups and differences in group dispersions. Going back to Figure 7.2, we might find that P_{s1}, i.e., the probability that student S will be a member of group 1, is .86, whereas P_{s2} is .14. This would indicate that S is most likely a member of group 1 (history). A new rule for deciding group membership is now possible.

Decision Rule III: $R_j \cap P_{ij} \geq P_{ik}, \qquad j, k = 1, 2, \ldots, g; \; j \neq k.$

Thus, an individual is assigned to that group for which his probability of group membership is highest.

This procedure requires computing g probabilities for each student. Although these probabilities can be extremely useful in research, workers in psychology and education are generally not familiar with this development. The computation of the many probabilities becomes feasible through use of the high-speed computer

---

[5] The values for p_j used in this expression can represent either *a priori* or posterior probabilities. They reflect the relative frequency with which group membership occurs in the mixed population. See, for example, Tatsuoka (1957).

and multiple-group-discriminant analysis. The role of discriminant analysis needs to be clarified, however.

An individual who lies in region R_j in the test space will also lie in R_j in the discriminant space, if group dispersion matrices are equal.[6] Therefore, under these conditions, the parameters estimated in equation 7.2 may describe the discriminant space rather than the test space, thus saving an enormous amount of computing time when the number of discriminant functions is substantially smaller than the number of tests, and the number of individuals to be classified is large (as is generally the case).

Experience seems to indicate that moderate departure from homogeneity of dispersion does not produce differences between test space and discriminant space results.[7] For this reason, and because it saves computation time, the classification program CLASSIF (pp. 148–149) is designed to read in the output of the discriminant-analysis programs of Chapter 6. This prior step reduces the dimensionality from the test space to the discriminant space. It also tests the significance of the group centroid differences, which is certainly a necessary preliminary to the computation of probabilities of group membership. Other methods of reducing the dimensionality prior to the application of equation 7.2 have been shown to yield unsatisfactory results [Rulon et al. (1954), Chapters 7–10].

Both classification χ^2's and probability of group membership are computed and reported in the CLASSIF program. Either Decision Rule I or III may be applied to the results. It should be noted that Rule II produces the same results as Rule III. Thus the comparisons of I and II we have given also apply to comparisons of I and III. Although Rules II and III minimize the frequency of misclassification,[8] certain applications may make Rule I more desirable. One difficulty with Rule III is that under certain conditions the region R_j will not exist for group j. That is, there may not exist sample points for which $P_{ij} > P_{ik}$ holds ($k = 1, 2, \ldots, g$; $k \neq j$). This occurs when p_j is small with respect to the relative frequency of membership in the other groups. There are ways of dealing with this problem, but they depend on the particular situation in which the classification procedures are to be applied. The examples of Section 7.2 illustrate these practical problems and possible solutions.

Another application of the centour score is in describing the extent of overlap among groups.[9] This is done by computing the centours for each of the group centroids in each of the group dispersions. For Figure 7.2, the group 2 centour for the group 1 centroid might be 95. This means that 95 per cent of group 2 is expected to lie outside the group 2 ellipse on which the group 1 centroid lies. The group 1 centour on which the group 2 centroid lies would also be 95 only if the dispersions for the two groups were equal.

[6] Lohnes (1961) has conducted a Monte Carlo study of this question and has also compared results using empirical data.

[7] See, for example, Rulon et al. (1954).

[8] Rao (1952), pp. 308–309 has proven that the number of correct classifications is maximal using these procedures, assuming multivariate normal distributions.

[9] Cooley (1958).

This procedure is especially useful where several groups are involved. Cooley's (1958) example consisted of nine groups; the matrix of centours of centroids is listed in Table 7.1. The centour C_{jk} is for the group j centroid in the group k dispersion. Here $C_{12} = 17$ indicates that an individual having the group 1 mean scores on the m variables would be "closer" to the center of the group 2 swarm

TABLE 7.1

Centours of the Centroids

Centroid	Group Dispersion								
	1	2	3	4	5	6	7	8	9
1	100	17	61	28	7	80	16	78	73
2	42	100	99	90	80	96	99	92	98
3	51	97	100	94	64	98	96	94	99
4	31	85	96	100	41	83	96	68	90
5	12	73	80	42	100	83	92	73	61
6	71	90	98	68	64	100	80	99	99
7	27	99	98	92	83	92	100	83	98
8	73	89	96	66	61	99$^+$	78	100	99
9	73	92	99	83	57	99	85	99	100

than would 17 per cent of the members of group 2. High values on the off-diagonals of the centour matrix indicate a high degree of overlap between the corresponding groups. Lack of perfect symmetry in the matrix is due to differences in dispersion for group pairs.

These centours of the group centroids can be easily computed by including the group mean vectors with the individual score vectors when the classification program is used. The χ^2's are then converted to centours by the procedures we have outlined. A similar table of probabilities may also be of interest and would be computed directly by the CLASSIF program.

One final point must be made concerning the difference between the classification procedures outlined in this chapter, including discriminant analysis, and classification based on regression analysis, outlined in Chapter 3. Rulon (1951a, 1951b) has described these differences in two very comprehensible articles, which the reader is encouraged to consult. The basic difference is that discriminant analysis, and the resulting centours and probabilities of group membership, are designed to answer the question, "What group am I most like?" Multiple-regression analysis, on the other hand, is concerned with the question, "In what group would I perform the best?"

One difficulty of regression analysis is that it almost always assumes that the individual in question is a member of the group. This is because the regression equations are based on individuals who have already entered a particular group. There are many selection factors operating before the individual becomes a member of the group. For example, chemistry majors might all tend to be high on mathematics aptitude. Thus, regression equations that attempt to predict performance as a chemistry major would not reflect the importance of mathematics aptitude, and misclassifications could result. In addition, classifications based on regression information would tend to overassign people to the less difficult tasks. As Kelley (1940) has pointed out, it seems unreasonable to have superior individuals spend their energies on inferior tasks. Regression prediction, when used alone, would tend to encourage that.

Rulon et al. (1954) and Tatsuoka (1957) have argued that the probability of group membership should be computed prior to the probability of success in a group. If it would first be established that individual i looks like members of group j, the latter difficulties mentioned would less likely occur. Tatsuoka (1957) has gone one step further and has shown how the probabilities for both membership and success in a group can be combined into a single probability statement. Unfortunately, however, this potentially useful technique has apparently not yet been applied in any investigation since Tatsuoka's original work.

7.2 Examples of Classification Procedures

In Section 6.2 multiple-discriminant analysis was illustrated with data from the Scientific Careers Study. The results from that example can be used to illustrate the computation of classification χ^2's and the probability of group membership.

Two different samples of students are involved here. In 1958, majors in science and engineering were randomly selected from the sophomore and senior classes of six eastern Massachusetts colleges. The discriminant analysis in Chapter 6 was based on the senior class sample. Three criterion groups were used: Research, applied science, and nonscience. Group membership of the senior sample was based on stated career plans 2 years after graduation from college.

Most of the sophomore sample graduated in June 1961, and their post college plans have also been determined through mailed questionnaires. Using these data we may determine the extent to which the regions of the test space occupied by the three senior groups are the same regions tending to be occupied by three similar sophomore groups.

The discriminant analysis of Section 6.2 yielded two discriminant functions. These are used to reduce the individual score vectors, the group mean vectors, and group dispersions from the six-dimensional test space to a two-dimensional discriminant space. The means and dispersions are reduced with the procedures and program described in Chapter 6. The individual discriminant scores are the vector products of discriminant vectors and test score vectors, as outlined in Section 6.1.

Using Decision Rule I we may divide the two-dimensional discriminant space into three mutually exclusive regions. The parameters Δ_j and μ_j for defining the bivariate normal distribution of group j are estimated using the dispersion matrix and means of the senior groups. These are reported for the test space in Tables 6.1 and 6.6. The group centroids and dispersions in the discriminant space are

TABLE 7.2

Group Centroids

Group	Function I	Function II
Research	.10	−.02
Applied science	−.03	.05
Nonscience	−.06	−.05

TABLE 7.3

Group Dispersions in Discriminant Space

$$\text{Research Group} = \begin{bmatrix} .00475 & -.00107 \\ -.00107 & .01329 \end{bmatrix}$$

$$\text{Applied science Group} = \begin{bmatrix} .01529 & .00216 \\ .00216 & .00814 \end{bmatrix}$$

$$\text{Nonscience Group} = \begin{bmatrix} .01301 & -.00047 \\ -.00047 & .01025 \end{bmatrix}$$

TABLE 7.4

Classification of Seniors, Rule I

		Group Entered				
		1	2	3		
Group Predicted	1	21	3	3	27	$\chi^2 = 39.09$
	2	7	14	11	32	$p < .001$
	3	5	8	24	37	
		33	25	38	96	

reported in Tables 7.2 and 7.3. The three classification χ^2's are then computed for each student according to equation 7.1 using the reported estimates $\mathbf{D}_g$ and $\bar{\mathbf{X}}_g$ in the discriminant spaces.

If a student's lowest χ^2 is for Group 1 (research), and if his post college career plans involve research in one of the natural sciences, this is a correct classification ("a hit"). Table 7.4 describes the hits and misses for the senior group, and Table 7.5 summarizes the sophomore classifications. The diagonal cell entries (from upper left to lower right) are the correct classifications; there is a greater proportion of hits for the senior group (62 per cent) than for the sophomore group (49 per cent). This is to be expected, since the discriminant space was divided into three regions which made the number of misclassifications for the seniors a minimum.

TABLE 7.5

Classification of Sophomores, Rule I

		Group Entered				
		1	2	3		
Group	1	11	3	9	23	$\chi^2 = 13.86$
Predicted	2	14	23	15	52	$p < .01$
	3	5	11	19	35	
		30	37	43	110	

TABLE 7.6

Classification of Seniors, Rule III

		Group Entered				
		1	2	3		
Group	1	25	6	6	37	$\chi^2 = 36.34$
Predicted	2	3	10	7	20	$p < .001$
	3	5	9	25	39	
		33	25	38	96	

TABLE 7.7

Classification of Sophomores, Rule III

		Group Entered				
		1	2	3		
Group	1	17	10	11	38	$\chi^2 = 22.84$
Predicted	2	4	16	5	25	$p < .001$
	3	9	11	27	47	
		30	37	43	110	

The sophomore hits represent actual predictions, whereas the senior "hits" only indicate the degree of minimum overlap among the three groups.

The results of using Decision Rule III are presented in Tables 7.6 and 7.7. There were 63 per cent "hits" for the senior sample and 54 per cent hits for the sophomores. Notice that Rule III tended to underassign to group 2, whereas Rule I tended to overassign to it. There are several reasons for this. Rule III assumes that the sophomores will select groups with the same relative frequency as did the seniors. Groups with low *a priori* probabilities tend to be underassigned by Rule

III. Rule I will overassign small groups because the relative frequency with which group membership occurs is not taken into account.

It is important to point out that the individual to be classified must be from the same mixed population as that from which the standard groups were drawn. In this example, the test space classificatory regions were defined in terms of three groups from the mixed population of senior males majoring in science and engineering in eastern Massachusetts colleges. If the groups to be distinguished among are known in advance, stratified random sampling of the mixed population is the appropriate procedure. However, in this case the groups of interest were defined in terms of postcollege decisions, and the individuals had to be selected and tested during their senior year. In such situations a straight random sampling is appropriate. The three groups used in this example exhausted the possible postcollege decisions for the population concerned. New individuals can be classified if they meet the criteria used in selecting the standard sample.

Institutions frequently face the task of selecting individuals to fill a particular quota (for example, armed services assignment, employee selection, college admissions). This is the task of selecting a quota of N_j for membership in group j from a pool of N applicants. If group homogeneity on m attributes is a primary consideration, then N classification χ^2's are computed, based on the group j dispersion of the "satisfied and satisfactory" members already in group j. After sequencing the χ^2's from low to high, the lowest N_j are selected. If g groups are involved, Rulon et al. (1954) have recommended that assignment begin with the group requiring the smallest quota. For the jth group assignment begins with the smallest χ_j^2 from among the individuals not yet assigned.

Another possible approach is to compute probabilities using the group quotas as the relative frequency of group membership. Assignment then begins with the group having the smallest quota, assigning those with the highest probabilities for that group. Figure 7.3 illustrates the advantage this has over the χ^2 quota method. Individual S resembles Group A more than any other group, yet he

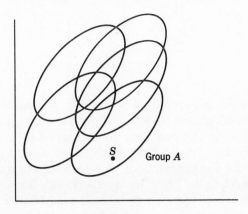

Figure 7.3

might not be assigned to A by the χ^2 approach. He *would* be assigned to A by the probability approach.

Table 7.8 illustrates a probability assignment procedure. The thirty sophomores

TABLE 7.8

Selection of Sophomores

		Group Entered				
		1	2	3		
Group "Assigned"	1	13	7	10	30	$\chi^2 = 11.93$
	2	7	19	11	37	$p < .02$
	3	10	11	22	43	
		30	37	43	110	

with the highest group 1 probabilities were assigned to group 1. From the remaining sophomores, thirty-seven were selected with the highest group 2 probabilities, and the rest were assigned to group 3. The "hits" in this case were no more numerous than those resulting from the use of Decision Rule I (both being 49 per cent). The procedure outlined here nevertheless seems the most efficient procedure when selecting a fixed quota for each group is the problem.

Flow Diagram for Classification χ^2's and Probabilities (CLASSIF Program)

INPUT
Read KG, M, N, GN_k, V_{xv}, $CENT_{xk}$ where KG is the number of groups, M is the number of original test variables, N is the number of functions in the reduced space, GN contains the numbers of subjects in each of the standardization groups, V is the matrix of discriminant vectors or factor loadings (row-wise), and CENT is the matrix of group centroids in the reduced space. (This program may be used in the test space by supplying a V matrix with 1's on the diagonal and 0's for all off-diagonal elements, i.e., an identity matrix). Throughout the diagram subscript ranges are: $k = 1, 2, 3, \ldots, KG$; $v = 1, 2, 3, \ldots, M$; $x = 1, 2, 3, \ldots, N$; $y = 1, 2, 3, \ldots, N$.
Set K = KG.

---

①

INPUT
Read DG_{xy} where DG is a group dispersion matrix in the reduced space.

SUBROUTINE
Call subroutine MATINV to compute the inverse of DG and place it in DG and to compute the determinant of DG and place it in DETERM.

$D_{xyK} = DG_{xy}$
$RATIO_K = GN_K / \sqrt{DETERM}$
$K = K - 1$

$=$ ⟨ Is K $\geq$ 0? ⟩ $>$ ⟶ ①

Set N1 = 1, N2 = 2, N3 = 3.

---

②

7.1 Flow Diagram for (CLASSIF Program) (Continued)

INPUT

Read XID, X_v where XID is a subject's ID number and X is that subject's score vector.

$DISC_x = 0$

$DISC_x = DISC_x + X_v \cdot V_{xv}$ forming a discriminant or factor score.

$DIF_x = DISC_x - CENT_{xk}$

$CHI_x = 0$

$CHI_x = CHI_x + DIF_y \cdot D_{yxk}$ (inside loops over x and y)   (outside loop over k)

$CHISQ_k = 0$

$CHISQ_k = CHISQ_k + DIF_x \cdot CHI_x$ forming the k group χ^2

$P2 = 0$

$P1_k = RATIO_k \cdot$ exponential function of $(-CHISQ_k/2)$

$P2 = P2 + P1_k$

$PROB = P1_k/P2$ forming the k group probability.

OUTPUT

Punch N1, XID, $DISC_x$ on a card, or set of cards.

Punch N2, XID, $CHISQ_k$ on a card, or set of cards.

Punch N3, XID, $PROB_k$ on a card, or set of cards.

(Program stops when there are no more subjects' score vectors in the input hopper or on the input tape.)

147

PROGRAM FOR CLASSIFICATION χ^2'S AND PROBABILITIES (CLASSIF)

```
C     CLASSIF.
C
C          THIS PROGRAM COMPUTES DISCRIMINANT SCORES, CLASSIFICATION
C     CHI SQUARES, AND PROBABILITY OF GROUP MEMBERSHIP, FOR UP TO 20
C     GROUPS, 20 FUNCTIONS, AND 50 VARIABLES. SUBROUTINES MATINV AND
C     SPUNCH ARE REQUIRED.
C
C     INPUT.
C          CARD ONE CONTAINS
C     COLS. 1-2  KG = NUMBER OF GROUPS
C     COLS. 3-4  M = NUMBER OF VARIABLES
C     COLS. 5-6  N = NUMBER OF FUNCTIONS.
C          CARD TWO CONTAINS THE NUMBER OF CASES PER GROUP REPRESENTING
C     THE A PRIORI PROBABILITIES.  THESE GROUP SIZES ARE IN FOUR
C     COLUMN FIELDS BEGINNING IN COLUMN 1.
C          THEN FOLLOW DISCRIMINANT VECTORS (AS COLUMNS), CENTROIDS, AND
C     GROUP DISPERSIONS IN DISCRIMINANT SPACE.  FORMAT FOR THESE CARDS
C     IS THAT OF DISCRIM AND RSPACE OUTPUT.
C          NEXT TWO(2) CARDS ARE SCORE CARD FORMAT.  STUDENT ID IS THE
C     FIRST VARIABLE IN THE CARD, AND IS READ IN F NOTATION ( 7-DIGIT
C     MAXIMUM).  THE TWO FORMAT CARDS ARE FOLLOWED BY THE SCORE CARDS.
C
C     OUTPUT.
C          ONLY PUNCHED OUTPUT IS PRODUCED.  THE TYPE OF OUTPUT IN A
C     CARD IS CODED IN COLUMN 1 AS FOLLOWS.
C               1 = DISCRIMINANT SCORES
C               2 = CLASSIFICATION CHI SQUARES
C               3 = PROBABILITIES OF GROUP MEMBERSHIP
C     IF MORE THAN ONE CARD PER OUTPUT TYPE PER PERSON IS REQUIRED,
C     CARDS ARE NUMBERED IN COLUMN 10.  STUDENT ID IS PUNCHED IN
C     COLUMNS 2-8.  COLUMN 9 CONTAINS A DECIMAL POINT.
      DIMENSION V(50,20), CENT(20,20), DG(50,50), D(20,20,20),
     1 RATIO(20), GN(20), X(50), DISC(20), DIF(20), CHI(20),
     2 CHISQ(20), P1(20), PROB(20), FMT(24) ,B(50)
 1000 FORMAT (3I2)
 1001 FORMAT (20F4.0)
 1002 FORMAT (5E14.7)
 1003 FORMAT (12A6)
 1004 FORMAT(10X5E14.7)
      READ 1000, KG, M, N
      READ 1001, (GN(K), K = 1, KG)
      DO 12 I = 1,M
   12 READ 1004, (V(I,J), J = 1,N)
      DO 14 K = 1,KG
   14 READ 1002, (CENT(I,K), I = 1,N)
      DO 20 K=1, KG
      DO 16 I = 1,N
   16 READ 1004, (DG(I,J), J=1,N )
      CALL MATINV(DG, N, B, 0, DETERM)
      DO 18 I=1,N
      DO 18 J=1,N
   18 D(I,J,K) = DG(I,J)
   20 RATIO (K) = GN(K) / SQRTF(DETERM)
      READ 1003, (FMT(I), I=1,24)
   22 READ FMT, XID, (X(I), I=1,M)
      DO 24 J=1,N
      DISC(J) = 0.0
      DO 24 I=1,M
   24 DISC(J) = DISC(J) +  (X(I)*V(I,J))
```

```
        CALL SPUNCH (DISC, N, XID, 1)
        DO 31  K = 1,KG
        DO 28  I = 1, N
  28 DIF(I) = DISC(I)-CENT(I,K)
        DO 30 J = 1,N
        CHI(J) = 0.0
        DO 30 I = 1,N
  30 CHI(J) = CHI(J)+(DIF(I)*D(I,J,K))
        CHISQ(K) = 0.0
        DO 31 I = 1,N
  31 CHISQ(K) = CHISQ(K)+(DIF(I)*CHI(I))
        CALL SPUNCH (CHISQ, KG, XID, 2)
  33 P2 = 0.0
        DO 34 K = 1,KG
        P1(K) = RATIO (K) * EXPF(-CHISQ(K)/2.0)
  34 P2 = P2 + P1(K)
        DO 36 K = 1,KG
  36 PROB(K) = P1(K)/P2
        CALL SPUNCH (PROB, KG, XID, 3)
  40 GO TO 22
        END




C     SUBROUTINE SPUNCH
C         THIS SUBROUTINE IS USED FOR PUNCHING OUT SCORE VECTORS,
C     TOGETHER WITH INDIVIDUAL IDENTIFICATION CODE.
C     DEFINITIONS OF SUBROUTINE ARGUMENTS.
C         X = VECTOR TO BE PUNCHED
C         M = NUMBER OF ELEMENTS IN VECTOR
C         XID = INDIVIDUAL IDENTIFICATION NUMBER (7-DIGIT MAXIMUM)
C         N = ONE INTEGER INDICATING VECTOR TYPE

C     OUTPUT.
C         COL. 1 = N
C         COL. 2-9 = XID IN F8.0
C         COL. 10 = SECTION NUMBER OF CARD (7 ELEMENTS/CARD)
C         COL. 11-80 = DISCRIMINANT SCORES, CLASSIFICATION CHI SQUARES,
C     GROUP MEMBERSHIP PROBABILITIES, FACTOR SCORES, ETC. IN 7F10.4

      SUBROUTINE SPUNCH (X, M, XID, N)
      DIMENSION X(20)
      J1 = 0
      J2 = 0
      JSEC = 0
  11 J1 = J2 + 1
      J2 = J1 + 6
      IF (J2 - M) 16, 14, 14
  14 J2 = M
  16 JSEC = JSEC + 1
      PUNCH 18, N, XID, JSEC, (X(J), J = J1, J2)
  18 FORMAT (I1, F8.0, I1, 7F10.4)
      IF (J2 - M) 11, 20, 20
  20 RETURN
      END
```

7.3 References

Cooley, W. W. (1958). The Application of a Developmental Rationale and Methods of Multi-variate Analysis to the Study of Potential Scientists. Unpublished dissertation, Graduate School of Education, Harvard University.

Cattell, R. B. (1949). "r_b and Other Coefficients of Pattern Similarity," *Psychometrika* **14**: 279–298.

Cronbach, L. J., and Gleser, G. C. (1953). "Assessing Profile Similarity." *Psychological Bulletin* **50**: 456–473.

DuMas, F. M. (1949). "The Coefficient of Profile Similarity." *Journal of Clinical Psychology* **5**: 123–131.

Kelley, T. L. (1940). *Talents and Tasks: Their Conjunction in a Democracy for Wholesome Living and National Defense.* Cambridge, Mass.: Harvard Education Papers, No. 1.

Lohnes, P. R. (1961). "Test Space and Discriminant Space Classification Models and Related Significance Tests." *Educational and Psychological Measurement* **21**: 559–574.

Rao, C. R. (1952). *Advanced Statistical Methods In Biometric Research.* New York: John Wiley and Sons, Chapter 8.

Rulon, P. J. (1951a). "The Stanine and the Separile: A Fable." *Personnel Psychology* **4**: 99–114.

——— (1951b). "Distinctions Between Discriminant and Regression Analysis and a Geometric Interpretation of the Discriminant Function." *Harvard Educational Review* **21**: 80–90.

———, Tiedeman, D. V., Langmuir, C. R., and Tatsuoka, M. M. (1954). *The Profile Problems: A Methodological Study of the Interpretation of Multiple Test Scores.* Cambridge, Mass.: Educational Research Corporation.

Tatsuoka, M. M. (1957). Joint-Probability of Membership and Success In a Group: An Index Which Combines Analysis as Applied to the Guidance Problem. Harvard Studies in Career Development, Report 6. Cambridge, Mass.: Harvard Graduate School of Education (mimeographed).

Tiedeman, D. V. (1954). "A Model for the Profile Problem," *Proceedings*, 1953 *Invitational Conference on Testing Problems.* Princeton, New Jersey: Educational Testing Service.

CHAPTER EIGHT

Factor analysis

8.1 Introduction to Factor Analysis

Factor analysis has become the generic term for a variety of procedures developed for the purpose of analyzing the intercorrelations within a set of variables. The variables may be test scores, test items, questionnaire responses, etc. Some procedures of factor analysis have been developed to explore a specific hypothesis regarding the basic structure of mental abilities. On the other hand, principal-components analysis is a generally useful procedure whenever the task is to determine the minimum number of independent dimensions needed to account for most of the variance in the original set of variables.

The historical development of this field illustrates the frequent controversies that occur as a new science or scientific technique emerges. Each pioneer seemed to feel his procedure was *the* method of factor analysis. Only recently have students of factor analysis begun to see that the different procedures are suitable for different purposes and usually involve different assumptions regarding the nature of human attributes. Harman (1960), Chapter 6, has done a comprehensive and thorough job of comparing in detail the factor solutions that have received the most attention. A brief general discussion of several aspects of factor analysis is presented here, followed by computational procedures.

One situation in which factor analytic techniques could be applied would be that of scaling a set of responses that sample a particular psychological or socio-logical domain. For instance, the investigator might have several responses to questionnaire items concerned with socio-economic status (SES). What this set of items measures in common defines the basic dimension for SES.

Figure 8.1 may clarify this point. Here X and Y represent two variables such as family income and prestige rating of father's occupation. In this test space model, individuals (or families) are plotted according to their reported values for X and Y (or some transformation of the reported values). The ellipse suggests the general outline of the bivariate swarm resulting from the plot of N individuals.[1]

---

[1] See Section 7.1 for more exact interpretations of the meaning of such an ellipse.

The X and Y exhibit a high positive correlation in this case. The task is to produce a composite score measuring what these variables have in common and producing a maximum variance among individuals. This is accomplished by projecting all points perpendicularly onto the principal axis of the ellipse (I). This procedure is called principal-components analysis. The principal axis, or component, defines the factor or basic dimension the variables are measuring in common. The principal axis should not be confused with regression lines, as indicated by the regression coefficients b_{xy} and b_{yx} in the diagram.

If a third variable is introduced, the test space is three-dimensional and the ellipse becomes an ellipsoid. In our example a third variable might be the assessed valuation of the family home, and the principal axis of the ellipsoid is again the best measure of what these variables have in common, socio-economic status in this case. As more and more variables are included, additional significant components of SES may appear, indicating that the domain is not unidimensional. Thus principal-components analysis not only reveals how several measures of a domain can be combined to produce maximum discrimination among individuals along a single dimension, but often reveals that several independent dimensions are required to define the domain under investigation adequately.

Another situation in which factor analysis may be used is that in which we wish to reduce the dimensionality of a set of variables by taking advantage of their intercorrelations. For instance, in an example presented in this chapter, forty-eight variables from the Rorschach Test were reduced to a more manageable sixteen dimensions. Principal-components analysis accomplished this by finding the principal axis of the hyperellipsoid in the forty-eight space (similar to the ellipse in the two space) along which there was maximum variance. Then a second axis was constructed, orthogonal to the first, along which the remaining variance was maximized (similar to Axis II in Figure 8.1). Finally, a third axis which was

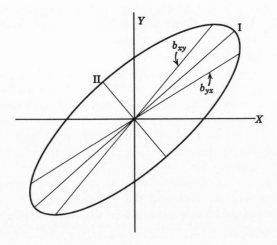

Figure 8.1

orthogonal to the first two was determined, and so on until "all" the variance is accounted for. At some point in the sequence of locating new axes in the ellipsoid, an insignificant amount of variance is found in the remaining dimensions, thus reducing the number of dimensions required.

The last use of factor analysis to be considered here is to find ways of identifying fundamental and meaningful dimensions of a multivariate domain. The investigation of mental abilities has received the most attention in this regard. Psychologists have identified and have agreed on a few of these primary mental abilities, or differential aptitudes, as they are sometimes called. This "construct-seeking" task of factor analysis is most frequently accomplished today by first conducting a principal-components analysis (or centroid analysis, which is a simplified approximation of the principal-components solution), and by then using the resulting principal factors as a set of reference axes for determining the simplest structure, or most easily interpretable set of factors, for the domain in question. This whole process, which Harman (1960) calls multiple-factor analysis, is most easily understood from the person space model.

The person space, or sample space as it is often called, is N-dimensional, where N is the sample size. The m tests are converted to standard score units and are plotted in the N space as points or vectors. That is, the scores of N subjects on test j locate a point for that test in the N space, and a line from the origin to that point becomes the vector representation of test j. The cosine of the angle between pairs of normalized test vectors is the correlation between the two tests. Figure 8.2 illustrates the sample space for the data in Table 8.1. Sample spaces of two dimensions are not very interesting because there are only two possible locations for a test vector, if standard scores are based on that particular sample of two. This is another demonstration that the correlation must be either $+1.00$ or -1.00 for the case where $N = 2$ ($\cos 0° = 1.00$ and $\cos 180° = -1.00$).

Now N dimensions are not needed to describe m vectors, where $m < N$. Think, for instance, of *two* test vectors in a *three*-dimensional space. The two test vectors define a plane, and only a plane is needed to describe the relationship between the two tests. The problem is to decide among the infinite sets of reference axes

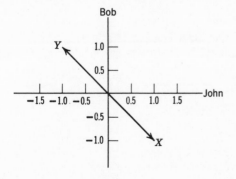

Figure 8.2

TABLE 8.1

Standard Score Roster

Name	X	Y
John	1	-1
Bob	-1	1

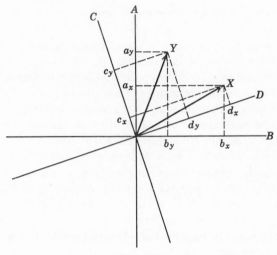

Figure 8.3

capable of adequately describing a particular configuration of tests. Figure 8.3 illustrates this problem by showing two of the pairs of axes which could serve as reference axes (factors) for describing the plane in which tests X and Y lie. Here axes A and B are rotated to positions C and D.

Principal-components analysis defines a unique set of reference axes for a given combination of m variables using the maximum variance criterion as described. That procedure does not usually result, however, in a satisfactory set of reference axes for psychological interpretation. A new set of axes is formed by rotating the derived principal-components axes. This rotation process can best be described by a fabricated example.

In order to illustrate the frequent advantages of rotation, one of the authors devised a set of eight scores for each of a hundred rectangles. First an arbitrary length L and width W were selected for each rectangle; then the eight scores were produced from the formulas of Table 8.2, where e_{mi} is a one-digit random number introduced as the error component on test m for individual i.

TABLE 8.2

Formulas for Scores on Eight Tests

Test	Formula
1	$X_{1i} = L_i$
2	$X_{2i} = W_i$
3	$X_{3i} = 10L_i + e_{3i}$
4	$X_{4i} = 10W_i + e_{4i}$
5	$X_{5i} = 20L_i + 10W_i + e_{5i}$
6	$X_{6i} = 20L_i + 20W_i + e_{6i}$
7	$X_{7i} = 10L_i + 20W_i + e_{7i}$
8	$X_{8i} = 40L_i + 10W_i + e_{8i}$

TABLE 8.3

Means, Standard Deviations, and Correlations for Eight Variables on One Hundred Rectangles

Variables	1	2	3	4	5	6	7	8
Means	17.8	11.7	190.6	119.1	476.3	591.5	416.1	831.3
S.D.	6.5	5.4	66.5	54.3	148.5	181.0	134.2	274.1
Intercorrelations								
1		.140	.987	.168	.931	.804	.597	.980
2			.160	.930	.491	.693	.877	.331
3				.185	.927	.807	.608	.972
4					.489	.671	.835	.347
5						.962	.848	.984
6							.950	.903
7								.743
8								

TABLE 8.4

Two Principal Components Accounting for 98.5 Per Cent of the Trace of R from Eight Rectangle Tests on One Hundred Subjects

	First Component	Second Component
Latent Root	5.96	1.93
Per Cent of Trace	74.4	24.1
Variable	Factor Loadings	
1	.8534	−.5188
2	.6337	.7623
3	.8578	−.4998
4	.6332	.7356
5	.9837	−.1761
6	.9923	.0776
7	.9264	.3664
8	.9391	−.3418

The intercorrelations among the eight scores were computed and the **R** matrix (Table 8.3) was subjected to a principal-components analysis, with the results displayed in Table 8.4. Notice that two components account for 98.5 per cent of the total variance in the battery of eight tests and that the first component is a general factor, whereas the second is a bipolar factor in which the tests dominated by length have negative loadings and those dominated by width have positive loadings.

A rotation was then performed on the matrix of adjusted factor loadings of the eight tests on the two principal components selected. The result (Table 8.5) was that the general factor was destroyed and two group factors were produced.[2]

In our example eight test vectors were located in an N-dimensional sample space ($N = 100$). The cosines of the angles between the eight test vectors, i.e., the intercorrelations, cause the vectors to tend to lie in a common plane within the N space. Principal-components analysis was used to define the tests, relative locations in the plane. The resulting reference axes are labeled I and II in Figure 8.4. The

TABLE 8.5

Two Rotated Factors from Varimax

Test	L Factor	W Factor
1	.997	.058
2	.089	.987
3	.989	.076
4	.103	.965
5	.909	.414
6	.772	.627
7	.554	.828
8	.967	.252

`coordinates of the termini of the eight test vectors in this two-dimensional factor space are listed in Table 8.4. The relative locations in the figure of the test vector termini are indicated by circled numbers, the numbers referring to the eight tests.

Axes I and II are not the only axes that can define this two-space. The axes resulting from principal-components analysis were rotated to positions A and B, and a new set of test coordinates were obtained. These are listed in Table 8.5. Figure 8.4 shows the location of axes L and W. These new, rotated axes might be preferable for purposes of interpreting the basic dimensions of the domain measured by the eight tests. This is because the new coordinates are more "simple" in the sense that a given variable tends to have a high coefficient for only one new axis, and each factor has zero, or near zero, coefficients for at least some of the variables.

The rotated solution consists of two distinct factors, length (variables 1, 3, 5, 6, and 8) and width (variables 2, 4, and 7). The components solution, on the other hand, produced one general factor and one bipolar factor. One general and $m - 1$ bipolar factors are typically the results of principal-components analysis. (Technically, m common factors are produced although not all of them are usually useful.)

Which of the infinite number of possible factor solutions is preferable is generally a theoretical question. We are familiar with rectangles, and so we tend to prefer the simple structure solution produced by rotation. Length and width are the two basic dimensions for rectangles; hence Factors L and W "make sense."

We could argue, however, that the principal-components solution is also interpretable. The first factor, I, is a general size or "bigness" factor and the second,

---

[2] The Varimax criterion was used in rotation here. This is described in Section 8.3.

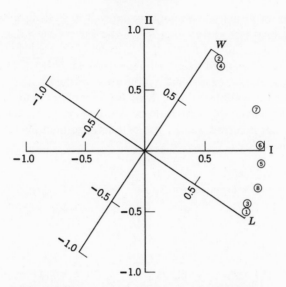

Figure 8.4. Test vector termini in two-space using two different factor solutions. Here I and II are the principal-components axes, and L and W are the Varimax-rotated axes.

bipolar factor, II, is length ($-$) versus width ($+$). The second factor would be dependent only on the relative lengths and widths of rectangles and independent of over-all size.

The new coordinates for the eight variables listed in Table 8.5 are the loadings for the corresponding factor. The loadings are the factor coefficients; an individual's score along factor I is the vector product of these loadings and his standardized test scores.[3] Thus both individuals and tests can be plotted in the factor space. The relative location of neither tests nor individuals is affected by the orthogonal rotation of factors. The interpretation of the factor solution alone is affected.

The brief description of factor analysis presented in this section is intended only as an introduction for the reader who has not been previously exposed to the procedures. The following discussion summarizes some of the basic mathematical concepts involved in factor analysis.

8.2   Mathematics of Principal-Components Analysis

Students of factor analysis have recognized for some time that the principal-components solution is the most desirable[4] way to obtain the initial factor structure of a correlation matrix, whether or not subsequent rotation is desired. The computer has made the procedure feasible as well as desirable. Principal-components analysis is therefore the solution outlined and programmed in this chapter.

[3] Computation of factor scores is described in Section 8.4.

[4] See Harman (1960), p. 179.

The basic task of principal components analysis is to determine, first, an axis in the m-dimensional test space along which the variance is a maximum; then a second axis, orthogonal to the first, which accounts for as much of the remaining variance as possible; a third axis, orthogonal to the first two; etc. Each new orthogonal axis accounts for a smaller proportion of the original variance.

This basic task is accomplished by solving for a set of m homogeneous equations which result from partial differentiation of the function to be maximized, subject to a restriction that is introduced by use of Lagrange multipliers.[5] The resulting equations may be written

$$
\begin{aligned}
v_1(1 - \lambda) + v_2 r_{12} \quad + v_3 r_{13} \quad &+ \cdots + v_m r_{1m} \quad = 0 \\
v_1 r_{21} \quad + v_2(1 - \lambda) + v_3 r_{23} \quad &+ \cdots + v_m r_{2m} \quad = 0 \\
v_1 r_{31} \quad + v_2 r_{32} \quad + v_3(1 - \lambda) + &\cdots + v_m r_{3m} \quad = 0 \\
&\quad \vdots \\
v_1 r_{m1} \quad + v_2 r_{m2} \quad + v_3 r_{m3} \quad &+ \cdots + v_m(1 - \lambda) = 0.
\end{aligned}
$$

(8.1)

Equations 8.1 can be written as matrices as follows:

(8.2)

$$
\begin{bmatrix}
(1 - \lambda_i) & r_{12} & r_{13} & \cdots & r_{1m} \\
r_{21} & (1 - \lambda_i) & r_{23} & \cdots & r_{2m} \\
r_{31} & r_{32} & (1 - \lambda_i) & \cdots & r_{3m} \\
\vdots & \vdots & \vdots & \ddots & \vdots \\
r_{m1} & r_{m2} & r_{m3} & \cdots & (1 - \lambda_i)
\end{bmatrix}
\cdot
\begin{bmatrix}
v_{1i} \\ v_{2i} \\ v_{3i} \\ \vdots \\ v_{mi}
\end{bmatrix}
=
\begin{bmatrix}
0 \\ 0 \\ 0 \\ \vdots \\ 0
\end{bmatrix}.
$$

Again, in matrix notation, $(\mathbf{R} - \lambda_i \mathbf{I})\mathbf{v}_i = \mathbf{0}$, $i = 1, 2, 3, \ldots, m$; where $\mathbf{I}$ is an identity matrix, $\mathbf{0}$ is a null vector, and $\mathbf{R}$ is the correlation matrix. There are m nontrivial solutions, each $\mathbf{v}_i$ representing the coefficients (transformation vector) for converting the m test scores to one of the new, uncorrelated factor scores.

The trivial solution would be to set $\mathbf{v} = \mathbf{0}$. For the nontrivial solutions, the determinant of the coefficient of $\mathbf{v}$ is zero: $|\mathbf{R} - \lambda \mathbf{I}| = 0$. The latter is the so-called characteristic equation, for which there are m possible values of λ (where $\mathbf{R}$ is an $m \times m$ correlation matrix). For a given root λ_i, the corresponding vector $\mathbf{v}_i$ can be obtained by substituting the λ_i in the set of equations 8.1 and solving for $\mathbf{v}_i$. (The elements of $\mathbf{v}_i$ are proportional to the cofactors of any row of $[\mathbf{R} - \lambda_i \mathbf{I}]$.)

Once again the need to compute latent roots and vectors in multivariate analysis becomes apparent (see Chapter 3, 4, and 5). Again, the subroutine used for this task in the system of programs provided is HDIAG. In this routine all the possible m roots and vectors are obtained so that the investigator can then determine how many factors are desirable for subsequent computations.

[5] Kendall (1957), Chapter 2, and Harmon (1960), Chapter 9. Two different restrictions are possible. Here $\Sigma_i v_i^2 = 1.00$ is used.

When the vectors are made normal (i.e., $\Sigma_{i=1}^{m} v_i^2 = 1.00$), the variance of each set of factor scores is λ_i. The vector $\mathbf{v}_1$ produces the factor scores of maximum variance, the variance being the value of the largest latent root λ_1. Two other useful properties of the latent roots are

$$\prod_{i=1}^{m} \lambda_i = |\mathbf{R}|, \qquad \sum_{i=1}^{m} \lambda_i = \sum_{j=1}^{m} r_{jj}.$$

That is, the continued product of the roots is the determinant of $\mathbf{R}$. In addition, the sum of the roots is equal to the trace of $\mathbf{R}$, the trace being the sum of the diagonal elements. Since the trace of $\mathbf{R}$ is the total variance to be accounted for, the sum of the roots associated with the preserved vectors divided by the trace of $\mathbf{R}$ is the proportion of variance accounted for by the resulting factor space.

If unities are used in the principal diagonal of $\mathbf{R}$, the *total* test variance is factor-analyzed. A large and continuing controversy among factor analysts concerns what ought to be placed in the diagonals of the matrix to be factored. The multiple-factor school argues that the common variance or communality of each variate must be placed in the diagonals.

When the task is construct seeking, as in multiple-factor analysis, it makes sense to eliminate from the analysis, if possible, the unique variance of each variable. The problem is that the true communalities are usually indeterminate. In the practical application of factor analysis, for uses described in Section 8.1, keeping unities in the diagonal seems to be one reasonable approach to the communality problem.[6]

When principal-components analysis is employed as the desired solution, the normalized vectors can serve as the factor score coefficients, at least when unities have been used in the diagonals of $\mathbf{R}$. When components analysis is used as the first stage in multiple-factor analysis, the normalized vectors are converted to the factor pattern by multiplying the elements of each vector by the square root of the corresponding latent root: $\mathbf{A} = \mathbf{\Lambda}^{1/2}\mathbf{V}$ where $\mathbf{\Lambda}^{1/2}$ is a diagonal matrix with $\sqrt{\lambda_i}$ as the diagonal elements, and where the m columns of $\mathbf{A}$ are the factor pattern coefficients.[7]

The elements of the ith row of $\mathbf{A}$ are the coefficients for the variable z_i on each of the factors. The matrix $\mathbf{A}$ is not symmetrical.

$$\mathbf{A} = \begin{bmatrix} a_{11} & a_{12} & a_{13} & \cdots & a_{1m} \\ a_{21} & a_{22} & a_{23} & \cdots & a_{2m} \\ a_{31} & a_{32} & a_{33} & \cdots & a_{3m} \\ \cdot & \cdot & \cdot & & \cdot \\ \cdot & \cdot & \cdot & & \cdot \\ \cdot & \cdot & \cdot & & \cdot \\ a_{m1} & a_{m2} & a_{m3} & & a_{mm} \end{bmatrix}.$$

[6] Kaiser (1960), Wrigley (1957), and Cooley and Mierzwa (1961). For an empirical consideration of this question, see Michael (1958).

[7] Harman (1960), p. 157.

If all the m factors are represented in $\mathbf{A}$, the sum of the squared loadings for a given row is equal to one:

$$\sum_{j=1}^{m} a_{ij}^{2} = 1.00.$$

If only p factors (p columns of $\mathbf{A}$) are selected for further computations, the sum of squared loadings for the i row in $\mathbf{A}$ is the proportion of variance of test i preserved in that particular factor solution:

$$\sum_{j=1}^{p} a_{ij}^{2} = h_{i}^{2}$$

where h_{i}^{2} is the observed communality of variable i when p factors are used.

One continuing concern in factor analysis is the problem of how many factors to preserve for further analysis. There seems to be little agreement on this question. Statistical considerations alone are not completely satisfactory, since the number of significant factors then depends on the size of the sample. (Even the "inveterate statistician" who insists on tests of significance can be frequently caught making arbitrary decisions on the significance level in order to include or exclude a particular factor!)

Kaiser has made a very practical suggestion for deciding how many factors to use. His recommendation is to use those factors with corresponding latent roots greater than one.[8] Since this rule applies only if unities are used in the diagonal, it gives another reason for beginning with unity as the communality estimate. A further advantage of using unities in the diagonal is seen in our consideration of computing individual factor scores (Section 8.4).

If the investigator is interested in seeing how close the resulting factor solution approximates the original intercorrelations of the battery, the correlation matrix can be reproduced easily. To see how this is done we must review the basic model for factor analysis. The linear model can be expressed as follows:

$$z_{ji} = a_{j1}F_{1i} + a_{j2}F_{2i} + \cdots + a_{jp}F_{pi} + a_{j}U_{ji}.$$

The standard score on test j for individual i is viewed as a linear function of p common factors and a unique factor, where a_{j1} is the factor coefficient for the first factor and F_{1i} is the factor score for individual i on the first factor. By preserving only the factors associated with the p largest roots of $\mathbf{R}$, we are essentially asserting that these p factors are the significant, reproducible common factors, and that the remaining $1.00 - h_{j}^{2}$ variance of test j is the unique component.[9]

If only the p common factors are used, then z_{ji} cannot be reproduced exactly from the factor model, but it can be approximated (z_{ji}^{*}).

[8] Kaiser (1960). Similar recommendations can be found in Harman (1960), p. 363, and Guttman (1954).
[9] Actually this is not completely consistent with definitions from multiple-factor theory. When we analyze the total test variance (using unities in the diagonal of $\mathbf{R}$), principal-components analysis yields m common factors. However, it seems reasonable to assert that the p factors which are preserved for rotation define the common factor space.

For two variables, the equations for individual i would be

$$z_{1i}{}^* = a_{11}F_{1i} + a_{12}F_{2i} + \cdots + a_{1p}F_{pi},$$
$$z_{2i}{}^* = a_{21}F_{1i} + a_{22}F_{2i} + \cdots + a_{2p}F_{pi}.$$

For uncorrelated factors, for instance those resulting from principal-components analysis, the reproduced correlation $r_{12}{}^*$ is obtained by multiplying the two equations, summing over i ($i = 1, 2, \ldots, N$), and dividing by N. For variables j and k, the result is:

$$r_{jk}{}^* = a_{j1}a_{k1} + a_{j2}a_{k2} + \cdots + a_{jp}a_{kp}.$$

The difference between $r_{jk}{}^*$ and the observed correlation r_{jk} is a measure of the lack of fit between the obtained factor model for the domain and the observed relations among the tests. These residual correlations ($\mathbf{R}_{res}$) can be obtained for the entire correlation matrix as follows:

$$\mathbf{R}_{res} = \mathbf{R} - \mathbf{AA'} \quad \text{since} \quad \mathbf{R}^* = \mathbf{AA'}.$$

This section has attempted to summarize the conclusions the authors drew as they applied factor analysis in their own research and to touch on some of the current controversies in the field. These recommendations may not represent the most elegant way of conducting factor analysis, but most of the suggestions for refinements tend *not* to affect the psychological interpretation of the factor solution.

8.3   Mathematics of Two Rotational Schemes

As indicated in Section 8.1, multiple-factor analysis involves two basic steps. First an initial set of reference axes is determined by use of a procedure like principal-components analysis. Then some rotational scheme that is designed to convert the obtained principal-factor pattern to a pattern of simple structure is employed. Thurstone's (1947) criteria for simple structure are the following:

(1) Each row of the factor matrix should have at least one zero.

(2) If there are m common factors, each column of the factor matrix should have at least m zeros.

(3) For every pair of columns of the factor matrix there should be several variables whose entries vanish in one column but not in the other.

(4) For every pair of columns of the factor matrix, a large proportion of the variables should have vanishing entries in both columns when there are four or more factors.

(5) For every pair of columns of the factor matrix there should be only a small number of variables with nonvanishing entries in both columns.

Although Thurstone's model for simple structure guided graphic rotation for many years, attempts to develop objective rotation methods directly from his principles proved fruitless. A major breakthrough, however, was made by Carroll (1953) when he proposed the first practical analytical[10] solution for the rotation

---

[10] Here, analytical means that the solution is independent of the investigators subjective judgments. Two investigators would arrive at the same solution.

problem. The high-speed computer, which began to be available to factorists at about the same time, made such procedures feasible. Soon several different computer approaches were available to the investigator who wished to use analytical rotations in multiple-factor analysis.

The first analytical schemes for rotation tended to focus on the problem of simplifying the rows of the factor matrix **A**. The loadings for each variable were modified so that each variable had high loadings on the fewest possible factors and zero or near-zero loadings on the remaining factors. Several investigators developed procedures for this type of analytical rotation.[11] Subsequently these procedures were all shown to be algebraically identical and have been classified as the Quartimax method.[12]

An alternative to Quartimax is the Varimax solution, which involves the simplification of columns rather than of rows of the factor matrix. The Varimax criterion for rotation is a development of Kaiser (1958). It has several advantages over the Quartimax method. The emphasis in Varimax is on "cleaning up" factors rather than variables. For each factor Varimax rotation tends to yield high loadings for a few variables. The rest of the loadings in the factor will be zero or near zero.

In the Varimax criterion, Kaiser defines the simplicity of a factor as the variance of its squared loadings:

$$V_j = \left[m \sum_i (b_{ij}^2)^2 - \left(\sum_i b_{ij}^2 \right)^2 \right] \bigg/ m^2$$

where b_{ij} is the new factor loading for variable i on factor j; $i = 1, 2, \ldots, m$, and $j = 1, 2, \ldots, p$. Then for the entire factor matrix, the Varimax criterion is:

$$(8.3) \qquad V = \sum_j V_j = \sum_j \left\{ \left[m \sum_i (b_{ij}^2)^2 - \left(\sum_i b_{ij}^2 \right)^2 \right] \bigg/ m^2 \right\} = \max$$

and V is the quantity maximized.

Experience with the Varimax criterion as defined in equation 8.3 soon revealed a slight bias in the resulting solutions. The rotation tended to produce factors which had disparate values for the sum $\Sigma_i b_{ij}^2$. This bias was removed by redefining the Varimax criterion as follows:

$$(8.4) \qquad V = \sum_j \left\{ \left[m \sum_i (b_{ij}^2/h_i^2)^2 - \left(\sum_i b_{ij}^2/h_i^2 \right)^2 \right] \bigg/ m^2 \right\} = \max$$

where h_i^2 is the communality of test i. Equation 8.4 defines the *normal* Varimax criterion. After rotation to the maximum value of V, each vector is readjusted by multiplying each row of the resulting factor matrix by the square root of the test's communality ($\sqrt{h_i^2}$). Rotation does not affect the values of the m communalities: $\Sigma_i b_{ij}^2 = \Sigma_i a_{ij}^2 = h_i^2$.

One important advantage of the Varimax solution is that the resulting factors

---

[11] Carroll (1953), Neuhaus and Wrigley (1954), Saunders (1953), and Ferguson (1954).

[12] Harman (1960), p. 301. This is true of Carroll's procedure only when restricted to the orthogonal case.

tend to be "invariant under changes in the composition of the test battery."[13] If the purpose of multiple-factor analysis is to allow inferences about the dimensionality or basic structure of some psychological domain on the basis of a sample of m tests drawn from that domain, this invariance property is of utmost importance. Small changes in the sample of tests used should not affect the basic inferences drawn.

If the reader is interested in the actual computational aspects of Varimax, he can see them by tracing through the flow chart of the Varimax program (Flow Diagram 8.2) while following Kaiser's (1959) outline for coding an electronic computer.

The final solution has the form $B = AT$, where T is the orthogonal transformation matrix chosen so that the elements of matrix B yield the desired maximum expressed in equation 8.3. The rotation is orthogonal because of the imposed restriction, $T'T = I$. The matrix A is the original factor pattern matrix resulting from principal-components analysis.

In addition to the orthogonal rotation methods like Varimax and Quartimax, a number of oblique solutions have been developed. In Carroll's (1953) pioneering effort, he produced both an orthogonal and an oblique solution. With the restriction of orthogonality, Carroll's original procedure is equivalent to the Quartimax. Without that restriction, the oblique Quartimin solution results. Kaiser's Varimax can also be modified to attain an oblique solution. Carroll has labeled the latter the Covarimin criterion, since it involves minimizing sums of cross products across column pairs of squared loadings (covariances).

Experience with Quartimin and Covarimin soon revealed that neither oblique solution was completely satisfactory. Carroll's Quartimin, which emphasized the simplification of rows (variables), produced factor axes that were too highly correlated, and Covarimin, which focused on simplifying columns (factors), tended to be biased toward orthogonal solutions. Recognizing these problems, Carroll developed the Oblimin class of oblique solutions, which incorporates the properties of both Covarimin and Quartimin in a way that allows the investigator to decide just how much obliqueness he can tolerate! The general Oblimin criterion can be written as follows, the b's having been made normal, as in Varimax:

$$(8.5) \qquad \sum_{j<k=1} \left(m \sum_i b_{ij}^2 b_{ik}^2 - \gamma \sum_i b_{ij}^2 \sum_i b_{ik}^2 \right) = \min$$

where again the problem is to find a transformation matrix T with the property that the elements of the resulting product $B = AT$ satisfy equation 8.5. The class of Oblimin solutions is obtained by varying γ. For $\gamma = 0$, equation 8.5 is equivalent to the Quartimin solution, and for $\gamma = 1$, it is the Covarimin equivalent. The more generally satisfactory value for γ seems to be .5, which Carroll calls the Biquartimin solution.[14]

[13] Kaiser (1958), p. 195.
[14] Carroll's program for Oblimin rotation was too lengthy for inclusion in this volume. Interested readers may obtain a FORTRAN listing of Oblimin by writing to W. W. Cooley.

8.4   Computation of Factor Scores

The factor scores are easily obtained from the principal factors when unities have been used in the diagonals of $\mathbf{R}$. The factor model presented at the end of Section 8.2 can be rewritten as follows:

$$F_{1i} = a_{11}z_{1i} + a_{21}z_{2i} + \cdots + a_{p1}z_{pi}.$$

This is the score on factor 1 for individual i. In other words, each of the p column vectors of $\mathbf{A}$ is multiplied by the standardized score vector of i to obtain the p factor scores for i.

Whenever communality estimates other than one are used, the solution is not as simple. The reader is referred to Harman (1960), Chapter 16, for a summary of recent developments in this area. See also Kaiser (1962).

8.5   Factor Analysis of the Rorschach Test

One of the instruments for personality assessment used in the Scientific Careers Study[15] is the individual Rorschach test. The statistical treatment of Rorschach scores presents a few problems, because the scores do not exhibit some of the essential properties of the more orthodox psychological-test scores. The most serious problem is the lack of normality in the distribution of the scores, which are frequency counts of types of responses, and which generally follow or approach the Poisson distribution.

Mosteller and Bush (1954) have suggested that the Freeman-Tukey square-root transformation is the most appropriate procedure for handling Rorschach scores. That is, $z = \sqrt{X} + \sqrt{X+1}$, where X is the observed frequency score. This transformation results in new scores for which the variances do not depend upon the true mean to any great extent.

Another aspect of the Rorschach test that has caused difficulty in quantitative treatment of the test is the partial dependence of the several scores on the total number of responses given. The results of this factor analysis indicate that the difficulty seems to be solved by forming a general productivity factor with which all the other factors are uncorrelated. This development is further discussed later.

The group used in the factor analysis report here consisted of 213 college males, majoring in one of the natural sciences or in engineering. The primary purposes of the analysis were:

(1) To reduce the test space of forty-eight dimensions to a factor space of somewhat fewer dimensions, and still preserve the common variance of the original Rorschach scores.

(2) To obtain factor scores that are even more normally distributed than the transformed Rorschach scores. The factor scores have the additional advantage of being uncorrelated, thus giving maximum information for a space of given dimensionality.

[15] Cooley and Mierzwa (1961).

TABLE 8.6

Means and Standard Deviations (Transformed Scores), $N = 213$

	Variable	Mean	S.D.
1	R	8.599	2.208
2	W	5.558	1.420
3	W	2.799	.938
4	D	5.640	2.374
5	Dd	2.194	1.318
6	S	1.806	1.039
7	M	3.021	1.291
8	FM	3.130	1.510
9	m, mF	1.727	.928
10	Fm	2.259	1.139
11	k, kF	1.147	.455
12	Fk	1.153	.456
13	K, KF	1.258	.578
14	FK	1.243	.546
15	F+	5.249	1.704
16	F−	2.419	1.312
17	Fc	1.856	1.147
18	c, cF	1.240	.539
19	C′FC′	1.564	.861
20	FC	2.473	1.247
21	CF	2.827	1.220
22	P	4.030	.951
23	Rej	1.290	.735
24	H	3.240	1.276
25	Hd	1.892	1.183
26	A	5.087	1.354
27	Ad	2.019	1.235
28	Aobj	2.030	.837
29	At	2.232	1.194
30	Sex	1.357	.675
31	Obj	2.686	1.552
32	Bot	2.045	1.109
33	N	1.952	1.113
34	Geo	1.455	.929
35	Art	1.452	.782
36	Embl	1.212	.525
37	Cloud	1.297	.609
38	Blood	1.162	.452
39	Fire	1.218	.499
40	Mask	1.089	.376
41	Abs	1.212	.591
42	Color	1.108	.402
43	A.At	1.400	.751
44	Food	1.218	.579
45	Smoke	1.127	.399
46	Expl.	1.455	.773
47	Cloth	1.127	.451
48	Sym	1.062	.265

(3) To eliminate most of the error variance in the scores by preserving only the common factors.

(4) To examine the factor structure of the Rorschach test for a nonpsychiatric population. Only a few such studies have been previously conducted.

The principal components analysis was conducted using unities in the diagonal, following the recommendations of Kaiser (1960). The means and standard deviations for the forty-eight transformed scores are reported in Table 8.6.

Sixteen latent roots were obtained which were greater than one; therefore, the sixteen corresponding vectors were the only ones preserved for further analysis.

TABLE 8.7

Latent Roots for the Principal-Components Analysis

Root number	Latent Root*	Cumulative Per Cent of Trace
1	9.367	19.51
2	3.511	26.83
3	2.311	31.64
4	2.060	35.94
5	1.772	39.63
6	1.684	43.14
7	1.614	46.50
8	1.474	49.57
9	1.354	52.39
10	1.290	55.08
11	1.206	57.59
12	1.155	59.99
13	1.107	62.30
14	1.079	64.55
15	1.021	66.68
16	1.002	68.76
	Trace = 48.00	

* These values are also the standard deviations for the corresponding factors, using the principal factor pattern as the factor coefficients.

The characteristic roots are reported in Table 8.7, which also shows that over two-thirds of the total variance is accounted for by these first sixteen factors (69 per cent).

The normalized vectors are converted to factor pattern coefficients by multiplying each element of the latent vector by the square root of the corresponding latent root. Thus the roots listed in Table 8.7 are the *standard deviations* along the corresponding principal factors, rather than variances, as is the case when the normalized vectors are used as the factor coefficients. Table 8.8 presents the

TABLE 8.8
Rorschach Principal Factor Pattern*

Factors

Variable	I	II	III	IV	V	VI	VII	VIII	IX	X	XI	XII	XIII	XIV	XV	XVI
1 R	−957															
4 D	−766	−366														
31 Obj	−679															
5 Dd	−649															
26 A	−633	−310														
15 F+	−618		−431													
27 Ad	−591	−426														
20 FC	−591															
17 Fc	−586															
10 Fm	−552							−342								
6 S	−536													386		
21 CF	−516	415														
33 N	−498	363														
2 W	−492	327					−340									
32 Bot	−481			−345												
8 FM	−463	−304	463													
19 FC,'C'F	−462															
22 P	−453		313													
16 F−	−446		−540													
9 m, mF	−424	529		322												
7 M	−418	−467		445												

* Only loadings greater than .300 are included and the decimal points have been dropped.

TABLE 8.8 (contd.)

	Variable	I	II	III	IV	V	VI	VII	VIII	IX	X	XI	XII	XIII	XIV	XV	XVI
37	Cloud	−411				338											
24	H	−407	−521		357												
14	FK	−403						320									
34	Geo	−402		−413									376				
25	Hd	−397	−467														
13	K, KF	−386	466							362							−305
18	cF, c	−356															
47	Cloth	−335			420				349								
38	Blood	−313					428					464					
29	At	−312			−428	−436							304				
11	k, kF	−301							−389							−480	
23	Rej	400	566														
46	Expl		433				331										
35	Art		388					−391									
45	Smoke			−308													
40	Mask				−332		471										434
12	Fk										345					358	
36	Embl					423				−367							
30	Sex					−614											
44	Food					−374			347				382				
42	Color						445					−319					−362
43	A.At							328		321							
28	Aobj								328	−307					352		
3	W								−308					459			
41	Abs									−438	−366		−313				
39	Fire												300				
48	Sym												392		416		

TABLE 8.9

Communalities of the Factor Solutions

	Variable	h^2
1	R	.969
2	W	.773
3	W	.688
4	D	.837
5	Dd	.616
6	S	.677
7	M	.852
8	FM	.706
9	m, m,F	.700
10	Fm	.622
11	k, kF,	.652
12	Fk	.706
13	K, KF	.693
14	KF	.516
15	F—	.837
16	F—	.670
17	Fc	.691
18	cF, c	.731
19	FC′, C′F	.674
20	FC	.584
21	CF, C	.717
22	P	.634
23	Rej	.618
24	H	.813
25	Hd	.668
26	A	.797
27	Ad	.693
28	Aobj	.680
29	At	.631
30	Sex	.685
31	Obj	.657
32	Bot	.565
33	N	.715
34	Geo	.699
35	Art	.584
36	Embl	.593
37	Cloud	.701
38	Blood	.635
39	Fire	.642
40	Mask	.693
41	Abs	.616
42	Color	.775
43	A.At	.678
44	Food	.760
45	Smoke	.590
46	Expl	.624
47	Cloth	.630
48	Sym	.740

TABLE 8.10
Rorschach Varimax Factor Pattern*

Factors

Variable	I	II	III	IV	V	VI	VII	VIII	IX	X	XI	XII	XIII	XIV	XV	XVI
16 F−	−66															31
37 Cloud	−64	37														
47 Cloth	−60						30									
15 F+	−53								−42							
34 Geo	−47							−41					−32		32	
1 R	−42		49	33	−32											
5 Dd	−41							−37								
4 D	−40		58		−31											
31 Obj	−38	30													31	
13 K, KF	−36	62														
27 Ad	−33		38					−40								
25 Hd	−31			53												
45 Smoke		70														
46 Expl		69					42									
9 m, mF		61														
10 Fm		39														
21 CF		39														
26 A			79													
22 P			73													
8 FM			71												40	
17 Fc			40											40		−47

* Only loadings greater than .300 are included and the decimal points have been dropped.

170

TABLE 8.10 (contd.)

Variable	I	II	III	IV	V	VI	VII	VIII	IX	X	XI	XII	XIII	XIV	XV	XVI
20 FC			35												40	
19 FC' C'F			34							−45						−52
38 Blood			32											38	32	
32 Bot			32													
7 M				88												
24 H				85												
29 At					−69											
30 Sex					−67											
44 Food					−38	−33							−43			
40 Mask						77										
39 Fire						−30	39									
41 Abs							72									
14 FK							30									
6 S								−69								
11 k, kF								−67			38					
36 Embl									−71							
43 A.At									38		39					
12 Fk										74						
18 c, cF											70					
33 N											54				31	
48 Sym												82				
3 W													74			
28 Aobj														78		
2 W															78	
23 Rej															−63	
35 Art															39	
42 Color																−83

principal factor pattern. Using the procedure outlined in Harman[16] for approximating the standard error of the factor loadings, we find that loadings greater than .29 are significant at the .05 level. Hence only loadings .30 or larger are reported in Tables 8.8 and 8.10.

The communalities, which give the proportion of the variance for each of the original variables which were preserved in the factor solution, are listed in Table 8.9. These range from .516 to .969. The communalities are the sums of the squared loadings across rows of the factor pattern. If all the forty-eight possible factors were used, these communalities would all be 1.00.

The sixteen factors were also rotated using the Varimax criterion for simple structure. The Varimax factor pattern is found in Table 8.10. Rotation was conducted in the hope that the new factors would be less difficult to interpret. The Varimax solution proved unsatisfactory, however. The nature of the Varimax criterion is such that *general* factors, if originally present in the principal-component solution, tend to be "destroyed" during rotation. Because the Rorschach responses very definitely exhibit a general factor (productivity), this property of Varimax rotation was undesirable.

The main reason for this undesirability is that quantitative Rorschach results are more easily interpreted if the general-response factor is partialed out. The initial principal-component solution seemed to accomplish just this by having a general-productivity factor independent of the other factors. During Varimax rotation, however, much of the variance associated with the first factor was distributed to the other factors, thus causing a person's location on any dimension (factor) to be partially a function of the number of responses given. The resulting Varimax loadings produced factor scores which were highly correlated. Hence, even though the orthogonal Varimax criterion was used for rotation, the resulting factors were not orthogonal (uncorrelated) in the original sample space (person space). Therefore the principal-components factors were used for computing factor scores and for subsequent analyses in the Scientific Careers Study.

[16] Harman (1960), p. 177.

8.1

Flow Diagram for Principal-Components Program (PRINCOMP Program)

INPUT

Read L where L = 0 if program is to start with the raw score vectors of subjects on the M tests, and L = 1 if program is to start with a previously computed M × M correlation matrix R.

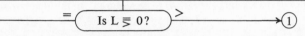

SUBROUTINE

Call subroutine CORREL, which computes from raw-score vectors of subjects on M tests the correlation matrix R and reports M and R to this program.

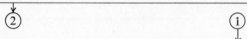

INPUT

Read M, R_{vw} where M is the number of variables and R is the correlation matrix. Throughout this diagram subscripts have the ranges: $v = 1, 2, 3, \ldots, M$; $w = 1, 2, 3, \ldots, M$.

SUBROUTINE

Call subroutine HDIAG, which computes the eigenvalues of R, placing them in the diagonal of R, and the eigenvectors of R, placing them in the columns of V.

$FRACT_v = 100 \cdot (R_{vv}/M)$ the percentage of the trace of R accounted for by each eigenvalue.

$ACCUM_1 = FRACT_1$

$ACCUM_x = ACCUM_x + FRACT_{x-1}$ where $x = 2, 3, 4, \ldots, M$, accumulated percentages.

$SR_w = \sqrt{R_{ww}}$

$X_{vw} = V_{vw} \cdot SR_w$ forming adjusted factor loadings required for entry to VARIMAX rotation program.

OUTPUT

Print, with labels, R_{vv}, $FRACT_v$, $ACCUM_v$.

Punch V_{vw}, X_{vw}.

| STOP |

Flow Diagram for Varimax Rotation (Condensed) (VARIMAX Program), including Subroutine VARMAX

INPUT
Read N, L, A_{vx}, K where N is the number of tests, L is the number of factors, A is the N ×L matrix of factor loadings, K is the number of iterations for which near equality of the Varimax criteria is to be required. In this diagram subscript ranges are $v = 1, 2, 3, \ldots, N;\ w = 1, 2, 3, \ldots, N;\ x = 1, 2, 3, \ldots, L;\ y = 1, 2, 3, \ldots, L.$

Set $TV_1 = 0$, NV $= 0$, $H_v = 0$.
$H_v = H_v + A_{vx}^2$
$H_v = \sqrt{H_v}$ forming the communalities.
$A_{vx} = A_{vx}/H_v$ normalizing A.

SUBROUTINE
Call subroutine VARMAX, which computes the value of the varimax criterion, TV_{NV}, for iteration number NV.

$AX_{vx} = A_{vx} \cdot H_v$ placing in AX the current A denormalized.

OUTPUT
Print, with labels, NV, TV_{NV}, AX_{vx}.

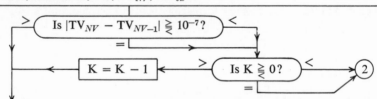

Compute for one pair of factors ϕ, an angle of rotation selected to maximize the Varimax criterion for this pair of factors. Repeat this computation for all pairs of factors to complete an iteration. For a detailed description of the analysis by which an angle of rotation is computed see H. F. Kaiser (1959). "Computer Program for Varimax Rotation in Factor Analysis." *Educ. Psychol. Meas.* **19**: 3.

$H_v = H_v{}^2$
$HN_v = 0$
$HN_v = HN_v + AX_{vx}{}^2$ forming the final communalities.
$HD_v = HN_v - H_v$ forming differences of final from original communalities.

OUTPUT
Print, with labels, H_v, HN_v, HD_v.
Punch AX_{vx}, the final rotated factor matrix.

STOP

Flow Diagram for Subroutine VARMAX

$SV = 0$
$NV = NV + 1$
$SA_x = 0$
$SA2_x = 0$
$SA_x = SA_x + A_{vx}{}^2$
$SA2_x = SA2_x + A_{vx}{}^4$
$SA_x = SA_x{}^2$
$V_x = (N \cdot SA2_x - SA_x)/N^2$ the variance for a factor.
$SV = SV + V_x$ the variance for the entire matrix.
$TV_{NV} = SV$

RETURN

PROGRAM FOR PRINCIPAL-COMPONENTS ANALYSIS [PRINCOMP (RAW)]

```
C       PRINCOMP (RAW).
C
C           THIS PROGRAM PERFORMS PRINCIPAL-COMPONENTS ANALYSIS.
C       BEGINNING WITH RAW SCORES, FOR UP TO 50 VARIABLES.  UNITIES ARE
C       USED AS THE COMMUNALITY ESTIMATES.
C
C       INPUT.
C           DATA AND CONTROL CARDS ARE SET UP AS REQUIRED BY SUBROUTINE
C       CORREL.  BE SURE TO SET L1 = 1 IN CORREL CONTROL.
C       SUBROUTINES HDIAG, MPRINT, AND MPUNCH ARE ALSO REQUIRED.
C
C       OUTPUT.
C           BESIDES THE REQUESTED OUTPUT FROM CORREL, THE FOLLOWING
C       ARE PRINTED.  ROOTS OF CORRELATION MATRIX, NORMALIZED LATENT
C       VECTORS, PERCENTAGE OF TRACE ACCOUNTED FOR BY THE ROOTS, AND THE
C       FACTOR LOADINGS.  ONLY 21 FACTORS ARE PUNCHED OUT, SEVEN PER CARD.
C       VARIABLE NUMBER IS PUNCHED IN COLUMNS 1-2, AND A 1, 2,OR 3 PUNCHED
C       IN COLUMN 4 INDICATES WHICH SET OF SEVEN FACTORS IS IN THAT CARD.

        DIMENSION FMT(36), FMR(36), X(50), SX(50), SS(50,50), SSD(50,50),
       1 D(50,50), R(50,50), XM(50), SD(50), FRACT(50)
        WRITE OUTPUT TAPE 2,2
      2 FORMAT ( 37H0PRINCIPAL-COMPONENTS FACTOR ANALYSIS)
        CALL CORREL (T, NG, SX, SS, SSD, D, R, XM, SD)
        M = T
        CALL HDIAG (R, M, 0, SS, NR)
        WRITE OUTPUT TAPE 2, 1
      1 FORMAT (28H0ROOTS OF CORRELATION MATRIX)
        WRITE OUTPUT TAPE 2,3, (R(I,I), I=1,M)
      3 FORMAT (5F14.7)
        WRITE OUTPUT TAPE 2,4
      4 FORMAT ( 19H1NORMALIZED VECTORS)
        WRITE OUTPUT TAPE 2,5
      5 FORMAT (38H NOTE THAT VECTORS ARE WRITTEN IN ROWS)
        DO 6  J=1,M
      6 WRITE OUTPUT TAPE 2,7,J, (SS(I,J), I = 1,M)
      7 FORMAT ( 8H0VECTOR I2, 7F10.6 / (10X, 7F10.6))
        DO 10  I=1,M
     10 FRACT(I)= (R(I,I) / T) * 100.0
        WRITE OUTPUT TAPE 2, 11
     11 FORMAT(52H0PERCENTAGE OF TRACE OF R ACCOUNTED FOR BY EACH ROOT)
        WRITE OUTPUT TAPE 2,3,(FRACT(I), I=1,M)
        DO 111 I = 2,M
    111 FRACT (I) = FRACT (I) + FRACT (I-1)
        WRITE OUTPUT TAPE 2,112
    112 FORMAT ( 23H0ACCUMULATED PERCENTAGE)
        WRITE OUTPUT TAPE 2,3, (FRACT (I), I = 1,M)
        WRITE OUTPUT TAPE 2,113
    113 FORMAT ( 25H1ADJUSTED FACTOR LOADINGS)
        DO 12 I = 1,M
     12 R(I,I) = SQRTF(R(I,I))
        DO 13 J = 1,M
        DO 13 I = 1,M
     13 SS(I,J) = SS(I,J) * R(J,J)
        DO 14 J = 1,M
     14 WRITE OUTPUT TAPE 2, 15, J, (SS(I,J), I = 1,M)
     15 FORMAT ( 8H0FACTOR I2, 7F10.6 / (10X, 7F10.6))
        N1 = 1
        N2 = 2
        N3 = 3
     17 FORMAT (I2, I2, 6X, 7F10.6)
        DO 16 I = 1,M
        PUNCH 17, I,N1, (SS(I,J), J = 1,7)
        PUNCH 17, I,N2, (SS (I,J), J = 8,14)
     16 PUNCH 17, I,N3, (SS(I,J), J = 15,21)
        CALL EXIT
        END
```

PRINCIPAL-COMPONENTS ANALYSIS [PRINCOMP (R)]

```
C       PRINCOMP (R).
C
C            THIS PROGRAM IS SIMILAR TO THE PREVIOUS ONE EXCEPT
C       THAT THE PROGRAM BEGINS WITH EITHER THE CORRELATION OR DISPERSION
C       MATRIX, RATHER THAN RAW SCORES.  MATRICES UP TO 50TH ORDER ARE
C       POSSIBLE, BUT THE DIMENSION STATEMENT COULD EASILY BE MODIFIED
C       IF LARGER MATRICES WERE NECESSARY.
C
C       INPUT.
C            CONTROL CARD 1 CONTAINS (COL. 1-2) M = NUMBER OF VARIABLES.
C       CARD 2 CONTAINS THE VARIABLE FORMAT FOR THE INPUT MATRIX.  THE
C       MATRIX FOLLOWS CARD 2.  SUBROUTINE HDIAG IS REQUIRED.
C
C       OUTPUT.
C            PRINTED OUTPUT INCLUDES THE ROOTS OF MATRIX, NORMALIZED
C       VECTORS, PERCENTAGE OF TRACE ACCOUNTED FOR BY THE ROOTS, AND THE
C       FACTOR LOADINGS.
C            LOADINGS FOR ONLY 21 FACTORS ARE PUNCHED OUT, SEVEN FACTORS
C       PER CARD.  VARIABLE NUMBER IS PUNCHED IN COLUMNS 1-2, AND A
C       1, 2,OR 3 PUNCHED IN COLUMN 4 INDICATES WHICH SET OF SEVEN FACTORS
C       IS IN THAT CARD.

        DIMENSION FMT(12), R(50,50), SS(50,50), IQ(50), FRACT(50),X(50)
        READ INPUT TAPE 4, 121, M
121 FORMAT (I2)
        READ INPUT TAPE 4,212, (FMT(I), I = 1,12)
212 FORMAT (12A6)
        DO 213  J = 1,M
213 READ INPUT TAPE 4, FMT, (R(I,J), I = 1,M)
        WRITE OUTPUT TAPE 2,214
214 FORMAT (19H0CORRELATION MATRIX)
        DO 215  J = 1,M
215 WRITE OUTPUT TAPE 2,216,(R(I,J), I = 1, M)
216 FORMAT (5 F 14.7)
        T = M
        CALL HDIAG (R, M, 0, SS, NR)
        WRITE OUTPUT TAPE 2, 1
  1 FORMAT (28H0ROOTS OF CORRELATION MATRIX)
        WRITE OUTPUT TAPE 2,3, (R(I,I), I=1,M)
  3 FORMAT (5F14.7)
        WRITE OUTPUT TAPE 2,4
  4 FORMAT ( 19H1NORMALIZED VECTORS)
        WRITE OUTPUT TAPE 2,5
  5 FORMAT (38H NOTE THAT VECTORS ARE WRITTEN IN ROWS)
        DO 6  J=1,M
  6 WRITE OUTPUT TAPE 2,7,J, (SS(I,J), I = 1,M)
  7 FORMAT ( 8H0VECTOR I2, 7F10.6 / (10X, 7F10.6))
        DO 10 I=1,M
 10 FRACT(I)= (R(I,I) / T) * 100.0
        WRITE OUTPUT TAPE 2, 11
 11 FORMAT(52H0PERCENTAGE OF TRACE OF R ACCOUNTED FOR BY EACH ROOT)
        WRITE OUTPUT TAPE 2,3,(FRACT(I), I=1,M)
        DO 111 I = 2,M
111 FRACT (I) = FRACT (I) + FRACT (I-1)
        WRITE OUTPUT TAPE 2,112
112 FORMAT ( 23H0ACCUMULATED PERCENTAGE)
        WRITE OUTPUT TAPE 2,3, (FRACT (I), I = 1,M)
        WRITE OUTPUT TAPE 2,113
113 FORMAT ( 25H1ADJUSTED FACTOR LOADINGS)
```

```
    DO 12 I = 1,M
12 R(I,I) = SQRTF(R(I,I))
    DO 13 J = 1,M
    DO 13 I = 1,M
13 SS(I,J) = SS(I,J) * R(J,J)
    DO 14 J = 1,M
14 WRITE OUTPUT TAPE 2, 15, J, (SS(I,J), I = 1,M)
15 FORMAT ( 8H0FACTOR I2, 7F10.6 / (10X, 7F10.6))
    N1 = 1
    N2 = 2
    N3 = 3
17 FORMAT (I2, I2, 6X, 7F10.6)
    DO 16 I = 1,M
    PUNCH 17, I,N1, (SS(I,J), J = 1,7)
    PUNCH 17, I,N2, (SS (I,J), J = 8,14)
16 PUNCH 17, I,N3, (SS(I,J), J = 15,21)
    CALL EXIT
    END
```

VARIMAX FACTOR ROTATION (VARIMAX), INCLUDING SUBROUTINE VARMAX

```
C      VARIMAX.
C
C          THIS PROGRAM WILL PERFORM VARIMAX ROTATION FOR UP TO 75
C      FACTORS AND 100 VARIABLES.
C
C      INPUT.
C          CARD 1 CONTAINS (COLS. 1-2) JOB NO., (COLS. 3-5) N = NO. OF
C      VARIABLES, (COLS 6-7) L = NO. OF FACTORS, (COLS 8-9) NVALUE = NO.
C      OF ITERATION CYCLES (USE 00 IF THIS TEST IS NOT DESIRED), (COLS
C      10-11) JTEST = NO. OF CYCLES NEW VARIANCE REQUIRED TO EQUAL OLD
C      VARIANCE, (COL 12) RORC = 0 IF AN INPUT CARD CONTAINS THE LOADINGS
C      FOR A VARIABLE, RORC = 1 IF AN INPUT CARD CONTAINS THE LOADINGS
C      FOR A FACTOR.
C          CARD 2 CONTAINS THE VARIABLE FORMAT FOR THE INPUT LOADINGS.
C      THE LOADINGS FOLLOW CARD 2.
C
C      OUTPUT.
C          THE RESULTS FOLLOWING EACH ITERATION CYCLE ARE PRINTED OUT.
C      THIS PRODUCES A LARGE QUANTITY OF PRINTOUT, BUT IT CAN EASILY BE
C      WRITTEN OUT OF THE PROGRAM IF NOT DESIRED.
C          NEW LOADINGS FOR UP TO 21 FACTORS ARE PUNCHED OUT, SEVEN
C      FACTORS PER CARD.  VARIABLE NUMBER IS PUNCHED IN COLS. 1-2, AND
C      A 1, 2,OR 3 PUNCHED IN COL.4 INDICATES WHICH SET OF SEVEN FACTORS
C      IS IN THAT CARD.

       DIMENSION A(100,75),V(75),TV(50),H(100),AX(100,75)
      1, HN(100), HD(100), FMT(12)
       COMMON A,V,TV,NV,N,L,FN,T,B,P
 1001 FORMAT(17H0NO.      VARIANCE)
 1002 FORMAT(1H I3,F20.8)
 1003 FORMAT(16H0  FACTOR MATRIX)
 1004 FORMAT(9H0VARIABLEI4/)
 1005 FORMAT(1H 10F11.4)
 1006 FORMAT(I2,I3,3I2,I1)
 1007 FORMAT (5E14.7)
 1008 FORMAT(27H0OLD H2   NEW H2   DIFFERENCE/)
 1009 FORMAT(F6.3,F8.3,F12.3,I8)
 1012 FORMAT(15H0   JOB NUMBER I2)
 1013 FORMAT (17H0VARIMAX ROTATION)
 1014 FORMAT(1H08X10HCYCLE NO.=I4)
 1015 FORMAT (12A6)
   24 READ INPUT TAPE 4, 1006, JOB, N, L, NVALUE, JTEST, RORC
      READ INPUT TAPE 4, 1015, (FMT(I), I=1, 12)
   25 WRITE OUTPUT TAPE 2, 1013
      WRITE OUTPUT TAPE 2, 1012, JOB
      IF (RORC) 26, 26, 28
   26 DO 27 I = 1,N
   27 READ FMT, (A(I,J), J=1,L)
      GO TO 29
   28 DO 20  J= 1,L
   20 READ INPUT TAPE 4, FMT, (A(I,J), I = 1, N)
   29 EPS=0.00116
      NC=0
      TV(1)=0.0
      LL=L-1
      NV=1
      FN=N
      CONS=1.0/SQRTF(2.0)
```

```
      DO 3 I=1,N
    3 H(I)=0.0
      DO 4 I=1,N
      DO 4 J=1,L
      H(I)=H(I)+A(I,J)*A(I,J)
    4 CONTINUE
      DO 5 I=1,N
      H(I)=SQRTF(H(I))
      DO 5 J=1,L
    5 A(I,J)=A(I,J)/H(I)
  222 CALL VARMAX
  102 LCYCLE=NV-2
      DO 6 I=1,N
      DO 6 J=1,L
    6 AX(I,J)=A(I,J)*H(I)
      WRITE OUTPUT TAPE 2, 1014, LCYCLE
      WRITE OUTPUT TAPE 2, 1001
      DO 7 I=2,NV
      LC=I-1
    7 WRITE OUTPUT TAPE 2, 1002, LC, TV(I)
      WRITE OUTPUT TAPE 2, 1003
      DO 8 I=1,N
      WRITE OUTPUT TAPE 2, 1004, I
    8 WRITE OUTPUT TAPE 2, 1005, (AX(I,J), J= 1,L)
      LV=NV-1
      IF(NV-50)9,999,999
    9 IF(LV-NVALUE)10,999,10
   10 IF(JTEST)13,13,16
   16 IF(ABSF(TV(NV)-TV(LV))-0.0000001)11,11,13
   11 NC=NC+1
   12 IF(NC-JTEST)13,999,999
   13 DO 500 J=1,LL
      II=J+1
      DO 500 K=II,L
      AA=0.0
      BB=0.0
      CC=0.0
      DD=0.0
      DO15I=1,N
      XX=A(I,J)
      YY=A(I,K)
      U=(XX+YY)*(XX-YY)
      V=2.0*XX*YY
      CC=CC+(U+V)*(U-V)
      DD=DD+2.0*U*V
      AA=AA+U
      BB=BB+V
   15 CONTINUE
      T=DD-2.0*AA*BB/FN
      B=CC-(AA**2-BB**2)/FN
      P=0.25*ATANF(T/B)
      TAN4P=T/B
      IF(T-B)1041,1433,1042
 1433 IF(T+B-EPS)500,1043,1043
 1043 COS4T=CONS
      SIN4T=CONS
```

```
         GOTO5000
 1041    TAN4T=ABSF(T)/ABSF(B)
         IF(TAN4T-EPS)8000,1100,1100
 1100    COS4T=1.0/SQRTF(1.0+TAN4T**2)
         SIN4T=TAN4T*COS4T
         GOTO5000
 8000    IF(B)1150,500,500
 1150    SINP=CONS
         COSP=CONS
         GOTO1000
 1042    CTN4T=ABSF(T)/ABSF(B)
         IF(CTN4T-EPS)9000,1200,1200
 1200    SIN4T=1.0/SQRTF(1.0+CTN4T**2)
         COS4T=CTN4T*SIN4T
         GOTO5000
 9000    COS4T=0.0
         SIN4T=1.0
 5000    COS2T=SQRTF((1.0+COS4T)/2.0)
         SIN2T=SIN4T/(2.0*COS2T)
         COST=SQRTF((1.0+COS2T)/2.0)
         SINT=SIN2T/(2.0*COST)
         IF(B)1250,1250,1300
 1300    COSP=COST
         SINP=SINT
         GOTO7000
 1250    COSP=CONS*COST+CONS*SINT
         SINP=ABSF(CONS*COST-CONS*SINT)
 7000    IF(T)1400,1400,1000
 1400    SINP=-SINP
 1000    X=COSP
         Y=SINP
         DO 100 I=1,N
         AIJ      =A(I,J)*X+A(I,K)*Y
         AIK      =-A(I,J)*Y+A(I,K)*X
         A(I,J)=AIJ
  100    A(I,K)=AIK
  500    CONTINUE
         GO TO 222
  999    DO 301 I=1,N
  301    HN(I)=0.0
         DO 303 I=1,N
         H(I)=H(I)*H(I)
         DO 302 J=1,L
  302    HN(I)=HN(I)+AX(I,J)*AX(I,J)
  303    HD(I)=HN(I)-H(I)
         WRITE OUTPUT TAPE 2, 1008
         DO 304 I=1,N
  304    WRITE OUTPUT TAPE 2, 1009, H(I), HN(I), HD(I), I
         N1 = 1
         N2 = 2
         N3 = 3
   17    FORMAT(2I2, 6X, 7F10.6 )
         DO 305  I = 1, N
         PUNCH 17, I, N1, (AX(I,J) , J = 1, 7)
         PUNCH 17,I, N2, (AX(I, J) , J = 8, 14)
  305    PUNCH 17, I, N3,  (AX(I,J) , J= 15, 21)
```

```
      CALL EXIT
      END



      SUBROUTINE VARMAX
      DIMENSION A(100,75),SA(75),SA2(75),V(75),TV(50)
      COMMON A,V,TV,NV,N,L,FN,T,B,P
      SV=0.0
      NV=NV+1
      DO 6 J=1,L
      SA(J)=0.0
      SA2(J)=0.0
    6 CONTINUE
      DO 8 J=1,L
      DO 7 I=1,N
      SA(J)=SA(J)+A(I,J)*A(I,J)
    7 SA2(J)=SA2(J)+(A(I,J)*A(I,J))**2
      SA(J)=SA(J)**2
    8 V(J)=(FN*SA2(J)-SA(J))/FN**2
      DO 9 J=1,L
    9 SV=SV+V(J)
      TV(NV)=SV
      RETURN
      END
```

FACTOR SCORES PROGRAM (FACTOR SCORE)

```
C       FACTOR SCORE.
C
C            THIS PROGRAM COMPUTES FACTOR SCORES FROM RAW SCORES FOR A
C       MAXIMUM OF 50 VARIABLES AND 20 FACTORS.
C
C       INPUT.
C            CONTROL   CARD 1 CONTAINS
C       COL 1-2 M = NUMBER OF VARIABLES
C       COL 3-7 CASES = NUMBER OF CASES
C       COL 8-9 NF = NUMBER OF FACTORS
C       COL 10 RORC = 0 IF A CARD CONTAINS LOADINGS FOR A GIVEN VARIABLE
C            (MATRIX IS IN CARDS AS ROWS).
C                RORC = 1 IF A CARD CONTAINS LOADINGS FOR A GIVEN FACTOR
C            (MATRIX IS IN CARDS AS COLUMNS).
C
C       CARD 2 DEFINES FORMAT FOR MEANS.
C       CARD 3 DEFINES FORMAT FOR STANDARD DEVIATIONS.
C       CARD 4 DEFINES FORMAT FOR FACTOR LOADINGS.
C       CARDS 5 AND 6 DEFINE FORMAT FOR THE SCORE CARDS.
C       STUDENT ID IS THE FIRST VARIABLE READ.   THE ID FIELD IS DEFINED
C       IN F NOTATION, WITH AN 8-DIGIT MAXIMUM.
C            BEGINNING WITH CARD 7 ARE THE MEANS,   FOLLOWED BY THE
C       STANDARD DEVIATIONS, FACTOR LOADINGS, AND FINALLY THE SCORE CARDS.
C
C       OUTPUT.
C            BOTH PRINTED AND PUNCHED OUTPUT IS PRODUCED.   AS A CHECK ON
C       INPUT, FACTOR LOADINGS ARE PRINTED OUT, A LINE OF PRINT BEING THE
C       LOADINGS FOR FACTORS, NOT VARIABLES.   SEVEN FACTOR SCORES ARE
C       PUNCHED PER CARD.   COLUMNS 1-8 CONTAIN STUDENT ID, COL. 9 IS A
C       DECIMAL POINT, AND COL. 10 IS THE NUMBER OF CARDS PER STUDENT.


        DIMENSION FMXM(12), FMS(12), FMV(12), FMX(24), X(50), XM(50),
       1 S(50), V(50,20), Z(50), F(20)
        READ INPUT TAPE 4, 11, M, CASES, NF, RORC
     11 FORMAT (I2, F5.0, I2, F1.0)
        READ INPUT TAPE 4,12, (FMXM(I), I=1,12), (FMS(I), I=1,12),
       1 (FMV(I), I=1,12),(FMX(I), I=1,24)
     12 FORMAT (12A6)
        READ INPUT TAPE 4, FMXM, (XM(I), I=1,M)
        READ INPUT TAPE 4, FMS, (S(I), I=1,M)
        IF (RORC) 13,13,15
     13 DO 14 I= 1,M
     14 READ INPUT TAPE 4, FMV, (V(I,J), J=1,NF)
        GO TO 170
     15 DO 16 J= 1,NF
     16 READ INPUT TAPE 4, FMV, (V(I,J), I= 1,M)
    160 FORMAT(22H0FACTOR COEFFICIENTS    )
    170 PRINT 160
        DO 161  J = 1,NF
    161 PRINT 162, (V(I,J), I = 1,M)
    162 FORMAT (10F10.4)
        PRINT 171
    171 FORMAT(14H1FACTOR SCORES)
     17 READ INPUT TAPE 4, FMX, XID, (X(I), I= 1,M)
        DO 18 I= 1,M
     18 Z(I) = (X(I) - XM(I))/ S(I)
        DO 19 J= 1,NF
        F(J) = 0.0
```

FACTOR SCORE PROGRAM (CONTINUED)

```
      DO 19 I = 1,M
19 F(J) = F(J) + Z(I) * V(I,J)
      NF = NF - 7
      IF (NF) 21, 21, 22
21 NF = NF + 7
      WRITE OUTPUT TAPE 2,20, XID, (F(I), I = 1,NF)
      PUNCH 20, XID, (F(I), I = 1,NF)
20 FORMAT ( F10.1, 7 F10.4 )
      GO TO 25
22 XID = XID + 0.1
      WRITE OUTPUT TAPE 2,20, XID, (F(I), I = 1,7)
      PUNCH 20, XID, (F(I), I = 1,7)
      XID = XID + 0.1
      NF = NF - 7
      IF(NF) 23, 23, 24
23 NF = NF + 14
      WRITE OUTPUT TAPE 2,20, XID, (F(I), I = 8,NF)
      PUNCH 20, XID, (F(I), I = 8,NF)
      GO TO 25
24 WRITE OUTPUT TAPE 2,20, XID, (F(I), I = 8,14)
      PUNCH 20, XID, (F(I), I = 8,14)
      NF = NF + 14
      XID = XID + 0.1
      WRITE OUTPUT TAPE 2,20,XID, (F(I), I = 15,NF)
      PUNCH 20, XID, (F(I), I = 15,NF)
25 CASES = CASES - 1.0
      IF (CASES) 26, 26, 17
26 CALL EXIT
      END
```

8.6 References

Carroll, J. B. (1953). "An Analytical Solution for Approximating Simple Structure in Factor Analysis." *Psychometrika* **18**:23–38.

Carroll, J. B. (1957). "Biquartimin Criterion for Rotation to Oblique Simple Structure in Factor Analysis." *Science* **126**:1114–1115.

Ferguson, G. A. (1954). "The Concept of Parsimony in Factor Analysis." *Psychometrika* **19**:281–290.

Guttman, Louis (1954). "Some Necessary Conditions for Common-Factor Analysis." *Psychometrika* **19**:149–161.

Harmon, H. H. (1960). *Modern Factor Analysis.* Chicago: University of Chicago Press.

Kaiser, H. F. (1958). "The Varimax Criterion for Analytic Rotation in Factor Analysis." *Psychometrika* **23**:187–200.

——— (1959). "Computer Program for Varimax Rotation in Factor Analysis." *Educational and Psychological Measurement* **19**:413–420.

——— (1960). Comments on Communalities and the Number of Factors. Read at an informal conference, "The Communality Problem in Factor Analysis," Washington University, St. Louis (dittoed).

——— (1962) "Formulas for Component Scores." *Psychometrika* **27**:33–37.

Kendall, M. G. (1957). *A Course in Multivariate Analysis* London: Charles Griffin and Co., Chapter 2.

Michael, W. B. (1958). "An Empirical Study of the Comparability of Factor Structure When Unities and Communality Estimates are Used." *Educational and Psychological Measurement.* **18**:347.

Mosteller, F., and Bush, R. R. (1954). "Selected quantitative techniques." In Lindzey, G. (Ed.), *Handbook of Social Psychology.* Cambridge, Mass.: Addison-Wesley, Vol. I, pp. 289–334.

Neuhaus, J. O., and Wrigley, Chas. (1954). "The Quartimax Method: An Analytical Approach to Orthogonal Simple Structure." *British Journal of Statistical Psychology* **7**:81–91.

Saunders, D. R. (1953). "An Analytical Method for Rotation to Orthogonal Simple Structure." *American Psychologist* **8**:428 (Abstract).

Thurstone, L. L. (1947). *Multiple-Factor Analysis.* Chicago: University of Chicago Press.

Wrigley, Charles (1957). "The Case Against Communalities." *Research Report*, 19. Berkely: University of California (mimeographed).

Reference for Example

Cooley, W. W., and Mierzwa, J. A. (1961). "The Rorschach Test and The Career Development of Scientists," Cambridge, Mass. *Scientific Careers Study*, Interim Report 5, Harvard Graduate School of Education.

CHAPTER NINE

Utility subroutines for numerical analysis

The flow charts in the preceding chapters have revealed how much the availability of certain subroutines has eased the task of coding the statistical analyses we have presented. It is questionable whether this set of programs would have materialized if it had been necessary to code the basic numerical analyses of inverses and eigenvalues required. Presumably the reader is not a mathematician, and certainly the authors are not, and therefore we may share a certain attitude of unconcern with how a numerical-analysis task gets done, as long as we have the comforting assurance that through the ministrations of a talented and slavish subroutine it does get done. It is so remarkably easy to "CALL MATINV" or "CALL HDIAG." In the service rendered research workers by the applied mathematicians who have developed and coded techniques and corresponding subroutines for matrix inversion and matrix diagonalization we see a clear example of the fruits of the division of labor. The purpose of this chapter is to provide acknowledgements and references for the two "work-horse" subroutines, MATINV and HDIAG, which the authors did not code, descriptions of the methods of LROOT and DIRNM which we did code, and FORTRAN listings of these four utility subroutines.

9.1 Computation of the Inverse of a Matrix by the Gauss-Jordan Method

The mathematics of the Gauss-Jordan method are not discussed since an excellent description of the procedure may be found in Orden (1960). The subroutine MATINV for which the FORTRAN listing is included here was prepared by Burton S. Garbow, Argonne National Laboratory, Applied Mathematics Division, Lemont, Illinois. The authors have relied heavily on Garbow's routine and have found it to be completely satisfactory. They are responsible for the flow chart. In the SHARE write-up of MATINV (SHARE 644) Garbow says of the method:

Jordan's method is used to reduce a matrix **A** to the identity matrix **I** through a succession of elementary transformations; $l_n l_{n-1} \cdots l_1 \mathbf{A} = \mathbf{I}$. If these transformations are simultaneously applied to **I** and to a matrix **B** of constant vectors, the result is $\mathbf{A}^{-1}$ and **X** where $\mathbf{AX} = \mathbf{B}$.

Computing time is approximately n^3 seconds where n is the order of the matrix of coefficients.[1] The subroutine is called with the instruction CALL MATINV (A, N, B, M, DETERM). The variables in the argument list are of course dummies, which may be replaced by the names of the corresponding variables in the main, or calling, program.

A is the matrix to be inverted.
N is the order of A.
B is the location of the criterion vector, if any.
M = 1 if equations are to be solved; if more than one criterion vector is
    involved, M is the number of column vectors in B; M = 0 if only the
    inverse and determinant of A are to be computed.
DETERM is the location where |A| is placed. On RETURN $\mathbf{A}^{-1}$ has replaced
    A and the solution vector, if any, has replaced B.

9.2 Computation of the Latent Roots and Vectors of a Real Symmetric Matrix by the Jacobi Method

No discussion of the mathematics of the Jacobi method is included here because a clear and complete account, with flow chart, is readily available in Greenstadt (1960). The subroutine HDIAG for which the FORTRAN listing is included here was prepared by F. J. Corbato, Associate Director, M.I.T. Computation Center, Cambridge, Mass., with the assistance of members of his staff. The reader will already have noted the authors' heavy reliance on this subroutine, which they have found completely satisfactory. The roots and vectors of large matrices are computed in approximately n^3 seconds, where n is the order of the matrix. If no eigenvectors are computed this time is reduced by about 40 per cent. This is the case when HDIAG is used as the basis of the calculation of the determinant as the continuous product of the eigenvalues.

The subroutine is called with the instruction CALL HDIAG (H, N, IEGEN; U, NR,)
where H is the matrix to be diagonalized.
    N is the order of H.
    IEGEN = 0 if eigenvalues and eigenvectors are to be computed;
    IEGEN = 1 if only eigenvalues are to be computed. On RETURN the
        eigenvalues are stored in the diagonal elements of H.
    U is the matrix in the columns of which the eigenvectors are stored.
    NR is the number of rotations executed by the subroutine.

---

[1] Time estimates here and in section 9.2 are for the IBM 704 computer.

9.3   Computation of the Largest Latent Root, and Its Vector, of a Real Square Matrix by the Iterative, or Power, Method[2]

The problem is to compute the largest eigenvalue and the associated eigenvector for a real square nonsymmetric matrix G, where G has been formed from two real symmetric matrices A and B, so that $G = B^{-1}A$. Given the problem $Gx = \lambda x$, choose a trial vector v_0. If v_0 is an eigenvector, Gv will be a multiple of v_0, the multiplication factor being the eigenvalue λ. In general, v_0 will not be an eigenvector. By iteration successive vectors may be produced from the multiplication $v_r = Gv_{r-1}$ where r is the number of iterations performed. For example, the first iteration produces $v_1 = Gv_0$. This iteration scheme will produce convergence to the eigenvector associated with the eigenvalue of largest absolute value, provided that the second largest eigenvalue is not equal to nor close to the first. Actually, the greater the separation of the largest root from the second root the faster the convergence. For this reason it may be desirable to solve the problem $G^2x = \lambda Gx = \lambda^2 x$, since the roots of G^2 will be better separated than the roots of G, and the vector is not affected by multiplication. It is also certain that there are no negative roots of G^2.

In the iteration scheme the approximation to the eigenvalue may be conveniently obtained by scaling each approximation to the eigenvector by dividing all its elements by its first element, which is the approximation to the eigenvalue. If the scaled approximation vector is called $\bar{v}_r$, then the next approximation vector is produced by $v_{r+1} = G\bar{v}_r$ and of course v_{r+1} is then scaled.

For statistical work at least, a sensible first trial vector is provided by putting 1.0 in each element of v_0. If it is desired to compute the smallest eigenvalue of G rather than the largest, substitute G^{-1} for G when calling LROOT. The subroutine is called with the instruction CALL LROOT (G, N, ROOT, VECT, L)
where G is the matrix for which the largest eigenvalue is desired.

> N is the order of G.
> L = 1 to print the results of each iteration;
> L = 0 if only the final root and vector are to be printed.
> On RETURN
> ROOT contains the largest eigenvalue of G;
> VECT contains the normalized eigenvector.

9.4   Computation of the Complete Set of Latent Roots and Vectors of a Real Square Nonsymmetric Matrix

The best-known method for approximating the complete set of eigenvalues and eigenvectors of a matrix, Jacobi's method, is restricted to real symmetric matrices. The matrix $G = B^{-1}A$ is nonsymmetric, although it is the product of two real symmetric matrices. The following algebra demonstrates that it is possible to get the roots and vectors of G by successive diagonalization of two real symmetric

[2] The authors acknowledge the assistance given them by Dr. Robert Owens, Department of Mathematics, U.N.H., in their study of this procedure. A good reference is Stephen H. Crandall (1956). *Engineering Analysis*. New York: McGraw-Hill Book Co., 1956, pp. 91–95.

matrices,[3] and this is the manner in which the authors compute multiple-discriminant functions and the complete set of canonical correlations.

$$(9.1) \qquad (\mathbf{B} - \theta\mathbf{I})\mathbf{h} = 0; \qquad \mathbf{B} = \mathbf{H}\mathbf{D}_\theta\mathbf{H}' = \mathbf{H}\mathbf{D}_\theta^{1/2}\mathbf{D}_\theta^{1/2}\mathbf{H}'$$

where $\mathbf{D}_\theta$ is the diagonal matrix of the eigenvalues of $\mathbf{B}$ and $\mathbf{H}$ contains the eigenvectors of $\mathbf{B}$ in its columns,

$$(9.2) \qquad (\mathbf{A} - \lambda\mathbf{H}\mathbf{D}_\theta^{1/2}\mathbf{D}_\theta^{1/2}\mathbf{H}')\mathbf{v} = 0,$$

$$(9.3) \qquad (\mathbf{D}_\theta^{-1/2}\mathbf{H}'\mathbf{A} - \lambda\mathbf{D}_\theta^{1/2}\mathbf{H}')\mathbf{v} = 0,$$

$$(9.4) \qquad (\mathbf{D}_\theta^{-1/2}\mathbf{H}'\mathbf{A}\mathbf{H}\mathbf{D}_\theta^{-1/2} - \lambda\mathbf{I})\mathbf{D}_\theta^{1/2}\mathbf{H}'\mathbf{v} = 0;$$

and letting $\mathbf{B}^{-1/2} = \mathbf{H}\mathbf{D}_\theta^{-1/2}$ and $m = \mathbf{D}_\theta^{1/2}\mathbf{H}'\mathbf{v}$,

$$(9.5) \qquad [(\mathbf{B}^{-1/2})'\mathbf{A}\mathbf{B}^{-1/2} - \lambda\mathbf{I}]\mathbf{m} = 0;$$
$$(\mathbf{B}^{-1/2})'\mathbf{A}\mathbf{B}^{-1/2} = \mathbf{M}\mathbf{D}_\lambda\mathbf{M}'; \quad \mathbf{V} = \mathbf{B}^{-1/2}\mathbf{M}.$$

where $\mathbf{D}_\lambda$ and $\mathbf{V}$ represent the diagonal matrix of eigenvalues and the matrix of eigenvectors (as columns) of $\mathbf{B}^{-1}\mathbf{A}$.

The steps by which the subroutine DIRNM computes the eigenvalue problem just described are

(1) Compute roots and vectors $(\mathbf{D}_\theta, \mathbf{H})$ of $\mathbf{B}$ by HDIAG.
(2) Form $1/\sqrt{\theta_i}$ for each root θ_i, giving as a vector the diagonal elements of the diagonal matrix $\mathbf{D}_\theta^{-1/2}$.
(3) Form $\mathbf{B}^{-1/2} = \mathbf{H}\mathbf{D}_\theta^{-1/2}$ by multiplying the ith column vector of $\mathbf{H}$ by $1/\sqrt{\theta_i}$, doing this for all i columns.
(4) Form $(\mathbf{B}^{-1/2})'\mathbf{A}\mathbf{B}^{-1/2}$ and compute its roots and vectors $(\mathbf{D}_\lambda, \mathbf{M})$.
(5) Form $\mathbf{V} = \mathbf{B}^{-1/2}\mathbf{M}$ and normalize the vectors in $\mathbf{V}$. The subroutine DIRNM is called by the instruction

CALL DIRNM (A, M, B, X, XL)

where A and B are the input matrices, both symmetric, of order M.

    Upon RETURN

    XL is a vector containing the eigenvalues of $\mathbf{B}^{-1}\mathbf{A}$.

    X is a matrix the columns of which contain the normalized eigenvectors.

9.5   Computation of the Latent Roots and Vectors of a Real Symmetric Matrix by the Exhaustion Method

Although the authors have generally utilized the Jacobi method for solving this problem, they are indebted to Mr. Bary G. Wingersky, Manager of the U.N.H. Computation Center, for calling to their attention the great utility of the exhaustion method of computing all the eigenvalues and eigenvectors of a real symmetric matrix. Mr. Wingersky points out that this method is particularly attractive for workers on smaller computers, because the required program is quite short. The

---

[3] The authors are indebted to Mr. Richard Willard, Statistical Analyst, Registrar's Office, M.I.T., Cambridge, Mass., who first explained this method to them.

method is described and proved in Faddeeva (1959) and in Kendall (1957). The latter speaks of it as a method of "extracting" components from a matrix.

The exhaustion method requires that the largest root and vector be provided. We have seen that the standard iterative procedure, incorporated in subroutine LROOT, is a good method of computing these. Given λ_1 and V_{1i} (a column vector) computed from A, the matrix $C1 = \lambda_1 V_{1i} V_{1i}'$ is formed and is subtracted from A, so that $A1 = A - C1$. The difference matrix $A1$ is then subjected to LROOT and a new λ and V are computed. These are λ_2 and V_{2i} of matrix A. Next $C2 = \lambda_2 V_{2i} V_{2i}'$ is formed, and $A2 = A1 - C2$. The matrix $A2$ is subjected to LROOT, and the process continues as long as there are nonzero roots of A to be found.

Kendall emphasizes that the convergence to a solution in LROOT may be accelerated by a factor of k if k is the power to which the matrix A is raised before being subjected to LROOT.

A flow diagram and FORTRAN listing for a subroutine (subroutine EXTRAC) incorporating the exhaustion method follow.

Flow Diagram for Matrix Inversion, Solution of Simultaneous Equations, and Determinant, by the Gauss-Jordan Method (Subroutine MATINV)

MATINV is called with the argument list (A, N, B, M, DET) where A is the matrix to be inverted, N is the order of the matrix, M is the number of column constant vectors, which are in B (M = 0 signals inversion only). On completion of the subroutine, A has been replaced by A^{-1}, | A | is in DET, and if M $\neq$ 0 the solution vectors have replaced the constant vectors in B.

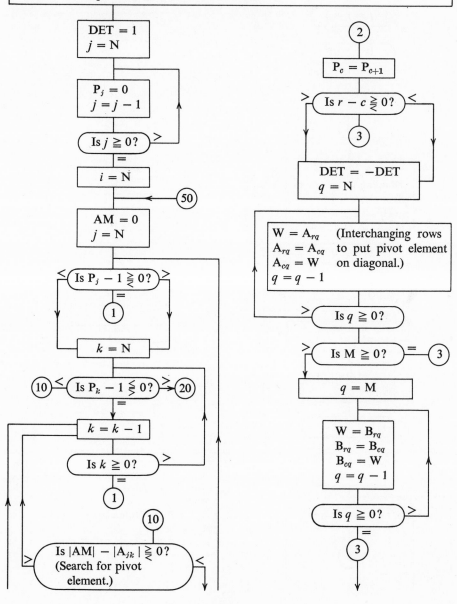

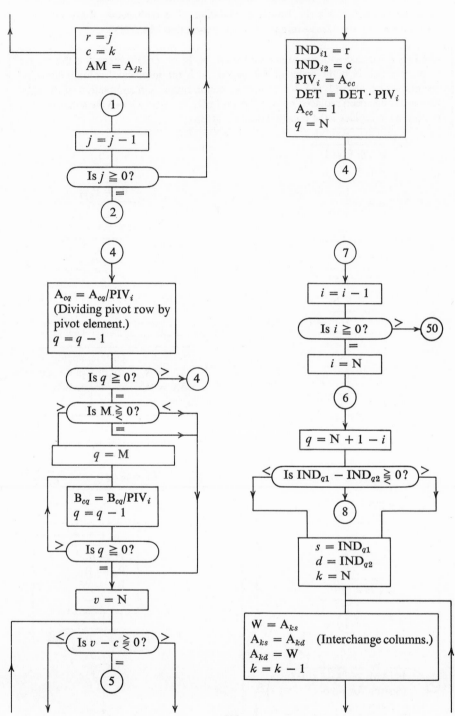

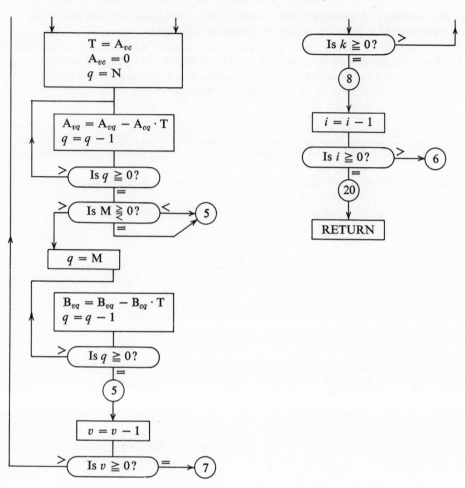

Flow Diagram for Standard Iterative Method for Largest Eigenvalue and Associated Eigenvector of a Real Square Matrix (Subroutine LROOT)

LROOT is called with the argument list (G, N, ROOT, VECT, L) where G is the $N \times N$ real square matrix to be diagonalized and is provided by the calling program. $L = 1$ to print out the results of each iteration, $L = 0$ if only the final root and vector are to be printed. Subscripts have the ranges:

$$v = 1, 2, 3, \ldots, N \qquad w = 1, 2, 3, \ldots, N.$$

TEST $= 10^{-7}$ determining the precision of the computation of a root and vector.

K $= 9$ determining the number of iterations allowed before the test of convergence is switched in.

IT $= 0$ IT becomes the number of the iteration in progress.

$V_v = 1$

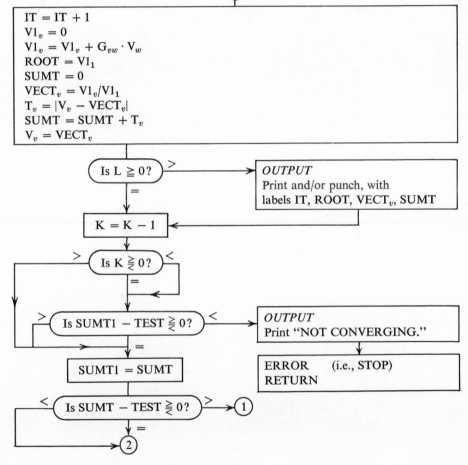

IT $=$ IT $+ 1$

$V1_v = 0$

$V1_v = V1_v + G_{vw} \cdot V_w$

ROOT $= V1_1$

SUMT $= 0$

$\text{VECT}_v = V1_v / V1_1$

$T_v = |V_v - \text{VECT}_v|$

SUMT $=$ SUMT $+ T_v$

$V_v = \text{VECT}_v$

Is L $\geqq 0$?

OUTPUT
Print and/or punch, with labels IT, ROOT, VECT_v, SUMT

K $=$ K $- 1$

Is K $\gtreqless 0$?

Is SUMT1 $-$ TEST $\gtreqless 0$?

OUTPUT
Print "NOT CONVERGING."

SUMT1 $=$ SUMT

ERROR   (i.e., STOP)
RETURN

Is SUMT $-$ TEST $\gtreqless 0$?

9.2. Flow Diagram for Subroutine LROOT (Continued)

$$\downarrow$$

(2)

$$\downarrow$$

SUMV = 0

SUMV = SUMV + $\text{VECT}_v{}^2$

DEN = $\sqrt{\text{SUMV}}$

$\text{VECT}_v = \text{VECT}_v/\text{DEN}$ normalizing the final vector.

$\text{GXX}_v = 0$

$\text{GXX}_v = \text{GXX}_v + \text{G}_{vw} \cdot \text{VECT}_w$ computing G · VECT.

$\text{XL}_v = \text{VECT}_v \cdot \text{ROOT}$ computing ROOT · VECT.

(The last two computations are a check, since GXX should be equal to XL.)

OUTPUT

Print, with labels, ROOT, VECT_v, GXX_v, XL_v.

Punch VECT_v.

(ROOT (the eigenvalue) and VECT_v (the eigenvector) are also reported to the main or calling program).

$$\downarrow$$

RETURN

Flow Diagram for Computation of Complete Set of Eigenvalues and Eigenvectors of the Equation $A \cdot X = B \cdot X \cdot \Lambda$ (Subroutine DIRNM)

DIRNM is called with the argument list (A, M, B, X, L) where A and B are the input matrices and are square and symmetric, M is the order of A and B, X is the matrix in which the eigenvectors will be placed columnwise, and L is the vector in which the eigenvalues will be placed. Throughout this flow diagram subscript ranges are: $v = 1, 2, 3, \ldots, M;\ w = 1, 2, 3, \ldots, M;\ x = 1, 2, 3, \ldots, M.$

SUBROUTINE

Call subroutine HDIAG to compute the eigenvalues of B (placing them in the diagonal of B) and the eigenvectors of B (placing them columnwise in X).

$S_v = 1/\sqrt{|B_{vv}|}$
$B_{vw} = X_{vw} \cdot S_w$
$X_{vw} = 0$
$X_{vw} = X_{vw} + B_{xv} \cdot A_{xw}$
$C_{vw} = 0$
$C_{vw} = C_{vw} + X_{vw} \cdot B_{xw}$ forming the matrix $B^{-1/2'} \cdot A \cdot B^{-1/2}$ of the notes.

SUBROUTINE

Call subroutine HDIAG to compute the eigenvalues of C (placing them in the diagonal of C) and the eigenvectors of C (placing them columnwise in X).

$L_v = C_{vv}$ placing eigenvalues in L.
$C_{vw} = 0$
$C_{vw} = C_{vw} + B_{vx} \cdot X_{xw}$

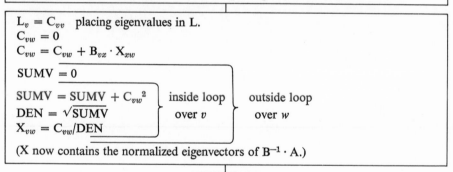

SUMV $= 0$

SUMV $=$ SUMV $+ C_{vw}^2$ inside loop   outside loop
DEN $= \sqrt{\text{SUMV}}$ over v over w
$X_{vw} = C_{vw}/\text{DEN}$

(X now contains the normalized eigenvectors of $B^{-1} \cdot A$.)

RETURN

9.4

Flow Diagram for Complete Eigenvalues and Eigenvectors of a Real Symmetric Matrix by the Exhaustion Method (Subroutine EXTRAC)

EXTRAC is called with the argument list (A, M, X, XL, K) where A is the matrix to be diagonalized, M is the order of A, and K is the number of positive (nonzero) roots to be extracted. On RETURN, the subroutine has placed the eigenvalues of A in the K elements of vector XL and the eigenvectors of A columnwise in the K columns of the $M \times K$ matrix X.

$$L = 1$$

SUBROUTINE
Call subroutine LROOT to compute the largest eigenvalue of A (placing it in ROOT) and the associated eigenvector (placing it in V).

$XL_L = \text{ROOT}$
$X_{iL} = V_i$
$A_{ij} = A_{ij} - V_i \cdot V_j \cdot \text{ROOT}$
$L = L + 1$
$K = K - 1$

In this box, the range of subscript $i = 1, 2, 3, \ldots, M; \ j = 1, 2, 3, \ldots, M.$

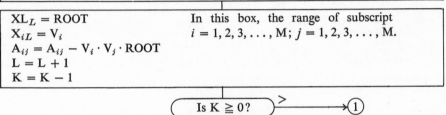

Is $K \geq 0$? $>$ ①

RETURN

MATRIX INVERSION BY THE GAUSS-JORDAN METHOD (MATINV)

```
C      SUBROUTINE MATINV.
C
C          PROGRAMMED BY BURTON S. GARBOW, ARGONNE NATIONAL LABORATORY,
C      AND REPORTED IN IBM 704-709 SHARE LIBRARY AS AN F402.
C          THIS SUBROUTINE COMPUTES THE INVERSE AND DETERMINANT OF
C      MATRIX A, OF ORDER N, BY THE GAUSS-JORDAN METHOD. A-INVERSE
C      REPLACES A, AND THE DETERMINANT OF A IS PLACED IN DETERM. IF
C      M = 1 THE VECTOR B CONTAINS THE CONSTANT VECTOR WHEN MATINV IS
C      CALLED, AND THIS IS REPLACED WITH THE SOLUTION VECTOR. IF M = 0,
C      NO SIMULTANEOUS EQUATION SOLUTIONS ARE CALLED FOR, AND B IS NOT
C      PERTINENT. N IS NOT TO EXCEED 50.
C      A, N, B, M, AND DETERM IN THE ARGUMENT LIST ARE DUMMY VARIABLES.
C
C
       DIMENSION IPIVOT(50), A(50,50), B(50,1), INDEX(50,2), PIVOT(50)
       COMMON PIVOT, INDEX, IPIVOT
       EQUIVALENCE (IROW,JROW), (ICOLUM,JCOLUM), (AMAX, T, SWAP)
C      INITIALIZATION
   10 DETERM=1.0
   15 DO 20 J=1,N
   20 IPIVOT(J)=0
   30 DO 550 I=1,N
C      SEARCH FOR PIVOT ELEMENT
   40 AMAX=0.0
   45 DO 105 J=1,N
   50 IF (IPIVOT(J)-1) 60, 105, 60
   60 DO 100 K=1,N
   70 IF (IPIVOT(K)-1) 80, 100, 740
   80 IF (ABSF(AMAX)-ABSF(A(J,K))) 85, 100, 100
   85 IROW=J
   90 ICOLUM=K
   95 AMAX=A(J,K)
  100 CONTINUE
  105 CONTINUE
  110 IPIVOT(ICOLUM)=IPIVOT(ICOLUM)+1
C      INTERCHANGE ROWS TO PUT PIVOT ELEMENT ON DIAGONAL
  130 IF (IROW-ICOLUM) 140, 260, 140
  140 DETERM=-DETERM
  150 DO 200 L=1,N
  160 SWAP=A(IROW,L)
  170 A(IROW,L)=A(ICOLUM,L)
  200 A(ICOLUM,L)=SWAP
  205 IF(M) 260, 260, 210
  210 DO 250 L=1, M
  220 SWAP=B(IROW,L)
  230 B(IROW,L)=B(ICOLUM,L)
  250 B(ICOLUM,L)=SWAP
  260 INDEX(I,1)=IROW
  270 INDEX(I,2)=ICOLUM
  310 PIVOT(I)=A(ICOLUM,ICOLUM)
  320 DETERM=DETERM*PIVOT(I)
C      DIVIDE PIVOT ROW BY PIVOT ELEMENT
  330 A(ICOLUM,ICOLUM)=1.0
  340 DO 350 L=1,N
  350 A(ICOLUM,L)=A(ICOLUM,L)/PIVOT(I)
  355 IF(M) 380, 380, 360
  360 DO 370 L=1,M
  370 B(ICOLUM,L)=B(ICOLUM,L)/PIVOT(I)
C      REDUCE NON-PIVOT ROWS
```

SUBROUTINE MATINV (CONTINUED)

```
      380 DO 550 L1=1,N
      390 IF(L1-ICOLUM) 400, 550, 400
      400 T=A(L1,ICOLUM)
      420 A(L1,ICOLUM)=0.0
      430 DO 450 L=1,N
      450 A(L1,L)=A(L1,L)-A(ICOLUM,L)*T
      455 IF(M) 550, 550, 460
      460 DO 500 L=1,M
      500 B(L1,L)=B(L1,L)-B(ICOLUM,L)*T
      550 CONTINUE
C         INTERCHANGE COLUMNS
      600 DO 710 I=1,N
      610 L=N+1-I
      620 IF (INDEX(L,1)-INDEX(L,2)) 630, 710, 630
      630 JROW=INDEX(L,1)
      640 JCOLUM=INDEX(L,2)
      650 DO 705 K=1,N
      660 SWAP=A(K,JROW)
      670 A(K,JROW)=A(K,JCOLUM)
      700 A(K,JCOLUM)=SWAP
      705 CONTINUE
      710 CONTINUE
      740 RETURN
          END
```

EIGENVALUES AND EIGENVECTORS OF A REAL SYMMETRIC MATRIX BY THE JACOBI METHOD (HDIAG)

```
C       SUBROUTINE HDIAG.
C
C           PROGRAMMED BY F. J. CORBATO AND M. MERWIN OF THE M. I. T.
C       COMPUTATION CENTER.
C
C           THIS SUBROUTINE COMPUTES THE EIGENVALUES AND EIGENVECTORS
C       OF A REAL SYMMETRIC MATRIX, H, OF ORDER N ( WHERE N MUST BE LESS
C       THAN 51), AND PLACES THE EIGENVALUES IN THE DIAGONAL ELEMENTS OF
C       THE MATRIX H, AND PLACES THE EIGENVECTORS (NORMALIZED) IN THE
C       COLUMNS OF THE MATRIX U.   IEGEN IS SET AS 1 IF ONLY EIGENVALUES
C       ARE DESIRED, AND IS SET TO 0 WHEN VECTORS ARE REQUIRED.  NR CON-
C       TAINS THE NUMBER OF ROTATIONS DONE.
C
C       H, N, IENGEN, U, AND NR OF THE ARGUMENT LIST ARE DUMMY VARIABLES
C       AND MAY BE NAMED DIFFERENTLY IN THE CALLING OF THE SUBROUTINE.
C
C       SUBROUTINE PLACES COMPUTER IN THE FLOATING TRAP MODE
C       THE SUBROUTINE OPERATES ONLY ON THE ELEMENTS OF H THAT ARE TO THE
C            RIGHT OF THE MAIN DIAGONAL.  THUS, ONLY A TRIANGULAR
C            SECTION NEED BE STORED IN THE ARRAY H.
        SUBROUTINE    HDIAG (H,N,IEGEN,U,NR)
         DIMENSION H(50,50), U(50,50), X(50), IQ(50)
        CALL EFM
        IF (IEGEN) 15,10,15
   10   DO 14 I=1,N
        DO 14 J=1,N
        IF(I-J)12,11,12
   11   U(I,J)=1.0
        GO TO 14
   12   U(I,J)=0.
   14   CONTINUE
   15   NR = 0
        IF (N-1) 1000,1000,17
C       SCAN FOR LARGEST OFF-DIAGONAL ELEMENT IN EACH ROW
C       X(I) CONTAINS LARGEST ELEMENT IN ITH ROW
C       IQ(I) HOLDS SECOND SUBSCRIPT DEFINING POSITION OF ELEMENT
   17   NMI1=N-1
        DO 30 I=1,NMI1
        X(I) = 0.
        IPL1=I+1
        DO 30 J=IPL1,N
        IF ( X(I) - ABSF( H(I,J))) 20,20,30
   20   X(I)=ABSF(H(I,J))
        IQ(I)=J
   30   CONTINUE
C       SET INDICATOR FOR SHUT-OFF.RAP=2**-27,NR=NO. OF ROTATIONS
        RAP=7.450580596E-9
        HDTEST=1.0E38
C       FIND MAXIMUM OF X(I) S FOR PIVOT ELEMENT AND
C       TEST FOR END OF PROBLEM
   40   DO  70  I=1,NMI1
        IF (I-1) 60,60,45
   45   IF ( XMAX- X(I)) 60,70,70
   60   XMAX=X(I)
        IPIV=I
        JPIV=IQ(I)
   70   CONTINUE
C       IS MAX. X(I) EQUAL TO ZERO, IF LESS THAN HDTEST, REVISE HDTEST
        IF ( XMAX) 1000,1000,80
```

```
 80    IF (HDTEST) 90,90,85
 85    IF (XMAX - HDTEST) 90,90,148
 90    HDIMIN = ABSF( H(1,1) )
       DO 110  I= 2,N
       IF (HDIMIN- ABSF( H(I,I))) 110,110,100
100    HDIMIN=ABSF(H(I,I))
110    CONTINUE
       HDTEST=HDIMIN*RAP
C      RETURN IF MAX.H(I,J)LESS THAN(2**-27)ABSF(H(K,K)-MIN)
       IF (HDTEST- XMAX) 148,1000,1000
148    NR = NR+1
C      COMPUTE TANGENT, SINE AND COSINE,H(I,I),H(J,J)
150    TANG=SIGNF(2.0,(H(IPIV,IPIV)-H(JPIV,JPIV)))*H(IPIV,JPIV)/(ABSF(H(I
      1PIV,IPIV)-H(JPIV,JPIV))+SQRTF((H(IPIV,IPIV)-H(JPIV,JPIV))**2+4.0*H
      2(IPIV,JPIV)**2))
       COSINE=1.0/SQRTF(1.0+TANG**2)
       SINE=TANG*COSINE
       HII=H(IPIV,IPIV)
       H(IPIV,IPIV)=COSINE**2*(HII+TANG*(2.*H(IPIV,JPIV)+TANG*H(JPIV,JPIV
      1)))
       H(JPIV,JPIV)=COSINE**2*(H(JPIV,JPIV)-TANG*(2.*H(IPIV,JPIV)-TANG*H
      1II))
       H(IPIV,JPIV)=0.
C       PSEUDO RANK THE EIGENVALUES
C       ADJUST SINE AND COS FOR COMPUTATION OF H(IK) AND U(IK)
       IF ( H(IPIV,IPIV) -  H(JPIV,JPIV)) 152,153,153
152    HTEMP = H(IPIV,IPIV)
       H(IPIV,IPIV) = H(JPIV,JPIV)
       H(JPIV,JPIV) = HTEMP
C       RECOMPUTE SINE AND COS
       HTEMP = SIGNF (1.0, -SINE) * COSINE
       COSINE = ABSF (SINE)
       SINE = HTEMP
153    CONTINUE
C      INSPECT THE IQS BETWEEN I+1 AND N-1 TO DETERMINE
C      WHETHER A NEW MAXIMUM VALUE SHOULD BE COMPUTED SINCE
C      THE PRESENT MAXIMUM IS IN THE I OR J ROW.
       DO 350 I=1,NMI1
       IF(I-IPIV)210,350,200
200    IF(I-JPIV)210,350,210
210    IF(IQ(I)-IPIV)230,240,230
230    IF(IQ(I)-JPIV)350,240,350
240    K=IQ(I)
250    HTEMP=H(I,K)
       H(I,K)=0.
       IPL1=I+1
       X(I) =0.
C      SEARCH IN DEPLETED ROW FOR NEW MAXIMUM
       DO 320 J=IPL1,N
       IF ( X(I)- ABSF( H(I,J)) ) 300,300,320
300    X(I) = ABSF(H(I,J))
       IQ(I)=J
320    CONTINUE
       H(I,K)=HTEMP
350    CONTINUE
       X(IPIV) =0.
```

```
      X(JPIV) =0.
C     CHANGE THE OTHER ELEMENTS OF H
      DO 530 I=1,N
      IF(I-IPIV)370,530,420
370   HTEMP = H(I,IPIV)
      H(I,IPIV) = COSINE*HTEMP + SINE*H(I,JPIV)
      IF ( X(I) -  ABSF( H(I,IPIV)) )380,390,390
380   X(I) = ABSF(H(I,IPIV))
      IQ(I) = IPIV
390   H(I,JPIV) = -SINE*HTEMP + COSINE*H(I,JPIV)
      IF ( X(I) -  ABSF(H(I,JPIV)) ) 400,530,530
400   X(I) = ABSF(H(I,JPIV))
      IQ(I) = JPIV
      GO TO 530
420   IF(I-JPIV)430,530,480
430   HTEMP = H(IPIV,I)
      H(IPIV,I) = COSINE*HTEMP + SINE*H(I,JPIV)
      IF ( X(IPIV) -  ABSF( H(IPIV,I)) ) 440,450,450
440   X(IPIV) = ABSF(H(IPIV,I))
      IQ(IPIV) = I
450   H(I,JPIV) = -SINE*HTEMP + COSINE*H(I,JPIV)
      IF ( X(I) -  ABSF( H(I,JPIV)) ) 400,530,530
480   HTEMP = H(IPIV,I)
      H(IPIV,I) = COSINE*HTEMP + SINE*H(JPIV,I)
      IF ( X(IPIV) -  ABSF( H(IPIV,I)) ) 490,500,500
490   X(IPIV) = ABSF(H(IPIV,I))
      IQ(IPIV) = I
500   H(JPIV,I) = -SINE*HTEMP + COSINE*H(JPIV,I)
      IF ( X(JPIV) -  ABSF( H(JPIV,I)) ) 510,530,530
510   X(JPIV) = ABSF(H(JPIV,I))
      IQ(JPIV) = I
530   CONTINUE
C     TEST FOR COMPUTATION OF EIGENVECTORS
      IF(IEGEN)40,540,40
540   DO 550 I=1,N
      HTEMP=U(I,IPIV)
      U(I,IPIV)=COSINE*HTEMP+SINE*U(I,JPIV)
550   U(I,JPIV)=-SINE*HTEMP+COSINE*U(I,JPIV)
      GO TO 40
1000  RETURN
      END
      SUBROUTINE EFM
      RETURN
      END
```

MAXIMUM EIGENVALUE AND EIGENVECTOR OF A NON-NEGATIVE DEFINITE MATRIX BY THE STANDARD ITERATIVE METHOD (LROOT)

```
C       SUBROUTINE LROOT.
C
C       LROOT COMPUTES THE MAXIMUM LATENT ROOT AND ASSOCIATED VECTOR OF G,
C       A SQUARE MATRIX OF ORDER N, WHICH IS THE PRODUCT OF B-1 A. THE
C       STANDARD ITERATIVE METHOD, OR POWER METHOD, IS EMPLOYED. BEFORE
C       CALLING LROOT STORE G, N, AND L=1 IF IT IS DESIRED TO PRINT
C       RESULTS OF EACH ITERATION, L=0 IF NOT.
C       G, N, ROOT, VECT, AND L OF THE ARGUMENT LIST ARE DUMMY NAMES AND
C       MAY BE NAMED DIFFERENTLY IN THE CALLING STATEMENT.
C
        SUBROUTINE LROOT (G,N,ROOT,VECT,L)
        DIMENSION G(50,50), VECT(50), V(50), V1(50), T(50), GX(50), XL(50)
        TEST = 0.00001
        IT = 0
        K = 6
C
        PRINT 21
     21 FORMAT (20H0G, THE INPUT MATRIX)
        DO 22  I = 1,N
     22 PRINT 8, (G(I,J),  J = 1,N)
        DO 1   I = 1,N
      1 V(I)  = 1.0
C
    100 IT = IT + 1
        DO 2   I = 1,N
        V1(I) = 0.0
        DO 2   J = 1,N
      2 V1(I) = V1(I) + G(I,J) * V(J)
C
        ROOT = V1(1)
        SUMT = 0.0
        DO 3   I = 1,N
        VECT(I) = V1(I)/ V1(1)
        T(I) = ABSF (V(I) - VECT(I))
        SUMT = SUMT + T(I)
      3 V(I) = VECT(I)
C
        IF (L) 10, 10, 4
      4 PRINT 5, IT
      5 FORMAT (15H0ITERATION NO. I3)
        PRINT 6, ROOT
      6 FORMAT (8H0ROOT = F14.7)
        PRINT 7
      7 FORMAT (7H0VECTOR)
        PRINT 8, (VECT(I),  I = 1,N)
      8 FORMAT (5F14.7)
        PRINT 9, SUMT
      9 FORMAT (8H0SUMT = F14.7)
C
     10 K = K - 1
        IF (K) 110, 110, 13
C       CONVERGENCE TEST SWITCHES IN AFTER FIVE ITERATIONS.
    110 IF (SUMT1 - SUMT) 11, 13, 13
C
     11 PRINT 12
     12 FORMAT (15H0NOT CONVERGING)
        CALL EXIT
C
     13 SUMT1 = SUMT
```

```
        IF (SUMT - TEST) 14, 14, 100
C
     14 SUMV = 0.0
        DO 141  I = 1, N
    141 SUMV = SUMV + (VECT(I)**2.)
        DEN = SQRF (SUMV)
        DO 142  I = 1, N
    142 VECT(I) = VECT(I) / DEN
C       VECT(I) HAS BEEN NORMALIZED
        DO 15  I = 1, N
        GX(I) = 0.0
        XL(I) = VECT(I) * ROOT
        DO 15  J = 1,N
     15 GX(I) = GX(I) + G(I,J) * VECT(J)
C
C       THE INTERESTING QUESTION NOW IS, HOW CLOSE ARE WE TO THE DESIRED
C       SITUATION WHERE GX = XL.
C
        PRINT 16, ROOT
     16 FORMAT (14HOFINAL ROOT = F14.7)
        PRINT 17
     17 FORMAT (25HOFINAL VECTOR, NORMALIZED)
        PRINT 8, (VECT(I),   I = 1,N)
        PRINT 18
     18 FORMAT (15HOG TIMES VECTOR)
        PRINT 8, (GX(I),   I = 1,N)
        PRINT 19
     19 FORMAT (18HOROOT TIMES VECTOR)
        PRINT 8, (XL(I),   I = 1,N)
C
    200 RETURN
        END
```

EIGENVALUES AND EIGENVECTORS OF A NONSYMMETRIC MATRIX OF THE FORM C = B-INVERSE*A (DIRNM)

```
C       SUBROUTINE DIRNM.
C
C       SUBROUTINE DIRNM, DIAGONALIZATION OF A REAL NONSYMMETRIC MATRIX
C       OF THE FORM B-INVERSE * A.
C       A AND B ARE M BY M INPUT MATRICES.  UPON RETURN VECTOR XL CONTAINS
C       THE EIGENVALUES OF B-1*A, AND MATRIX X CONTAINS THE EIGENVECTORS
C       IN ITS COLUMNS, NORMALIZED. SUBROUTINE HDIAG IS REQUIRED.
C       A, M, B, X, AND XL ARE DUMMY NAMES AND MAY BE CHANGED IN THE
C       CALLING STATEMENT.
C
        SUBROUTINE DIRNM (A, M, B, X, XL)
        DIMENSION A(50,50), B(50,50), X(50,50), XL(50)
         CALL HDIAG (B, M, 0, X, NR)
        DO 1  I = 1, M
    1 XL(I) = 1.0 / SQRF(ABSF(B(I,I)))
        DO 2  I = 1, M
        DO 2  J = 1, M
    2 B(I,J) = X(I,J) * XL(J)
        DO 3  I = 1, M
        DO 3  J = 1, M
        X(I,J) = 0.0
        DO 3  K = 1, M
    3 X(I,J) = X(I,J) + B(K,I) * A(K,J)
        DO 4  I = 1, M
        DO 4  J = 1, M
        A(I,J) = 0.0
        DO 4  K = 1, M
    4 A(I,J) = A(I,J) + X(I,K) * B(K,J)
C       A NOW CONTAINS B-1/2PRIME * A * B-1/2 OF THE NOTES.
        TRACE = 0.0
        DO 10  I = 1, M
   10 TRACE = TRACE + A(I,I)
        PRINT 11, TRACE
   11 FORMAT (33HOTRACE OF B-1/2PRIME *A* B-1/2 = F14.7)
        CALL HDIAG (A, M, 0, X, NR)
        DO 5  I = 1, M
    5 XL(I) = A(I,I)
        SUMR = 0.0
        DO 12  I = 1, M
        SUMR = SUMR + XL(I)
   12 PRINT 13, I, XL(I)
   13 FORMAT (12HOEIGENVALUE I2,F14.7)
        PRINT 14, SUMR
   14 FORMAT (22HOSUM OF EIGENVALUES = F14.7)
        DO 6  I = 1, M
        DO 6  J = 1, M
        A(I,J) = 0.0
        DO 6  K = 1, M
    6 A(I,J) = A(I,J) + B(I,K) * X(K,J)
        DO 9  J = 1, M
        SUMV = 0.0
        DO 7  I = 1, M
    7 SUMV = SUMV + (A(I,J)**2.)
        DEN = SQRF (SUMV)
        DO 8  I = 1, M
    8 X(I,J) = A(I,J) / DEN
    9 CONTINUE
C       COLUMNS OF X(I,J) ARE NOW NORMALIZED.
        RETURN
        END
```

SUBROUTINE FOR EXTRACTION OF EIGNEVALUES AND EIGENVECTORS OF A REAL SYMMETRIC MATRIX BY THE EXHAUSTION METHOD (EXTRAC)

```
C      SUBROUTINE EXTRAC.
C
C          THIS SUBROUTINE COMPUTES SUCCESSIVE ROOTS AND VECTORS OF
C      MATRIX A, WHERE A IS A REAL SYMMETRIC MATRIX, BY THE STANDARD
C      ITERATIVE PROCEDURE, USING SUBROUTINE LROOT, AND EXTRACTS THESE
C      SUCCESSIVE SOLUTIONS FROM A, THUS EXHAUSTING A IN A SERIES OF
C      STEPS.  M, THE ORDER OF A, IS LESS THAN 51.  K, IN THE ARGUMENT
C      LIST, IS THE NUMBER OF EIGENVALUES TO BE EXTRACTED (I.E., THE RANK
C      OF A).  THE SUBROUTINE PLACES THE EIGENVALUES IN DESCENDING ORDER
C      IN THE ELEMENTS OF VECTOR XL, AND THE EIGENVECTORS IN THE COLUMNS
C      OF MATRIX X. (NOTE THAT A, M, X, XL, AND X ARE DUMMY VARIABLE
C      NAMES.) SUBROUTINE LROOT IS REQUIRED.
C
C      SUBROUTINE EXTRAC (A, M, X, XL, K)
C
       DIMENSION A(50,50), X(50,50), XL(50), V(50)
       L = 1
     1 CALL LROOT (A, M, R, V, 0)
       XL(L) = R
       DO 2  I = 1, M
       X(I,L) = V(I)
       DO 2  J = 1, M
     2 A(I,J) = A(I,J) - V(I) * V(J) * R
       L = L + 1
       K = K - 1
       IF (K) 3, 3, 1
     3 RETURN
       END
```

9.6   References

Faddeeva, V. N. (1959). *Computational Methods of Linear Algebra*. New York: Dover Publications, pp. 225–233.

Greenstadt, John (1960). "The Determination of the Characteristic Roots of a Matrix by the Jacobi Method." In A. Ralston and H. S. Wilf (Ed.) (1960). *Mathematical Methods for Digital Computers*. New York: John Wiley and Sons, Chapter 7.

Kendall, M. G. (1957). *A Course in Multivariate Analysis*. New York, Hafner Publishing Co., pp. 22–25.

Orden, Alex (1960). "Matrix Inversion and Related Topics by Direct Methods." In A. Ralston and H. S. Wilf (eds.) (1960). *Mathematical Methods for Digital Computers*. New York: John Wiley and Sons, Chapter 2.

Index

(Names occurring in references are indicated by *r.*, those in footnotes by *n.*)